TAKING PLACE

TAKING PLACE

The Spatial Contexts of Science, Technology and Business

ENRICO BARALDI

HJALMAR FORS

and

ANDERS HOULTZ

Editors

Science History Publications/USA
Sagamore Beach
2006

First published in the United States of America
by Science History Publications/USA
a division of Watson Publishing International
Post Office Box 1240, Sagamore Beach, MA 02562-1240, USA
www.shpusa.com

Library of Congress Cataloging-in-Publication Data

Taking place: the spatial contexts of science, technology, and business / Anders Houltz,
   Hjalmar Fors, and Enrico Baraldi, editors.
       p.   cm.
   Includes bibliographical references and index.
   ISBN 0-88135-252-7 (alk. paper)
   1. Space in economics.   2. Space (Architecture)—Social aspects.   3. city
planning—Technological innovations.   4. Regional planning—Technological innovations.
5. Technology—Social aspects.   6. Spatial behavior.   I. Title: Spatial contexts of science,
technology, and business.   II. Houltz, Anders.   III. Fors, Hjalmar.   IV. Baraldi, Enrico.

HT388.T35 2006
307.1'216—dc22

                                                                    2005057629

Design and typesetting by Publishers' Design and Production Services, Inc.
Manufactured in the U.S.A.

CONTENTS

v

PART IV   ACROSS AND BEYOND SPATIAL SCALES

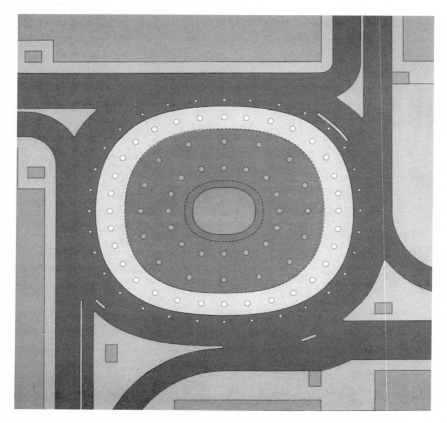

The superellipse roundabout and fountain of Sergels torg in Stockholm. The little circles represent skylights, adding light to the underground pedestrian level below the fountain. The image differs in some details from the final design of the place. (*Teknisk Tidskrift* 1966, p. 11).

Introduction

ANDERS HOULTZ, HJALMAR FORS,
ENRICO BARALDI

In 1959, a city planning team was considering the future shape of what was to become Stockholm's new central plaza, Sergels torg. The problem had both practical and aesthetic aspects. The architects wanted a truly modern place, which combined beauty with a smooth flow of traffic, both pedestrian and vehicular. For a solution they turned to science, or more specifically, to the Danish writer, scientist and philosopher Piet Hein. Hein combined two geometrical figures, the rectangle and the ellipse, into a so-called superellipse, defined by the equation $x^{2\frac{1}{2}} + y^{2\frac{1}{2}} = 1$. Delighted by the mathematical simplicity and beauty of the solution, the architects completed the square by constructing a roundabout in the shape of a superellipse embracing a huge fountain, and beneath it, a vast pedestrian space connecting the square to the main hub of the Stockholm underground railway system.[1]

This case of techno-scientific place creation can be used to illustrate the central themes of this book. When completed, Sergels torg was a "now," cast in concrete. With its surrounding buildings, the plaza still remains a highly accomplished large-scale manifestation of international modernism in architecture—a style meant to fit into any urban metropolis, regardless of the local conditions and free from ties to the specificity of place. Sergels torg was conceived of as a kind of non-place, a square that was not really a square and a public space meant for movement and flow rather than enduring activity. In that sense, it was the ultimate expression of the modern condition, and a concrete illustration of philosopher Martin Heidegger's words: "[In modern space] every place is equal to every other."[2]

However, even Sergels torg, a place completely imbued with modernist ideology, did not conform to Heidegger's dictum. With people's everyday use and rapidly visible wear, with substantial criticism and gradual reevaluation, layer upon layer of meaning has been

added. Today, Sergels torg is Stockholm's main venue for mass
demonstrations and public celebration of sporting achievements; but
also, on a less happy note, it has become the main meeting place for
pushers and drug addicts. The square is still imbued with ideology,
but it is a symbol open to differing interpretations. Carved out of the
historical central district of Stockholm with bulldozers, it stands as a
representative of an epoch and a society in which science and industry were believed to present the model solutions to problems of all
kinds, and were inseparable from political power. At the same time,
and for better or worse, this place is a constant remainder of the fact
that master plans rarely succeed in retaining control of places used by
people.

   This book deals with places that, like Sergels torg, have been
shaped by various interactions of science, technology and industry.
We treat place as an essential factor for understanding the workings
of such actors as municipalities, companies, scientists and scientific
institutions. We discuss the embodiment of ideas and power relationships in actual architectural structures—as in the case of Sergels
torg—and how the creation of organized places can create or reverse
flows of people, ideas, wealth or commodities. But we also analyze
the opposite process whereby people, ideas and artefacts continuously change or distort the intended "nature" of places. Accounting
for the heterogeneous character of places casts a special light on the
complexities of science, technology and industry, and focussing on
places reveals new traits of the interplay between science, technology
and industry.

MAIN THEMES AND QUESTIONS

Science, ultimately expressed in the shape of the superellipse, was indeed symbolically embedded in the construction of Sergels torg. The
interaction between science, technology and industry in the actual
making and reshaping of the plaza is, however, an altogether more
difficult matter to investigate. Nevertheless, the first of four main
questions addressed by this anthology relates to this issue:
*1. How are techno-scientific and industrial places constructed, by
whom and for what purposes?*

   Furthermore, the example of Sergels torg shows that the correspondence between vision and outcome in the shaping of places is
often complex and fraught with conflict. Or, to rephrase the matter
into our second question:

2. How are the ideals and the conceptualization of a place related to its concrete realization?

Moreover, to be fully understood, places must be studied in context rather than as isolated microcosms. Sergels torg was intended as a central hub in a complicated urban texture; it is interrelated to, and corresponds with, a multitude of other places. More clearly than any other part of the city, it connects to suburban life in the outer areas of Stockholm. In a symbolic way it also relates to urban centers in different countries of a similar or comparable origin and function. This leads to our third question:

3. How do different places interact and what does this mean to the actors involved?

The fourth and final question relates to the third one, but focuses on connections and exchange on a more concrete level, focusing attention on the actual journeys from one place to another made by people, artefacts and ideas:

4. How do techno-scientific and industrial objects, ideas and actors move between places?

Our first and second questions above focus on *single places*, isolated for analytical purposes from other places. This permits us to stress the complexity of each single place, its textured substance and its relational nature, while hinting at the heterogeneous nature of all places. Our third and fourth questions focus instead on *the connections between separate places*. In this way, we can stress that places can be seen as isolated only for analytical purposes, whereas they are always susceptible to external influences. This second approach therefore helps us to understand better the nature of places by recognizing that they also interact and mutually affect each other by the movements of actors, artefacts and ideas between them. We will return to these four questions in the concluding chapter.

RELATING SPATIAL CONTEXTS TO SCIENCE, TECHNOLOGY AND INDUSTRY

In disciplines such as human geography and even economics, issues of spatiality have always been in focus, but there is also emerging a large literature on the subject, with its starting point in other disciplines. A common denominator of the authors of this anthology is an interest in the field of STS—Science and Technology Studies. A majority of the chapters are written by historians of science, technology and industry, while the other large group of contributors comes from the field of business studies. With this mix of contributions, we intend to show how historical and present-day actors strive to influence flows of techno-scientific and economic resources. In exploring issues like these, our historical perspective also has bearings on the contemporary making of science policy. If we want to stand even a chance of creating innovative environments based on the interaction between science, technology and business, it is essential to know how such places emerged in the past, including the processes that shaped them. As we will argue in our closing chapter, this is a problem that the makers of science policy have not taken seriously enough.

This anthology can also be seen as an attempt to bring a sense of concreteness to the concept of the "seamless web" of interactions that constitutes science, technology and business.[3] We use several ideas from economic and human geographers in order to discuss the importance of places and spatial contexts for social, technical and economic processes. Such processes will be contextualized within several types of spatial structures and within specific places in order to understand the mutual interplay between *spatiality* and *sociality*. However, the goal is not simply to contextualize social, technical and economic processes, but to take the further step of *socializing* space, that is, to unravel the dynamics by which places are created and imbued with values and symbols by means of social interactions.

It is worth mentioning that the network of researchers who have produced this book shares a common interest: that is, to present a criticism of, and alternatives to, simplifying and normative models for understanding the interaction between industry, science and technology.[4] One such model is the linear model, which suggests a simple and predictable relationship between basic research and new technology with its industrial applications, the one leading with necessity to the other. Although contested for decades by scholars from different disciplines, the linear model has a tendency to return in new guises.[5] In bringing historical disciplines and business studies closer together, one of our aims is to find theoretical approaches that might serve as viable alternatives to the linear model as a standard explanation of technological development.

TAKING PLACE SERIOUSLY

By using the title *"Taking Place,"* we want to underline that place is subject to actors and their actions, consciously or unconsciously claiming, using and shaping places. We also want to point out the need for a historical perspective. Historical and current events also *take place*, in the most literal sense, and as they unfold they become interlaced with place, and thus impossible to understand properly without taking place into consideration.

But what is place, and what does it mean? To begin with, *place* is a useful analytical concept for the study of the interactions of science, technology and industry. We emphasize place because this concept, and the sense of embodiment that it carries, can be anchored to socioeconomic relationships in a more concrete way than can space. The definition of *space,* on the other hand, remains a bone of contention. Indeed, the interpretation of the concept of space may be said to be a philosophical field in its own right.[6]

However, place and space are notions that presuppose one another. Space implies relationships and flow, proportions and relative distances, whereas place is located and bounded. Place also has its own materiality, whether it is a spot on the floor or a whole city. A place has specific characteristics—social, cultural, and historical as well as physical and economic. It is by no means static, but it is limited and individual. It may be a landscape—natural or artificial— or architecture—a building or a set of buildings. It may be a territory, controlled and marked by borders or boundaries. A place may also be a specific set of resources. Places are physical and geographical, but they can also be social, cultural, and even mental. The boundaries of a place are not, however, definite or unproblematic. Rather, they are permeable and constantly negotiated, disputed and maintained by the interests and actions of people. Places relate to the surrounding world and are perceived differently by different people. As cultural geographers have shown, both space and place are culturally produced. Culture takes place, but it also *makes* place.[7]

By presenting studies from different disciplines and covering a wide variety of cases, this volume makes the claim that the singularity and uniqueness of specific places should be studied if one aspires to understand how science, technology and business interplay in modern society. Thus, Heidegger's statement that every place is equal to every other in modern space can be upheld only in theory, if at all. Indeed, the disregard of the significance of place could be seen as a part of the modernist stance, connected to the modern vision of frictionless motion through space.[8]

THE CONTRIBUTIONS TO THIS ANTHOLOGY

The fourteen chapters in this anthology tackle spatial issues from different vantage points and accordingly describe and analyze very different types of places, from laboratories to cities, whole regions and countries. Places come in several shapes and sizes, from the smallest and most physically constrained to the widest and most open ones. The anthology proceeds basically from small to larger places. On an ideal spatial scale, we distinguish between *micro*, *meso*, and *macro* places.[9] These notions are primarily used to distinguish between different types of studies, and between different types of theoretical interests. The section on micro-places discusses physically constrained places, such as single buildings. Collections of several micro-places, built and natural, and the connections between them, are dealt with in the following section on meso-places. The third section includes chapters presenting macro-places, ranging from regions to whole countries and nations. Eleven of the fourteen chapters focus on one dominant type of place, while the three essays in the final part of the anthology move freely on our spatial scale, thus putting emphasis across and beyond, rather than on a specific spatial level.

Part One: Starting in Micro-places

The opening chapter of the book is a study by Hjalmar Fors in which the first chemical laboratory of Uppsala University is considered as a focal point of the social forces surrounding eighteenth-century science. Fors draws attention to the fact that the creation of specialized buildings for science heralded important social changes, new roles for the scientific enterprise and a growth in the social status of researchers. He argues that science could be a tool for professors who wished to dissociate themselves from the small-town artisan environment that had previously been the setting for university scholarship. Instead, they joined forces with the state, and became spokespersons of the scientific enlightenment. But even in this period, laboratories were contested spaces. Whereas the Uppsala chemical laboratory had originally been built as a nexus for the spreading of chemical knowledge to large audiences, it was later redefined as a closed "workshop," turning out high-quality research and high-status chemical specialists.

In the volume's second chapter, Emma Shirran uses the architecture of a women's clinic in the university town of Lund as a starting point for discussing the breakthrough of a new clinical ideal in western medicine. By reconstructing the clinic as seen from the perspective of the medical doctor, the medical student, the nurse/midwife and the patient, she shows its built-in patterns of social inclusion and exclusion. Thus, the clinic is shown to be an expression of the power, and ultimate control over resources, of the doctors, displacing the previous comparatively independent status of Swedish midwives. Shirran shows how medical innovation (bacteriology), spatial reorganization (clinical obstetrics) and social change (as women in increasing numbers entrusted their pregnant bodies to hospital care) all played parallel parts in a process of social change that ushered in a new era of technocratic practice in obstetrics and gynaecology.

Sven Widmalm's chapter studies the research institute and laboratory of The Svedberg as an embodiment of modernist science. On the one hand, the building's standardized modules, lack of ornamentation, and above all, interior flexibility, made it a model for other modernist laboratory buildings. On the other, the laboratory's heavy machinery was not only highly *inflexible*, but also designed to perform tasks in a fairly limited number of areas. Thus Widmalm points to an inherent paradox in the modernist ideal of science, and shows that large investments in heavy equipment open new avenues for research but simultaneously limit alternative possibilities. Svedberg's laboratory, which a simple architectural analysis might suggest to be a celebration of modernist, scientific flexibility, turns out, on closer scrutiny, to be dependent on inflexible technology and a meticulously designed spatial, organizational, and scientific context.

Part Two: Crossing Meso-places

In the fourth chapter, Jenny Beckman broadens the spatial perspective by discussing the construction of an entire academic area, placed in the pastoral setting of Frescati outside Stockholm. In 1904 it was decided to move the Swedish Museum of Natural History from its previous urban premises to a new and spacious building on the outskirts of the city. Relocating the institution contributed to a redefining of its role and function. It also gave birth to visions of a new institutional focal point for scientific Stockholm—the Science City. Beckman links the notion of the Science City to questions of distance and accessibility, scientific exclusivity and public education. As her essay shows, the Science City embraced not one but several contending visions. While all of these visions had something to contribute to the shaping of the Science City, neither they nor the concrete spatial conditions alone proved determinative for the outcome.

Maja Fjæstad's article deals with the security and the boundaries of FR-0—the first and only experimental nuclear fast reactor in Sweden. The reactor, located in Studsvik not far from Stockholm, was in operation from 1964 to 1971. What was the real purpose of the thick walls surrounding the compound—to keep the potential dangers in, or to keep people out? As Fjæstad observes, the physical measures to protect the population from radiation in case of accident served simultaneously to exclude the public from insight into activities at the reactor. The boundaries created were not just of a physical nature; they were practical, legal *and* social. From discussing the boundaries of the site of nuclear power, Fjæstad proceeds to address questions concerning the boundaries of the nuclear engineering profession itself and the exclusive role of the expert.

The sixth chapter also connects place to professional expertise. In this chapter, Per Lundin examines the way in which Swedish city planners in the mid-1900s imposed their visions of rational spatial order on the urban landscape. By claiming the objectivity, rationality and universality of science, they gained a position as providers of expert knowledge, giving the arguments for the universal model solution applied, for instance, in Sergels torg. Urban space became a venue where power relations were established, exerted and manifested. Lundin shows how the principles of modernist city planning were based on a metaphorical view: the city can be understood as, and treated like, a machine, with traffic as its prime mover. This metaphor implied a city that was intelligible, possible to measure and quantify scientifically, and thus possible to plan and control.

Arne Kaijser's contribution discusses the way in which technology transforms places and creates spaces. The focus here is not, however, on the intricate and condensed systems of urban infrastructure, but rather on the impact of technology in a rural community, a place on the periphery. Kaijser studies the way in which infrasystems were introduced and received from the 1870s to the late 1900s in a limited and relatively isolated area, the parish of Malexander in the region of Östergötland in southern Sweden. The peripheral spatial character of the place is an important point of departure for the study. The "meso-place" of Malexander became more and more closely connected with the outer world by technology. This, in turn, fundamentally changed the conditions of landscape, economics and everyday life. From railways and steamboats to the internet, technological systems contributed to the transformation of Malexander from a place characterized by a diverse agricultural economy and controlled by a single powerful employer, the ironworks and manor of Boxholm, into a place dominated by summer residents and commuters.

Part Three: Moving to Macro-places

In the 20th century, large-scale hydropower construction became a symbol of progress and modernization. In her study, May-Britt Öhman explores an unpleasant side of these large technoscientific projects, by discussing the expropriation of territories of indigenous peoples in northern Sweden and the "invisibilization" of indigenous inhabitants. In particular, she analyzes the impact of a hydropower dam on the culture and livelihood of reindeer-herding Sami along the Lule river in northern Sweden. Of special interest is Öhman's discussion of the side effects that modernity carries with it, as it encroaches on its peripheral places. She shows how the alterations and the "industrialization" of the landscape led to the destruction of the traditional ways of Sami reindeer-herding, followed by a forced adoption of the production modes and lifestyles of mainstream modern Swedish culture.

Chapter nine, by Håkan Håkansson, Annalisa Tunisini and Alexandra Waluszewski, discusses the Italian district around Pesaro. The authors present a dynamic and interactive perspective on place, viewed as open to the influence of other places. A place is both the result of inter-firm interactions and a main source of company development. Thus place is an important resource in industrial networks, where firms shape and utilize it in their activities. But place is also a rather special type of resource, because it colors the other resources in business networks with particular features. This theoretical discussion is supported by an empirical description of how the Italian machine producer Biesse affects and is affected by specific places and by the place-related features of such key resources as products, facilities, organizational units and business relationships.

Enrico Baraldi and Torkel Strömsten tackle the relation between places and resources by focussing on the networks that connect two rather special resources—scientific knowledge and venture capital. The empirical ground for such a discussion is the journey from a scientific idea born at Uppsala University (Sweden) to a finished product that was commercialized in 2001–02 by ParAllele, a biotech firm in Silicon Valley. The authors pay special attention to the other resources (besides science and capital) that were combined during this journey of development, leading to the progressive increase in the economic value of the original scientific idea. A wealth of resources from several places in the world of science, technology and industry interacted and, by bearing the imprints of their places of origin, these resources affected and shaped the development process.

Concluding the section on macro-places, Francesco Ciabuschi and Mats Forsgren apply a network-inspired view of business management to the study of multinational corporations (MNCs). This chapter advances theoretical arguments for the importance of specific local places for innovations, even within the very epitome of the globalized organization, that is, the large multinational firm (see below Baraldi for a concrete application in IKEA). In fact, specific countries and regions include local networks of co-located suppliers and customers that inspire and stimulate the innovative ability of the local subsidiaries of any MNC. On the other hand, if a subsidiary is heavily embedded in its local network, the very same places may hinder the transfer of a locally developed innovation to subsidiaries in other countries. The reason is that in such cases a strong local network may oppose the pressure for global standard routines and solutions coming from the headquarters of the MNC.

Part Four: Across and Beyond Spatial Scales

Chapter twelve in this volume, by Enrico Baraldi, relies on the same theoretical perspective and analytical model as Håkansson et al. (see above). Baraldi's study expands the discussion of how a firm utilizes specific places and the place-related features of resources. The giant furniture retailer IKEA provides a concrete example of how a company playing on the global arena still actually needs to exploit the heterogeneity of certain specific places (as implied also by Ciabuschi and Forsgren, above). Furthermore, IKEA needs to combine a wealth of place-specific features that are embedded in the resources that it employs in its innovation and routine activities. Such combination takes place across the three spatial scales presented above, from micro places (e.g., IKEA's retail stores) to macro places (i.e., countries such as China and Sweden), through meso places (i.e., the main cities where IKEA is present).

Olof Ljungström's study relates a centrally located micro-place, the ethnographic museum, to the periphery of world cultures. The study thus delineates the emergence of the ethnographic museum and its role in the European colonial enterprise. The overarching aim is to gain an understanding of how these developments were connected to an epistemological shift towards a new concept of vision in the 19th-century sciences of man. Focusing on a continental European development with its main nodes in France, the Netherlands, Germany and Denmark, Ljungström makes a contribution to a research field that hitherto has relied primarily on British and U.S. sources. Ljungström argues that museums served as liminal places, acting as intermediaries "between the field and its practices, and the finished texts of scholarly discourse and theory." In these places, new visual practices developed and were transferred to the sciences of culture. Ultimately, Ljungström studies how the construction of museum spaces reconstructed vision, and how visual displays and practices enabled a modernity of vision to replace older forms of visual order.

In the concluding study of this anthology, Henrik Mattsson brings together the three spatial scales—micro, meso and macro places—into holistic "bundles." These analytical constructs are borrowed from time-geography, a theoretical approach within human geography, and are applied by Mattsson to a stylized example from the biotech field. The modelling of time-geography shows that science, instead of being a universal and place-unbounded process, takes place concretely, inside specific places where several elements—scientists, businessmen, institutions, infrastructures, etc.—meet in time and space. Mattsson also advances the idea that innovations emerge more easily when actors break those rules and norms that forbid them to move between certain institutional and geographical places. This sort of liberation allows individuals to encounter several places, which they can then bind together or influence to develop their projects. This also shows how difficult it is to stimulate and steer science and innovation by means of public policies that stick to the established geographical and institutional boundaries.

The main observations of the anthology are finally summed up in a concluding chapter written by the editors. Our conclusions stress the importance of place and directly address the four central questions raised earlier in this introduction.

NOTES

1. *Expressen*, July 14, 1964. See also Martin Gardner: "The 'superellipse': A curve that lies between the ellipse and the rectangle," *Scientific American*, September 1965, 223–234.
2. Martin Heidegger, "The Age of the World Picture," in *The Question Concerning Technology and Other Essays* (1969; New York, 1993).

3. Different points of departure and foci are possible when discussing this topic. For instance, the interplay between science, technology and industry can be studied by using *artefacts* as a focal category: see Sven Widmalm (ed.), *Artefakter: Industrin, vetenskapen och de tekniska nätverken* (Hedemora, 2004).

4. This issue is also central to the research project from which this book originates: "Scientific Research–Technological Change–Industrial Renewal" (or, in Swedish, *Vetenskaplig forskning–Teknisk förändring–Industriell förnyelse*). This multi-disciplinary project, funded by the Bank of Sweden's Tercentenary Foundation, engages four Swedish institutions: the Office for History of Science and the Department of Business Studies at Uppsala University, and the Office for Industrial Heritage Studies and the Department of History of Technology at the Royal Institute of Technology, Stockholm.

5. For a recent discussion of this question, see Karl Grandin, Nina Wormbs & Sven Widmalm (eds.), *The Science-Industry Nexus: History, Policy, Implications* (Sagamore Beach, 2004).

6. See Phil Hubbard, Rob Kitchin and Gill Valentine, "Editor's introduction," in *Key Thinkers on Space and Place* (London, 2004), 3–6.

7. Peter Jackson, *Maps of Meaning: An Introduction to Cultural Geography* (London, 1989).

8. The historian of philosophy Edward S. Casey has shown how the notion of place has experienced a gradual decline in philosophical discourse throughout the modern period. While space from Descartes onwards has remained a key notion, place has generally been neglected. As Casey puts it, places have been considered "merely momentary subdivisions of a universal space, quantitatively determined in its neutral homogeneity." Edward S. Casey, *The Fate of Place: A Philosophical History* (Berkeley, 1997), quotation on p. 134.

9. Thomas J. Misa, "Retrieving Sociotechnical Change from Technological Determinism," in Merrit Roe Smith and Leo Marx (eds.), *Does Technology Drive History? The Dilemma of Technological Determinism* (Cambridge, 1994), 115–141.

ACKNOWLEDGEMENTS

The editors would like to thank Karin Sennefelt, Alexandra Walus-zewski, and Sven Widmalm for valuable comments on the introduction and conclusion, as well as Bernard Vowles, for his English proof reading. We would also like to thank the Bank of Sweden's Tercentenary Foundation (Riksbankens jubileumsfond) for its generous financial support, both of the present anthology, and of the research school "the VTI-project" which brought together the editors, as well as many of the contributors. VTI is a joint research school on graduate level, organized by the Department for History of Science and Ideas and the Department of Business Studies at Uppsala University, and the Department of History of Science and Technology at the Royal Institute of Technology, Stockholm.

PART I

Starting in Micro-Places

Amateur chemist Carl August Ehrenswärd interrupted in his laboratory by a Lady. Portrait of artist, late 18th century. Photography by Åsa Lundén from the collections of Nationalmuseum, NMH-71/1970.

J. G. WALLERIUS AND THE LABORATORY OF ENLIGHTENMENT

HJALMAR FORS

In 1995 the department of hydrology at Uppsala University moved out of the premises it had occupied since 1965. Major repairs were carried out in the building, as it was prepared for its new tenant, the department of psychology. When I sneaked in, during the workers' lunch hour, there were still some laboratory workbenches left and a large amount of piping was still attached to the walls. I had paper and pen ready. Originally, the house had been built as the first chemical laboratory of Uppsala University, and I wanted to find out if there remained any traces of the original interior as it existed at the time of its first occupant, Sweden's first professor of chemistry, Johan Gottschalk Wallerius, or of his successor, Torbern Bergman. Almost no interior walls had been moved since Bergman's day, and I quickly found the door to a small room, located where Wallerius had installed the chemical furnaces of his laboratory. Inside the door there was a storeroom, containing thousands of tiny bottles of water. From the labels, I could deduce that they contained water collected from lakes all over the country. The hydrologists had left them behind, and they were probably soon to be thrown away.[1]

For me to find a twentieth-century collection of specimens of water in the innermost chamber of Wallerius's old laboratory was a very strange experience. In Wallerius's chemical theory, water was the source of all things, and the substance to which all things would return, when the world ended. The theory was based on an ancient

---

I would like to thank Prof. Anders Lundgren and Drs. Karin Sennefelt and Hanna Östholm for their valuable comments on earlier drafts of this paper.

3

idea, that water was the primordial substance from which all other objects were generated, and that it was changed through a process of
transmutation into earth, metals, plants and animals.[2] Wallerius had
published a work, the *Hydrologia*, that ordered the "water realm"
into a Linnaean system of classes, orders, genera, species and vari-
eties. A project that, given this theoretical background, was both useful to society and scientifically relevant.[3] In Wallerius's system,
lake-water, such as that found in the abandoned collection of the hydrologists, was the fifth genus in the order of earth waters in the class
of common, or sweet waters. The closest relatives in the system were
the genera "standing earth water" and ice.[4] I was in no doubt that
some traces of Wallerius's spirit remained in the old house.

Can the study of a building add anything to the knowledge of the
scientific activity that has taken place there? Is it possible to draw
conclusions about a scientist's views of science, his theories and scientific practice by studying the rooms that he shaped in order to conduct his business?[5] This paper is an attempt to do just that. It is my
intention to take Wallerius's laboratory building as a point of departure for a study on the social circumstances surrounding eighteenth-
century science. More precisely, the study attempts to outline under
which social circumstances chemistry became institutionalized as a
science in a Nordic university setting.

By doing this, I aim to lead the discussion of eighteenth-century
chemistry away from the study of the genealogy of thoughts and theories. History of science has merged, more or less completely, with
sociology of science in recent decades, and accepted the premise that
the science of the past should not be judged on the merits of the science of later ages. Nevertheless, there is still a tendency to perceive
eighteenth-century chemistry as an orderly progression from alchemy
to the chemical revolution. However, as F. L. Holmes persuasively argues, such a description gives a deeply flawed view of eighteenth-century chemistry.[6] By taking places and social practices into account as
well as theories, this paper attempts to show that if we want to understand scientific change, we must consider the whole context.[7] In
history of science, there is still a tendency to believe that only that
which seems strange needs to be explained, while that which seems
recognizable can be left unexplained. This is where sociology of science can make its greatest contribution to history of science, since its
object is precisely to study what seems perfectly normal and to show
that we really do not know very much about it.[8] It is my belief that
such an approach is necessary. If the aim is to achieve some under-

standing of, for example, what eighteenth-century science was all about, we must put aside the notion that late eighteenth-century science is any "closer" to us and easier to understand than its predecessor of the early part of the century.[9] This paper mainly describes Johan Gottschalk Wallerius's position in a controversy that he fought out with his younger contemporary Torbern Bergman. If I might seem to cast Bergman in the role of "the bad guy," it should not be taken as a reflection of my views on his character. I do it primarily in order to put the notion of "progress" aside. Science does not move forward from worse to better: It adapts to new circumstances, and transforms along with the societies of which it forms a part.

J. G. Wallerius, and Uppsala University's first chemical laboratory, are well suited for a study of this kind. One reason for this is Wallerius's public controversy with Bergman, his successor, who inherited the chair and the building. The controversy forced both professors to state clearly their views on the proper uses of the laboratory building, and on the role of the chemist in society. Although Wallerius's laboratory was re-equipped and refurbished by Bergman, it must be stressed that there was much more continuity than disruption when it came to how the "laboratory," the room for chemical operations, was equipped and used. As Holmes has noted, "Until late in the eighteenth century no major technological changes altered the character of the chemical laboratory as a material or social setting."[10] The fight between Wallerius and Bergman was fought on an ideological, theoretical, methodological and personal battleground. But the equipment and operations that they used were only a small part of the issue, and the importance of the laboratory as a room for the investigation of nature was not an issue at all.[11]

When his laboratory was erected, Wallerius was already a well-known and respected chemist. His breakthrough had been his mineralogy, published in 1747. It has been characterized by historian of science Theodore Porter as "[t]he representative mineralogical treatise of the first half of the eighteenth century" and was published, all in all, in nine editions in five languages.[12] According to his autobiography, Wallerius began teaching chemistry in Uppsala from a private laboratory in 1735, using demonstrations from Hermann Boerhaave as a base, but writing his own lectures to accompany them. He continued his studies of chemistry, mineralogy and assaying, while also teaching anatomy and physiology. (On some occasions he used his laboratory for vivisecting dogs.) During the period 1747–50, he presided over two public defences of dissertations with chemical content.

Figure 1. Johan Gottschalk Wallerius. Plaster medallion by J. T. Sergel. Photo: Kungliga Vetenskapsakademien (The Royal Swedish Academy of Sciences).

He was most likely the author of both. He received a newly instituted chair in chemistry, metallurgy and pharmaceutics in 1750.[13]

Wallerius had petitioned the university authorities for a new laboratory as early as 1746, but it was only after he had been awarded the newly established professorship that a search for a suitable building began. Wallerius's first choice was the ground floor of the university's astronomical observatory, located close to the university's botanical garden on Uppsala's main trading street. Eventually, he had to settle for a site on the southern outskirts of town.[14]

The laboratory building was built just by the river, close to the town's southern gate, beneath the southern tower of Uppsala Castle. It was first erected as a free-standing one-storey stone building, designed and planned by Wallerius himself. There are no extant drawings of the exterior of this first building. According to Åke Stavenow, it must have looked squat and clumsy by the aesthetics of the time.[15] Wallerius was not happy with the exterior either. It was finished in 1754, but before that, as early as in March 1753, he petitioned the university for a tower or similar superstructure to be built on the central part of the roof. He argued that it was desirable for the house to look more like the other buildings of the university and that an addition would make it possible to see from the exterior that it belonged to university. For a small cost, the building would gain a handsome appearance, and there would also be the benefit of extra space for the university's mineral collection.[16]

The official look that Wallerius strived for was clearly that exhibited in two other buildings of Uppsala University. Gustavianum, the university's main building where most lectures were held, had an anatomical theatre built as a tower centrally placed on the roof.[17] There was also an observatory tower on the astronomical observatory. The building had been erected 1739–41 for Anders Celsius, and now housed his successor, Mårten Strömer.[18]

Wallerius's petition shows that he must have had some awareness of the symbolic functions of these superstructures as representational architecture. The towers highlighted the importance of the buildings that they formed a part of, and conferred status on those who used them. The anatomical theatre was more or less disused in the mid-eighteenth century. Regarding the tower of the observatory, the situation was similar. Since the observatory was located on Uppsala's main trading street, observations were disturbed both by lights from the neighbors and by vibrations from passing carts. The building was quickly acknowledged as a total failure as a site for practical astronomy. Thus, the main function of the observatory was as a space for teaching, and a place were astronomical instruments could be seen by, and demonstrated to, students. It was, functionally, the place for display of a collection.[19] Given these circumstances, Wallerius's interest in a tower was, most likely, a sign of his desire for symbolic recognition of his new chair—both by creating a visual/structural similarity between his building and other official buildings of the university, and also through his desire to display the university's mineral collection inside a tower. Wallerius's personal control over such a space would have implied a significant increase of status, for him personally, and for chemistry as a science. It would also have made Wallerius's laboratory an obvious site of interest for any *savant* visiting Uppsala University. In modern language, it would have made his laboratory a tourist attraction.[20]

It should not surprise us that Wallerius's request for a tower was denied by the other professors in the university's ruling body. The finished building turned out to be a rather unassuming house. It was

clearly visible from the ships that anchored in the town's harbor, but the main entrance was to the west, facing the street leading into Uppsala from the south. The house was reached by means of a long, straight path. Thus the front of the one-storey house must have been partly obscured from the street by the fences and trees of its own garden. The building was erected on the south-western outskirts of town, but it was a small town, and it would have required no more than a fifteen-minute walk to reach Linnaeus's botanical garden, located on the opposite outskirts on the north-eastern side.[21]

As Svante Lindqvist has noted, the foremost setting for eighteenth-century science was "the prosperous home in an urban environment where crafts were practised."[22] However, as the eighteenth century progressed, a number of specialized buildings for the pursuit of science came to be erected. In Sweden, the universities were a driving force behind the erection of new buildings for science. An explanation of this trend was a successful marriage of interests between enterprising individuals within the university system and leading politicians in their capacities as state officials. The former sought the patronage of the latter, and the politicians obliged the university men by diverting the resources of the country's universities towards clients

Figures 2 and 3. The university's main building, Gustavianum, (previous page) and its Astronomical Observatory (this page). Note the centrally placed towers on the roofs of the buildings. Engravings by Fredric Acrel. Photo: Repro-och fotoenheten/Kungliga Biblioteket (National Library of Sweden).

that supported their policies. Those who wooed for patronage could, for example, write pamphlets that outlined the utility of their science to the state and plead for resources. The physician Abraham Bäck wrote a pamphlet on the usefulness of a new hospital, the engineer Carl Knutberg argued for a mechanical laboratory, Anders Celsius held forth on the astronomical observatory that had been built for him. J. G. Wallerius wrote eloquently on how important it was to continue to support chemistry after he had been promised his new laboratory.[23] Men such as these pursued a successful strategy. Chairs of chemistry, economics and other practically oriented university subjects were founded, and several hospitals, observatories and chemical and mechanical laboratories were erected in Sweden, primarily in Stockholm and the university towns Åbo, Lund and Uppsala, in the 1730s, 40s and 50s.[24]

Most of the new buildings were not erected as monumental buildings or palaces, but built on the template of the town house, looking rather much like the homes of any moderately wealthy merchant or craftsman.[25] There was also a functional similarity to such buildings, since the laboratories, observatories, hospitals and botanical gardens often also contained the living quarters of the professor who used the facilities, and of his family. Traditionally, professors had done much of their teaching from their own homes, and when need arose for specialized equipment, like books, instruments and collections, they bought these objects at their own expense. Alix Cooper has argued that the focus of historians of science on formal institutions has obscured the fact that early modern scientific inquiry often took place in the home of the investigator and "often constituted a family project."[26] Thus it should be no surprise that the new institutional buildings evolved from the template of the private homes of the professors. Furthermore, early modern Scandinavian universities had a corporativistic character. Professors privately owned their own teaching materials, they were embedded in strong local family networks, and chairs tended to be inherited from one generation to another within the same family. According to Matti Klinge, Åbo (Turku) University in Finland, which was then a part of the Swedish kingdom, functioned as a family community. Chairs were often divided up between influential academic families.[27] Similar patterns can be identified in Uppsala.[28] Thus there was a similarity on several levels between the university academics and the craftsmen and small-town merchants that were their neighbors, and with whom they cooperated and intermarried.[29] Their homes served as the main place of work, and their networks, businesses and craft secrets, and the tools of their trades, were passed on from the parents to the children of the household.[30] In the words of Alix Cooper "the extended household was responsible both for its members' material maintenance and for cultural reproduction more generally, for the transmission of customs and practices from one generation to the next."[31]

The appearance of university-owned houses built for the teaching of specific sciences, and equipped with highly specialized and expensive equipment, was a novelty in these environments. Clearly, the new buildings were not simply town houses. They were also institutional buildings.[32] Wallerius recognized this with his requests that his laboratory should look impressive and have a tower that singled it out as an official building. His house, along with the others of its kind, were semi-public places: The professor who had his apartments in one of these buildings could not refuse access to his house to certain parts of the public, in particular the students (and indeed had no interest in doing so). But other groups, too, had access. The professor, his wife and their children, assistants, servants, lodgers, relatives and visitors all made use of the building.[33] In a building such as Wallerius's *Laboratorium Chemicum*, or the house in Linnaeus's botanical garden, there was a flow of people who had a right to visit and who were encouraged to come. As both a private dwelling and a public teaching space, the status of these new buildings was to some degree open to negotiation. Where would the line be drawn between private and public?

Inside Wallerius's building there was a division between the private apartments to the left, and the laboratories to the right. When Wallerius described the laboratories in his autobiography, he specifically mentioned that the larger room, the auditorium, was intended for public demonstrations, whereas the smaller room, the laboratorium, was for private tuitions. However, his chemical experiments, and also the manufacturing of medicines for which he had received a privilege, most likely took place in the smaller laboratory.[34] Thus the right side of the building was wholly reserved for Professor Wallerius, the public man who performed his duties. (However, the left side of the building would by no means have been closed to students, relatives, lodgers and visitors.) On the right side, there were further divisions, the larger laboratory had a row of windows facing the river and the street behind the building. When Wallerius performed his public lectures and demonstrations, it was probably possible for passers-by to look in at him through the windows. The smaller laboratory had

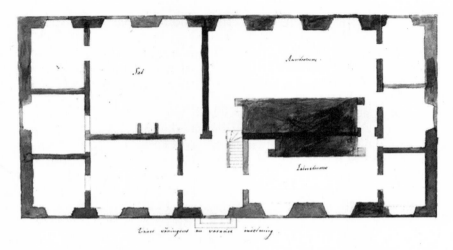

Figure 4. Floor plan of Wallerius's *Laboratorium Chemicum* in Uppsala, drawn after the city fire of 1766. The "auditorium" is located in the upper right half of the plan, the "laboratorium" is located at the bottom right. Note the large black-marked zone; that most likely marked the location of built-in chemical furnaces and hoods to collect fumes produced during chemical demonstrations and experiments. Photo: Reprosektionen/ Uppsala Universitetsbibliotek (Uppsala University Library).

two windows overlooking the garden. It would have been difficult to get a clear view of what was happening in there, unless one entered the garden of the house through its main entrance and approached its main door.

Does this general layout tell us something about the chemical activities of the inhabitants? In a well-known article, Owen Hannaway has written about the seventeenth-century humanist scholar and alchemist, Andreas Libavius, who was a major opponent of the secret-mongering of the alchemy of his day.[35] In his *Commentariorum alchymiae*, part one, Libavius asserted that the alchemist should not abandon civic responsibility and isolate himself from society. Libavius also described what he saw as an ideal house for an alchemist. In his opinion, the alchemist's house should be a free-standing building in its own grounds. Inside the house, there would be a wall, separating the public part of the house, where the alchemist assumed his civic responsibilities by receiving his friends and clients, from the laboratory, which was a private space where he and his assistants pursued

Figure 5. Uppsala, seen from the south in an engraving by Fredric Acrel. The *Laboratorium Chemicum*, as rebuilt by Bergman after the Uppsala fire of 1766, is the stone building in the bottom right corner. In Wallerius's time the building would have been lower, but the location of the laboratory room (its windows are hidden behind a tree) would have been the same. Photo: Reprosektionen/ Uppsala Universitetsbibliotek (Uppsala University Library).

the great work of alchemy. Libavius's plans were, as Hannaway has shown, strongly polemical against paracelsian influences in alchemy, and in particular against Tycho Brahe, the famous astronomer, and his plans, published in 1598, for the observatory Uraniborg, which also sported an alchemical laboratory in the basement. However, despite his distaste for secrecy, Libavius still characterized alchemy as a private activity, for which a private and secluded space was needed.[36]

When this early seventeenth-century vision of the accessible house is compared to Wallerius's laboratory, it becomes clear that Wallerius had taken the ideal of openness one step further. Wallerius's house was a free-standing building in its own grounds, sharing one important characteristic with the ideal of Libavius. Inside the building, however, the laboratory of Wallerius had four doors, one of which led to the main hallway and was easily accessible from the outside. Furthermore, the inside of the laboratory was clearly visible through two large windows, placed just to the right of the main entrance. Whereas Libavius had stressed that alchemy should be performed in seclusion, Wallerius had no such ambition for his chemistry (especially since eighteenth-century chemistry often had to be performed with open windows). Wallerius's laboratory was an open space, designed for ease of access for air, light, visitors, instruments and chemicals. Compared to his auditorium, the laboratory was secluded. However, it was quite accessible and transparent to those who had business with Wallerius or his family, such as the public students, who had to pass by its windows and door in order to listen to the lectures in the auditorium. Furthermore, in his autobiography Wallerius mentioned the laboratory as a place where private students received instruction, and not as a secluded place for the contemplation of nature.[37] This is important and gives a hint about how he perceived his chemistry. It was to be a transparent craft that was to be performed in the open, for the benefit of the public. Wallerius's laboratory and the chemistry performed there were clearly products of enlightenment sentiments.

Apart from the family life that went on in Wallerius's laboratory building, it was also a place were chemicals and minerals were purified and transformed, and systematized and accumulated in collections. Charcoal and water were carried inside to be consumed in quantity. Books and articles from all over Europe were bought and brought inside, read and re-read. Letters and mineral specimens from a number of scientific correspondents were received and answered. The defining and most important activity, however, was not the production of novel research. It was, as Wallerius himself emphasized in his autobiography, the teaching of students.[38] There were students of two kinds, those who visited the public lectures, and those who paid extra money to participate in the private seminars. A glance in the university's catalogue of lectures for the years 1751–66 shows that Wallerius's public lectures covered such diverse fields as the doctrine of salts, agrarian chemistry, history of chemistry, the composition of natural bodies, the theory of the bodies of the mineral realm, and the composition and analysis of bodies of the vegetable and animal realms. In his private lectures, he covered hydrology, pharmaceutical preparations, mineralogy, metallurgy, and several other subjects. According to Wallerius's autobiography, most lectures started with one hour of chemical demonstrations, and concluded with one hour of explanation of the phenomena that just had been demonstrated.[39]

Older alchemy was a secret art. Alchemists' emphasis on secretiveness contributed to the ideal that the laboratory should be a secluded space. Not even with Andreas Libavius could the alchemical laboratory take the step from private to public space. Alchemy was not a public enterprise in the way that chemistry would later become.[40] The relationship between alchemy and chemistry is a longstanding debate that I will not address here. I agree, however, with B. J. T. Dobbs, that chemistry's dissociation from alchemy was a slow step-by step process. According to Dobbs, the first step of this process was taken by (al)chemists who gained the intent and ambition to publicly publish their findings in a clear and open manner, although they worked with alchemical experiments and used alchemical terminology. Later, (al)chemists also started to describe the transformations of matter using the new, mechanistic terminology, abandoning the flowery poetic language and metaphors traditionally used. It was towards the end of this process that chemistry, in some kind of modern sense, was born.[41]

It is in this later tradition that Wallerius can be found. One of his many undertakings was to translate alchemical experiments and theory into a mechanist language in order to make it available to the public and useful to the state. He also published manuscripts by Urban Hiärne, one of the foremost Swedish alchemists of the seventeenth century.[42]

It was, among other things, these scientific aims that made Wallerius a part of the enlightened currents of his time. One of the more surprising connections between Wallerius and the French Enlightenment is that it was none other than the Baron d'Holbach who translated Wallerius's mineralogy and hydrology into French, working

from the German editions.[43] Was there something tangible in the
work of this Swedish professor that attracted French radicals? Even
though Wallerius was a highly religious and pious man, his views on
the transformation of matter had a strong mechanist foundation. Thus
they could be used by those who had other purposes.[44] To Wallerius,
however, such descriptions were part of a greater story. They explained the workings of God's Creation and were in no way opposed
to the revealed truth of biblical scripture.[45]

There was, however, something in Wallerius's works that was even
more attractive to those who attempted to break down the old order of
society and replace it with something new. Alchemists were not the
only secret-mongers in early modern society. Craftsmen dealt in secrets, too. "Progressive" forces in eighteenth-century society perceived
guilds as exclusive groups that guarded their privileges aggressively.[46]
The secrets of the trades were transmitted only to those whom the masters had chosen as their successors, and were ideally to remain within
the family of the master. Crafts could only be pursued by those who
had the privileges and who accepted the authority of the guilds. This
system was said to conserve ancient techniques, to be non-competitive
between craftsmen, and to ensure the high quality of the products.
Craftsmen had no particular interest in their businesses being public,
nor in their being open to inspection by foreign agencies or groups.[47]

By incorporating certain crafts into an overarching chemical science, which was publicly taught at universities, and published in articles, dissertations and monographs, Wallerius and other chemists
joined up with the values of the Enlightenment. The enlightenment of
matter joined hands with the enlightenment of society through the
connecting link of utility. According to its practitioners and many others, it was during the eighteenth century that chemistry became a useful science at the service of society.[48] Simultaneously, it was also seen
to pursue an honest and open search for truth. For these reasons,
chemistry and its practitioners could serve as welcome contrasts to
disobliging craftsmen, secretive alchemists, hypocritical priests and
other opponents of reason and common sense.[49]

In this, too, our professor played a not insignificant part. At the
beginning of the eighteenth century, there was still no unified chemistry. Instead, one could talk of three different crafts: pharmacy, assaying and alchemy, in which chemical processes were used.[50] They
had greatly differing terminology and there was little contact between
them. But they had one thing in common: they were practiced in
closed rooms, where (ideally) their practitioners transformed natural

substances into useful and valuable things. The laboratory of the pharmacist was first and foremost a place where medicines were mixed and manufactured. The chamber of assaying was a place where metals and minerals were assayed and analyzed. Assayers were often employed by the mining industry, but their procedures were also used by craftsmen engaged in fine metalwork, such as goldsmiths. Alchemists, finally, also conducted their work in laboratories. There, the secrets of nature were unveiled through the manipulation of material substances. Successful alchemy would yield the most valuable substance of all: the philosopher's stone that could turn common metals into gold and give its owner eternal life. In a sense, there was a straight line from the alchemical laboratories of the seventeenth century to the chemical laboratories of the eighteenth. However, it was mainly through the combination of alchemy with pharmacy and assaying, and the ideological accommodations that it went through as a consequence, that early eighteenth-century chemistry emerged, as an art that was distinct from alchemy.[51]

But chemistry's transformations did not end there. Historian of science Lissa Roberts has argued that three stages can be identified in eighteenth-century chemistry's transformation from art to science. From about the 1720s to the 1740s, "chemistry was publicly defined and accepted as an art." But it was during the two latter stages, the second from about 1740 to the mid-1780s and the third from the mid-1780s to the end of the century, that it emerged as a systematic science.[52] Without going too deeply into Robert's argument, I would argue that chemistry's usefulness was established on the premise that it was a functional art/craft, but it could be elaborated because it portrayed itself as a useful science.[53] It would give birth to inventions, medicines, alloys, dyestuffs and many other useful products. Chemistry's increased pretensions to utility emerged from its connection with, and assimilation of, crafts. By claiming to be useful, the chemists could increase their social status. They could also obtain patrons, money, and resources on the promise of new products, and on the promise that they could rationalize and improve crafts and industries.[54] The early concept of chemistry as an art still retained strong connections with the craft environments that saw its birth. The art of chemistry had comparably low social status, while the systematic science of chemistry was to be an enterprise associated with high social status. The continuing rise in the status of chemistry, and of the chemists themselves, was to happen in conjunction with a successful dissociation from the science's craft roots, and it is in part as a symbolic dissociation from the crafts that we should perceive Wallerius's request for a more imposing building. Another strategy, however, was to impose chemistry as a controlling and improving instance, superior to the crafts in the hierarchical order of society. Wallerius achieved his hierarchical superiority through an ingenious use of the concept of chemical theory.

According to Wallerius, it was necessary that science should be based on theory, but it was equally necessary that it should have practical applications. Theory without practice was of no value, and practice without theory was not science at all. Functioning practices, however, such as assaying procedures, became applied science if they could be explained theoretically, and were performed by a chemist. Alchemical theories, operations and recipes could also be incorporated.[55] Thus correct theory separated the sciences from the arts, and also provided the unifying framework for chemical knowledge. Wallerius's chemistry was an empirical, collecting and systematic science. It accumulated and organized facts from a number of non-scientific fields, as well as from nature. On a conceptual level, this activity was similar to that of Linnaeus. But whereas Linnaeus directed his search towards the animal and plant realms, Wallerius sought to systematize not only the mineral and water realms, but also the human crafts with a bearing on chemistry, and their products. In a very concrete meaning, he sought to enlighten obscure craft practices, and organize and rationalize them. These activities were, of course, best performed from a position of social superiority.

The strength of Wallerius's vision was that he managed to incorporate previously rather disparate crafts into a unified discipline, whose practice was conducted out in the open. Theoretically, this union was achieved through the distinction between *chemia pura* and *chemia applicata*, an organizing dichotomy that was created to guide chemical investigations. When the chemist was interested in processes that were of economic importance to society, he was doing *chemia applicata*, or applied chemistry. When his primary concern was the descriptions of the transformations of nature and the investigation of the ultimate structure of matter, he concerned himself with *chemia pura*, or pure chemistry. In the words of the German historian of chemistry, Christoph Meinel:

> By establishing the subject on the formula 'pure and applied chemistry' Wallerius tightly joined the way the discipline saw itself to the great and forward-looking trends of his time, the philosophical

rationalism and scientism of the Enlightenment as well as to the programme of general usefulness which was to culminate in utilitarianism.[56]

To conclude: Wallerius subordinated the crafts to science. His dichotomy between *chemia pura* and *chemia applicata* structured chemistry. Since chemistry concerned itself with the scientific betterment of the crafts, it became useful. Thus, in Wallerius's person, many of the values that Libavius had called for in the civic-minded alchemist actually found their expression. In a sense, he can be said to have embodied many aspects of Libavius's scientific ideal. Libavius had been of the opinion that an alchemist should be at the service of the public and the state. According to Hannaway, three elements of ideological importance were incorporated into Libavius's chemical house. First, the conviction that a politically and socially engaged life (*vita activa*) was superior to a life in stillness and contemplation (*vita contemplativa*). Second, that the family was the basis for a sound society, and that the alchemist should be a *paterfamilias*. Third, that the ideal alchemist should hold a public office: "We want him to cultivate *humanitas* in a civil society and to bring luster to his profession by an upright household, so that he may strive for every virtue and be able to assist with his friends as an aid and counsel to his country."[57]

What was more fitting, then, than that the public office should consist in spreading knowledge of chemistry, as did the position of a university professor? The work of the chemist was to take what was hidden and obscure, and to make it transparent and comprehensible to reason. Through this, the chemist also served the public good, since he published the knowledge he collected. In the lecture rooms of the *Laboratorium Chemicum*, rational knowledge of how the world actually worked was transmitted to the students, and through them, to society. So far, the vision of Wallerius corresponded well to the general aims of eighteenth-century "enlightened" reformers.[58] In a broader sense, he defended his place among them, and he was also a leading chemical ideologue of the central part of the eighteenth century. Wallerius should not, however, be seen as being of unique importance in this regard. He was not so much unique, as a prominent representative of a larger, and broader, movement. According to Lisbet Koerner, "enlightenment" took on a specific meaning in the northern European, Baltic context. It "meant a material, universalizing, utilitarian, rational, and encyclopaedic style of thought."[59] Wallerius was a strong exponent of this style of thought, and also corresponded quite well to Koerner's characterization of the typical exponents of the tradition that carried it: "Baltic naturalists had strong family resemblances. Typically they were Lutherans, of German or Scandinavian origins, and from modest homes. [. . .] They belonged to European-wide correspondence networks; they were in close contact with one another; they subscribed to a broad idea of the 'new science'; and they were civil servants."[60] Armed, as he was, with a new and powerful identity, Wallerius was able to orient himself away from the craft surroundings that had previously been the setting for university scholarship. At the same time as there emerged institutional buildings, the users of these buildings dissociated themselves from the values of their craft surroundings.[61] Henceforth, professors were not craftsmen, but the superiors of craftsmen, who exposed their knowledge, constructed theories from it, and returned to them only in order to inspect and reform their activities.

There were, however, other depths in this professor that complicated the picture. Wallerius spent the later half of his life fighting the views of his younger contemporaries, and in particular those of his successor Bergman. Wallerius did not take well to losing his influence over chemistry, and he could not accept the changes that his science underwent from the 1760s onwards. Instead, he steadfastly continued to defend views that, as the century progressed, were viewed as more and more antiquated. An important aspect of his thinking was that the chemistry he sought to spread was more or less complete. It contained an ordering theory, which also endowed chemistry with a high social status (see above) and it had a set of practices that encompassed both empirical collecting and laboratory trials. This was, except for some minor details, a non-negotiable, and finished chemical system.[62] In short, Wallerius already knew the truth, and all that was left to do was to announce it to the world. Simultaneously, among Wallerius's younger contemporaries, a stream of new discoveries led to the dawning realization that the chemists' knowledge of the physical world was incomplete, and that revolutionary change was imminent.[63] However, given his point of departure, Wallerius's emphasis on teaching becomes readily understandable. Indeed, Wallerius's laboratory building can be likened to a church, or perhaps a cathedral of enlightenment, where Wallerius, as a high priest of chemistry, preached his knowledge to the world, accompanied by the liturgy of chemical demonstration.

This interpretation also explains the intense dislike that Wallerius showed towards his successor Bergman, and his opposition to the claims of the younger chemists who, with increasing insistence, tried to overthrow his chemical world-view. Almost immediately after his retirement, Wallerius started a controversy with his successor. Bergman soon came to detest the older chemist and managed, quite successfully, to discredit Wallerius as a part of his general defence against his predecessor's attacks. Bergman's views on Wallerius subsequently came to gain wider and wider currency among Swedish scientists and soon Wallerius's influence on the development of chemistry was all but forgotten.[64] The following quotation illustrates Bergman's wrath. It is taken from a letter to Wargentin, the secretary of the Swedish Academy of Sciences:

> At the outset he [Wallerius] thought that he could break me with his yelling, but providence has turned all his anger to my benefit. [. . .] He has done the greatest harm to himself and has in a way survived himself, since when he wanted to do wrong to others, he laid himself open, and it is increasingly clear, that the old man has never made a reliable experiment, [or] any real discovery. He twists and turns hypotheses in order to make them suitable to the experiments of others, and how far he has succeeded lies plain to the public.[65]

Bergman's observation that Wallerius had never made "a reliable experiment" was clearly unfair. But underlying the anger was an epistemological difference between the two professors. It concerned their views on the meaning and interpretation of experiments. Wallerius emphasized the empirical collection of facts, whereas Bergman emphasized the controlled laboratory experiment. According to Bergman, chemical facts were primarily produced in chemical laboratories, by means of experiments. They were not collected from books or from craft practices. In another critical passage, Bergman stated:

> A number of experiments, made during a succession of ages, are collected; and an accurate and attentive consideration is thought sufficient to unravel the chain of causes. Thus a philosopher at his table, surrounded with books, undertakes to penetrate the arcana of nature, and to deal out truths as if by inspiration; and [. . .] pronounces concerning substances, which, far from examining as he should, he has never so much as seen.[66]

The emphasis on the importance of experiment was a rhetorical commonplace in eighteenth-century science.[67] This critique, aimed at such chemists as had made no true commitment to the experimental method, was, however, in all likelihood aimed at Wallerius.[68] Although important, laboratory experiments had no privileged position in Wallerius's chemistry. They were part of a larger chemical enterprise that also included, for example, systematic mineralogy in the Linnaean tradition.[69] Wallerius, however, was not alone in trusting the collection of experiments "made during a succession of ages." Chemists, then as today, had to trust each other's experiments and collect information from several sources.[70] What we see here is rather a shift in emphasis, from a broad empirical program of collecting chemical information (it might be called a "Linnaean" collecting and ordering of specimens, whether they were rocks, texts or chemicals) to a narrower program of analysis and synthesis in a laboratory.[71]

Viewed in this manner, the conflict between Wallerius and Bergman was a disagreement about what gave the most valuable knowledge: empirical collecting of facts or controlled laboratory experiments. The difference had important implications for the way that they perceived teaching, and also for the way that they organized their laboratory and teaching spaces. This becomes evident when we take a look at how Bergman had the laboratory in Uppsala rebuilt after he had received the chair in 1767.[72] The year before, the laboratory had burned in a great city fire. The fire had left only the inner and outer walls, and some fireproof crucibles and mortars. This meant that Bergman could rebuild the house according to his own preferences. He was also permitted to add a second floor.

The architect, however, was Carl Johan Cronstedt.[73] The house became a rather typical building of the period. It could have been the home of any affluent merchant or tradesman. With its nice proportions and typical rococo exterior, there was not much that signalled that the building was built as a chemical laboratory. Bergman chose to use the second floor as his private apartments. The ground floor contained a long gallery for the mineral collection, a small laboratory and a kitchen, along with a number of storage chambers. The main change to the ground floor was that there was no longer an auditorium were chemical demonstrations could be performed publicly on a regular basis. Bergman performed his demonstrations in the chemical laboratory, where he also did his research work. This was a conscious move, since he was of the opinion that there should be a strong link between the place where chemical facts were taught, and where they were produced:

> The laboratory is also the auditorium, because all the doctrines of
> this science should be confirmed with clear trials.[74]

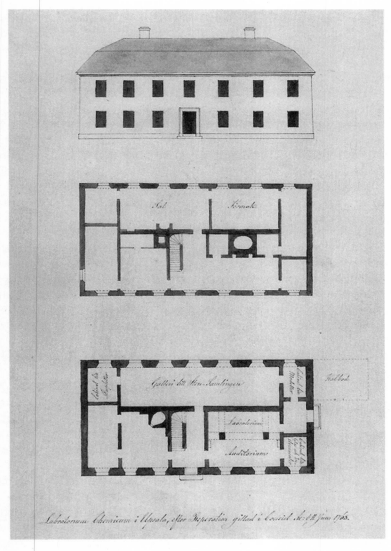

Figure 6. Floor plan of Bergman's *laboratorium chemicum*. Wallerius's smaller laboratory has been slightly enlarged and is marked as both "auditorium" and "laboratorium" (bottom image, lower right). The most imposing room of the building is the gallery for the collection of minerals, which faced the river and was flanked by a chamber for models of industrial installations on the right and a chamber for duplicates on the left (bottom image, top). Photo: Reprosektionen/ Uppsala Universitetsbibliotek (Uppsala University Library).

But the teaching of students was of less importance to Bergman than to Wallerius. While his predecessor had engaged in a didactic and utilitarian enlightenment enterprise, which was very much embedded in the local context of Nordic universities and mining districts, Bergman, in the words of Theodore Porter, "sought truth through rational classification and utility in the growth of learning." He oriented himself away from the local Swedish context and sought an audience of international theoretical chemists.[75] He was also different from his predecessor in that he wanted to show clearly that his laboratory was a place were a chemical investigator conducted his work. In his autobiography, he included a description of the different furnaces, bellows and pieces of chemical equipment that a chemist needed. Instead of following any of Wallerius's schemes, he based his public lectures on an enlarged edition of Teophil Scheffer's lectures at the Board of Mines' Laboratory in Stockholm. Scheffer's lectures consisted mostly of practical recipes and advice on preparing and separating chemical substances. Bergman added some theoretical discussions in the footnotes, but the impression of the lectures as a very practical course in the craft of analysis and synthesis remains.[76] Simultaneously, his advanced, private students took part in the "real" research and became, so to speak, apprentices in experimental chemistry. The process that Wallerius had initiated, of separating chemistry from crafts such as pharmacy, assaying and dyeing, was not continued by Bergman. The subordination of crafts was upheld, however. Wallerius had motivated the superiority of chemistry by applying superior theory to the crafts. Bergman on the other hand, motivated chemistry's elevated position by calling attention to the superiority of the experimental method. To him, there was no need to argue that the methods of the man of science were superior to those of the craftsman. It was self-evident, and needed only to be demonstrated.[77]

In addition, students were taught mining economy and mineralogical natural history. The largest room in Bergman's house was a gallery for the mineral collection. This room took up the space where Wallerius had had his large auditorium, and also his salon. Furthermore, Bergman had a smaller room with models of different machines and industrial installations such as furnaces used in the Swedish mining industry. There was also a second collection of minerals, comprising Swedish minerals organized geographically, according to where they had been found. Bergman's students could get a good overview of the installations, methods and materials of the Swedish mining industry, without leaving his laboratory.[78] If they wanted chemical theory, they had to take his private seminars, where the focus, however, lay on experimental methods. Thus there is no doubt that Bergman washed the slate clean of Wallerius's chemical program.

Wallerius was very critical. In his autobiography there are several passages that criticize the changes that Bergman had wrought on his laboratory and in the teaching of students.

> I did not want anything to be missing in the Laboratories, but the dearth and discomfort for the Professor, became all the greater. Now it is the other way around.[79]

This was a criticism of Bergman, who had had a second floor built, but had decided to use it as his private apartment. Wallerius, on the other hand, claimed that he had wanted to have a second floor, but would have used it to store the mineral collection. According to Wallerius, it was absolutely necessary that the minerals should not be stored on the first floor, since the water from the river seeped into the building during the spring flood. The moisture made the minerals fall apart and changed their colors. Probably he also thought that they transmuted into something different, but it would have been ill-timed to say that in the 1780s. It was of course also bad that the auditorium had been removed. Since Bergman had become professor, Wallerius stated, there had been no public chemical demonstrations, and hardly any medicines had been manufactured, despite the privilege.[80] What Wallerius implied was that Bergman had neglected his duties as a teacher, he had not produced any significant quantities of medicine, and he had put his own comfort before the preservation of the mineral collection of the university. In short, he had not done his duty as a chemist, citizen and servant of the public.

Bergman never criticized Wallerius in public, although he vented his spite against him in private correspondence. But he answered Wallerius's criticism in a more subtle manner, by attacking Wallerius's scientific method. As has been indicated, he had little interest in public demonstrations and the spreading of chemical knowledge to the general public. Instead, he attempted to strengthen the links between teaching and experimentation. Bergman probably saw this as a necessity. From the 1750s onwards, there was a constant stream of new chemical information and a number of new substances were described and discovered. There was also a healthy discussion on how to interpret theoretically new chemical matters of fact. Chemistry was fast becoming a very complex science. Probably Bergman found it difficult to sift out a suitable curriculum of known "truths" to demonstrate to the students in this new atmosphere of discovery. Furthermore, the ethos of chemical investigators during the 1760s, 70s and 80s was that one should avoid putting forward assertive statements on chemical theory. As Joseph Priestley put it, "when all the facts [. . .] are collected, the system will form itself."[81] Instead of teaching theory, Bergman focused on research, and his advanced students were taught to become knowledgeable chemists in their own right.

But, Bergman's turning of the tables on Wallerius had a price. Just as Wallerius claimed, Bergman had turned his back on the public mission of chemistry. Wallerius had built a laboratory in order to spread useful knowledge and to demonstrate the truths of chemistry to as large an audience as possible. His building was a teaching space, a laboratory built for enlightenment, not for research. In Bergman's laboratory building there were two main areas where students were taught. The gallery where the mineral collection was stored was probably for the use of the public students, but it was ill-suited for the performance of chemical demonstrations. Although the public students could view models and minerals, the operations of chemistry became a hidden activity, reserved for those who could afford to pay for the private seminars. Those who could visit these seminars could expect to achieve a high level of analytical competence in a more informal setting. They were apprentices in a highly effective research laboratory. However, this new laboratory room was suspiciously similar to the ancient craft workshops, in which secrets were passed from one generation of craftsmen to the next. Thus Bergman closed the doors of his laboratory to the public. With him, chemistry re-entered the private sphere. But it was not the private sphere of any poor craftsman. Henceforth, chemistry would be an elite enterprise, taught at universities to those who could afford it, and pursued by high-status professionals and wealthy amateurs.

Bergman's two-storey building can be taken to signal this new ideal. Lacking a tower, it did not seek public recognition as a place of importance. Rather it was to be sought out by such people that already knew of it. However, its formal plan and well-proportioned architecture signalled that it was an important place, built for someone with aesthetic sensibilities and high status. Someone who not only aspired to belong to society's elite, but had already gone a long way towards that goal.

Figure 7. Exterior of Bergman's *Laboratorium Chemicum* and garden. Note the four well-dressed gentlemen with hats and canes that are depicted as walking towards the entrance. Engraving by Fredric Acrel. Photo: Repro-och fotoenheten/ Kungliga Biblioteket (National Library of Sweden).

NOTES

1. The building's institutional history is the following: 1753–1858, dept. of chemistry and mineralogy; 1860s–1922, the university's printshop "Berlingska boktryckeriet"; 1923–1927, dept. of hygiene and bacteriology; 1936–1964, institute of racial biology; 1965–1995, dept. of hydrology; 1997 to date, dept. of psychology. During the 1995–97 renovation, many of the interior walls were torn down and new ones were erected. The above-mentioned room is now part of the student cafeteria.
2. Tore Frängsmyr, *Geologi och skapelsetro: Föreställningar om jordens historia från Hiärne till Bergman* (Uppsala, 1967) 246–68.
3. Hjalmar Fors, "Vetenskap i alkemins gränsland: Om J. G. Wallerius Watturiket," *Svenska Linnésällskapets Årsskrift* (1996–97) 33–60.

4. Johan Gottschalk Wallerius, *Hydrologia: Eller Wattu-riket indelt och beskrifvit Jämte Inledning til Vattuprofvers anställande* (Stockholm, 1747) introduction (*"företal"*), fol., 0. Wallerius's hydrological system was a companion piece to his great mineralogical work, the *Mineralogia: eller Mineralriket, indelt och beskrifvit* (Stockholm, 1747). Together the two works were intended to be an outline of a description of all material substances that could be found on Earth.

5. A resounding and inspiring "yes" to these questions can be found in Adi Ophir and Steven Shapin, "The place of knowledge: A methodological survey," *The Place of Knowledge: The Spatial Setting and its Relation to the Production of Knowledge, Science in Context* 4:1 (1991) 3–21. For a general discussion of early laboratories, see Maurice Crosland, "Early laboratories c. 1600–c. 1800 and the location of experimental science," Annals of Science 62:2 (2005).

6. I perceive the argument of this paper as an elaboration of that presented in Frederic Lawrence Holmes, *Eighteenth-Century Chemistry as an Investigative Enterprise* (Berkeley, 1989) 4–10.

7. Ophir and Shapin, "The Place of Knowledge," 3–6. The overall perspective is strongly influenced by Owen Hannaway, "Laboratory Design and the Aim of Science: Andreas Libavius versus Tycho Brahe," *Isis*, 77 (1986) and by Steven Shapin, "The house of experiment in seventeenth-century England," *Isis* 79 (1988).

8. Bruno Latour and Steve Woolgar, *Laboratory Life: The Construction of Scientific Facts* (Princeton, 1986) 27–32. Bruno Latour, *Science in Action: How to Follow Scientists and Engineers through Society* (Cambridge, MA, 1987) 15–6.

9. Holmes, *Eighteenth-Century Chemistry*, 14–6.

10. Ibid., 17–20, quotation on 18.

11. See also Hannaway "Laboratory Design and the Aim of Science," 585.

12. Theodore M. Porter, "The promotion of mining and the advancement of science: The chemical revolution in mineralogy," *Annals of Science* 38 (1981) 553. William A. Cole, *Chemical Literature 1700–1860: A Bibliography with Annotations, Detailed Descriptions, Comparisons and Locations* (London, 1990) 554–5.

13. Johan Gottschalk Wallerius, "Johan Gottschalk Wallerius' självbiografi: Med inledning utgiven av Nils Zenzén," *Lychnos* 1953, 235–259, 245, 248, 250. The dissertations were *An et Quosque Chemia resolvat Corpora Naturalia in illas, a quibus fuerunt composita, Partes?* (Uppsala, 1748) and *Origine et Natura Nitri* (Uppsala, 1749).

14. Carl Ehrenpreus, "Kanslerbref om laboratorium chemicum, Stockholm d. 24 febr. 1752" in, Claes Annerstedt, *Upsala Universitets Historia Bihang 4: Handlingar 1749–1776* (Uppsala, 1912), 75–6. Ulf Göransson, "Uppsala universitet och äganderätten till vissa fastigheter och byggnader för institutionsändamål," unpublished report, (1993), Archive of Uppsala University, 78–80.

15. Åke Stavenow, "Sjuttonhundratalets Upsala: Ett bidrag till stadens byggnadshistoria under frihetstiden," *Upplands Fornminnesförenings Tidskrift* 38 (1923) 188. Wallerius, "Wallerius' självbiografi," 251.
16. Johan Gottschalk Wallerius, "Ödmjukt Memorial" dated 30.03.1753, registered 19.05.1753. Uppsala Universitets Arkiv E3a:53, 461–2. at Uppsala University Library (UUB).
17. Göran Lindahl, *Universitetsmiljö: byggnader och konstverk vid Uppsala Universitet* (Uppsala, 1957) 77–80. Carl Forsstrand, "Uppsala på Linnés tid," *Svenska Linnésällskapets Årsskrift* (1924) 20.
18. Lindahl, *Universitetsmiljö*, 81. Sten Lindroth, *Svensk lärdomshistoria: Frihetstiden* (Stockholm, 1978) 305–6, 311.
19. I do not know, however, if the observatory tower itself was used to exhibit the instruments.
20. As a measure of Wallerius's success in establishing the importance of the building, it can be mentioned that twelve pages in Johan Benedict Busser's description of Uppsala of 1773 were dedicated to the foundation of the chair of chemistry, the erection of the building and the history of the university's mineral collection, which was stored in it. Full references were given to five works by Wallerius, the building appeared on the volume's accompanying map of the town of Uppsala, and was also shown on an engraving (reproduced at the end of this article). Johan Benedict Busser, *Utkast till beskrifning om Uppsala* 2 (Uppsala, 1773) 142–53.
21. For an overview of Uppsala in the mid eighteenth-century, see Forsstrand "Uppsala på Linnés tid," 15–21.
22. Svante Lindqvist, "The spectacle of science: An experiment in 1744 concerning the Aurora Borealis," *Configurations: A Journal of Literature, Science and Technology* 1 (1993) 63.
23. Svante Lindqvist, *Technology on Trial: The Introduction of Steam Power Technology into Sweden, 1715–1736* (Uppsala, 1984) 23–27. Lindroth, *Frihetstiden*, 305–6, 432–435. Johan Gottschalk Wallerius, *Bref om Chemiens Rätta Beskaffenhet Nytta och Wärde* (Stockholm & Uppsala, 1751).
24. Hjalmar Fors, *Mutual Favours: The Social and Scientific Practice of Eighteenth-Century Swedish Chemistry* (Uppsala, 2003) 36–38.
25. An example is the exterior of the house erected as an anatomical theatre and chemical laboratory at the university of Åbo 1759–64, that "showed all the typical traits of a stone building in Finland in the mid-eighteenth century[.]" Rainer Knapas, "C universitetets byggnader" in M. Klinge, R. Knapas, A. Leikola and J. Strömberg, *Kungliga Akademien i Åbo 1640–1808: Helsingfors Universitet 1640*-1990 1 (Helsinki, 1988) 268 (author's translation). However, monumental institutional buildings were erected by universities towards the end of the eighteenth-century, in particular the new botanical institution at Uppsala (finished in 1807). Ibid., 284.
26. Alix Cooper, *Homes and Households*, 2–8, due to be published in K. Park and L. Daston (eds.), *Cambridge History of Science, vol. 3: Early Modern*

Science (Cambridge: Cambridge University Press, forthcoming). See also Londa Schiebinger, *The Mind Has No Sex?: Women in the Origins of Modern Science* (Cambridge, MA & London, 1989) 66–7, 79.

27. Matti Klinge, "B Universitetet som institution" in M. Klinge, R. Knapas, A. Leikola and J. Strömberg, *Kungliga Akademien i Åbo 1640–1808: Helsingfors Universitet 1640*-1990 1 (Helsingfors, 1988) 222–238.

28. Sven Widmalm, *Mellan kartan och verkligheten: Geodesi och kartläggning, 1695–1860* (Uppsala, 1990) 173–4.

29. Klinge, "Universitetet som institution," 222–225, 237. On cooperation between craftsmen and academics in eighteenth-century Uppsala, see Sven Widmalm "Gravören och docenterna: Cosmographiska sällskapet i Uppsala 1758–1778" in G. Broberg, G. Eriksson and K. Johannisson (eds.), *Kunskapens trädgårdar: Om institutioner och institutionaliseringar i vetenskapen och livet* (Stockholm, 1988) 86–91, 100–1. See also Fors, *Mutual Favours*, 169–175. On marriages (and in particular J. G. Wallerius's attempts to squirm out of two promises of marriage) see Henrik Schück, *Från det forna Uppsala: Några kulturbilder* (Stockholm, 1917) 168–183.

30. The most prominent example from eighteenth-century Uppsala is of course Linnaeus. He managed to reserve his chair for his son, Carl von Linné the younger, who held it until his death in 1783. Lindroth, *Frihetstiden* 186, 239.

31. Cooper, *Homes and Households*, 11–12, 17, quotation on 8.

32. For an overview of academic architecture in northern Europe, see Knapas, "universitetets byggnader," 254–65.

33. Wallerius, like many other professors, took in students as lodgers, as is apparent from the acknowledgment in Johannes Kempe (respondent) and J. G. Wallerius (praeses), *De indole maris mortui* (Dissertation: Uppsala, 1751). On Wallerius's family and children, see C. E. Bergstrand, *Johan Gottschalk Wallerius som landtbrukskemist och praktisk jordbrukare* (Stockholm, 1885).

34. Wallerius, "Wallerius' självbiografi," 251–2. Nils Sundquist, "Laboratorium Chemicum: En förnämlig byggnad från 1700-tals-Upsala," *Upsala Nya Tidning* 20.11.1937, 12.

35. Hannaway's article has been much criticized for giving a flawed view of Libavius's alchemy and placing too great an emphasis on the openness of Libavius's chemical house. For the purposes of the present article, it is however Hannaway's astute reading of Libavius as an ideologue that is most relevant. It is not Libavius the alchemist who concerns us here, but Libavius the civic humanist who also was an alchemist. The fact that Libavius innovatively managed to combine these two rather different roles seems to have eluded Hannaway's critics. Hannaway, "Laboratory design and the aim of science." Jole Shackelford, "Tycho Brahe, laboratory design, and the aim of science: Reading plans in context," *Isis* 84 (1993). William R. Newman, "Alchemical symbolism and concealment: The chemical house of Libavius," in P. Galison and E. Thompson (eds.), *The Architecture of Science* (Cambridge, MA & London, 1999).

36. Hannaway, "Laboratory Design and the Aim of Science," 598–600.

37. Wallerius, "Wallerius' självbiografi," 251.
38. Research had no given place at eighteenth-century universities; professors were hired to teach. They conducted research, if any, in their spare time. Fors, *Mutual Favours*, 38–41.
39. Wallerius, "Wallerius' självbiografi," 252. "Catalogus Lectionum Publicarum 1751–64" and "Catalogus Praelectionum" in *Programmata Upsaliensia*, vol. 4, 1745–1772, collection of small prints in a single volume (UUB). Wallerius published his lectures in the monumental *Chemia Physica* (Stockholm, 1759).
40. Hannaway, "Laboratory design and the aim of science," 599–605. Newman, "Alchemical symbolism and concealment," 70–2.
41. Betty J. T. Dobbs, *The Foundations of Newton's Alchemy: or "The Hunting of the Greene Lyon"* (Cambridge, 1975) 26–35. See however, Lawrence Principe, *The Aspiring Adept: Robert Boyle and his Alchemical Quest* (Princeton, 1998) 8–10, for an important note of caution. I must emphasize that I do not perceive this process of dissociation as progress, on the part of chemistry, from something bad to something better. Rather it is a separation of two traditions, both of which are still alive today, but which have different goals and perceptions of nature.
42. Sten Lindroth, "Urban Hiärne och Laboratorium Chymicum," *Lychnos* 1946–47.
43. Cole, *Chemical Literature 1700–1860*, 557. D'Holbach translated works by several German and Swedish chemists. Henry Guerlac, "Some French antecedents of the chemical revolution," *Chymia: Annual Studies in the History of Chemistry* 5 (1959) 100–1.
44. Ursula Klein, "The chemical workshop tradition and the experimental practice: Discontinuities within continuities," *Science in Context* 9:3 (1996) 280.
45. Frängsmyr, *Geologi och skapelsetro*, 232–3.
46. Henry Guerlac, "Some French antecedents of the chemical revolution," 99.
47. See, however, Pamela Long, "Invention, secrecy, and theft: Meaning and context in the study of late medieval technical transmission," *History and Technology* 16 (2000) 224–9, 237–8.
48. Jan Golinski, "Utility and audience in eighteenth-century chemistry: Case studies of William Cullen and Joseph Priestley," *British Journal for the History of Science* 21 (1988) 1–2.
49. Fors, *Mutual Favours*, 99–102.
50. There were of course many others. Wallerius's views on how academic chemistry could reform the diverse "chemical" processes of crafts and commerce can be found in *Bref om chemiens rätta beskaffenhet nytta och wärde* (Uppsala & Stockholm, 1751).
51. Klein, "The chemical workshop tradition," 253–9, 266–7. Crosland, "Early laboratories," 245.
52. Lissa Roberts, "Filling the space of possibilities: Eighteenth-century chemistry's transition from art to science," *Science in Context* 6 (1993) 512.

53. See also Anders Lundgren, "Bergshantering och kemi i Sverige under 1700-talet," *Med hammare och fackla* 29 (1985) 96.
54. For an excellent discussion based on British examples, see Golinski, "Utility and audience," 13–15. For the Swedish example, see above.
55. Wallerius's views on alchemy are clearly expressed in the only surviving letter from him to Torbern Bergman. He was of the opinion that chemistry was indebted to alchemy for many siginficant discoveries, and that such alchemists as were guided by common sense should be distinguished from ignorants and impostors. [J. G. Wallerius] to T. Bergman, undated, unsigned, in Svensk brevväxling till T. Bergman, G21, (UUB).
56. Christoph Meinel, "Theory or practice? The eighteenth-century debate on the scientific status of chemistry," *Ambix* 3 (1983) 127.
57. Hannaway, "Laboratory Design and the Aim of Science," 606–7. Libavius, quoted from ibid., 607. For a differing view, see Newman, "Alchemical symbolism and concealment."
58. Lisbet Koerner, "Daedalus Hyperboreus: Baltic Natural History and Mineralogy in the Enlightenment" in W. Clark, J. Golinski and S. Schaffer (eds.), *The Sciences in Enlightened Europe* (Chicago & London, 1999) 389.
59. Lisbet Koerner, "Daedalus Hyperboreus: Baltic Natural History and Mineralogy in the Enlightenment" in W. Clark, J. Golinski and S. Schaffer (eds.), *The Sciences in Enlightened Europe* (Chicago & London, 1999) 389.
60. Ibid. 398.
61. This process was also of central importance in the exclusion of women from science that occurred during this period. Schiebinger, *The Mind Has No Sex?* 96.
62. It would take us too far from the present topic to investigate Wallerius's chemical world-view. See, however, Fors, *Mutual Favours*, 76–80. For an excellent overview of the preoccupations of experimental chemistry and chemical theory in the eighteenth-century, see Klein, "The chemical workshop tradition."
63. Roberts, "Filling the space," 51.
64. In the previous Swedish research, in particular, Wallerius's importance has been constantly downplayed. For a discussion on this, see Fors, *Mutual Favours*, 68–72.
65. T. Bergman to P. W. Wargentin, November, 1778. In Bergianska avskriftssamlingen 18, in the Archives of the Royal Academy of Sciences, Stockholm (KVA).
66. Torbern Bergman, *Physical and Chemical Essays: Translated from the Original Latin of Sir Torbern Bergman [...] by Edmund Cullen* 1 (London, 1784) xxiii.
67. Lisa Rosner, "Eighteenth-Century Medical Education and the Didactic Model of Experiment" in P. Dear (ed.), *The Literary Structure of Scientific Argument: Historical Studies* (Philadelphia, 1991) 182.
68. It contains several references to Bergman's academic battle with Wallerius. An example is the following, most likely a reference to Wallerius's belief

that all natural objects had their genesis in water: "the purity of truth is corrupted by preconceived opinions concerning the genesis and metamorphosis of matter." Bergman, *Physical and Chemical Essays*, xxiv. For an elaboration of this argument, see Fors, *Mutual Favours*, 83–91.

69. Fors, "Vetenskap i alkemins gränsland." For a survey of the Swedish tradition of mineralogical classification in the eighteenth century, see Lundgren, "Bergshantering och kemi," 103–20. For the international perspective, see Porter, "The promotion of mining and the advancement of science," 543–570. For Wallerius's contribution, ibid., 553–555.

70. For an enlightening discussion on eighteenth-century views on experiments, see Rosner, "Eighteenth-Century Medical Education," 182–199.

71. "The truth is that Bergman trusted laboratory circumstances more than nature itself. Although unable to create nature's original materials, chemists could create structured spaces within which bodies might be combined either in apparent imitation of nature or with results unknown to the natural world. [. . .] In other words, chemists might recast the world as one great chemical workshop." Roberts, "Filling the space of possibilities," 526.

72. Bergman's strong emphasis on laboratory experiment is also evident in the textbook he used, Torbern Bergman (ed.), *H. T. Scheffers chemiske föreläsningar: Rörande salter, jordarter, vatten, fetmor, metaller och färgning* (Uppsala, 1775).

73. Anders Franzén, *Laboratorium Chemicum och gravkapellet, kv Munken, Uppsala stad: Dokumentation av utvändiga snickerifärger Förslag till exteriör färgsättning*, unpublished report, Uppsala, 1995, 4, 7. Cronstedt probably worked under the constraints of sketches made by Bergman; see Torbern Bergman, "Torbern Bergmans självbiografi" in *Uppsala Universitets Årsskrift 1916 program 3*, Äldre svenska biografier 3–4 (Uppsala, 1916) 90.

74. Ibid., 91.

75. Porter, "The promotion of mining," 561. On Bergman's attitude, see for example T. Bergman to B. Bergius, January 1772 in Bergianska Brevsamlingen vol. 16, 190 (KVA).

76. Bergman (ed.), *H. T. Scheffers chemiske föreläsningar*. However, theoretical considerations are always built into any teaching material. For a discussion on some of the reasons behind Bergman's edition and use of this textbook, see Fors, *Mutual Favours*, 96–103.

77. Ibid.

78. Bergman, "Bergmans självbiografi," 90–1.

79. Wallerius, "Wallerius' självbiografi," 251.

80. On laboratories as manufactories, see Ernst Homburg, "The rise of analytical chemistry and its consequences for the development of the German chemical profession (1780–1860)," *Ambix* 46 (1999) 5–6.

81. Roberts, "Filling the space," 51, 519–533. On Bergman's position, ibid., 524–528. Quotation from ibid., 520.

BIRTH OF A TECHNOCRATIC DELIVERY
Spatial Reorganization and Ritual Characteristics of Obstetric Care in Early Twentieth-Century Sweden

EMMA SHIRRAN

INTRODUCTION

Like few other institutions of western society, the hospital has manifested itself in twentieth-century culture by a strong and successful combination of visual representation—through architectural potency—and cultural impact, by the gradual growth of its authority and influence on people's lives. Resembled only by the prison and its close relative, the asylum, the hospital has grown into the core of western life in less than 150 years. Beneath, or rather embedded in, this development lie the rapid professionalization of medical doctors and the creation of new and complex social relations and hierarchies, together with a gradual but meticulously carried out construction of boundaries around the medical disciplines. A public once scared of a literally infectious hospital milieu has been won over by great promises of scientific progress and salvation through medical liturgy. The price has been an ever-increased medicalization of the body—a tendency that can be perceived as stronger within certain areas, such as those touching upon the female reproductive cycle and, most of all, upon the process of giving birth. As an immediate result of new insights regarding antisepsis and the thereupon depending science of bacteriology, puerperal fever was brought to a minimum, thereby drastically lessening mortality rates in Europe's and North America's lying-in wards and hospitals. In fact, bacteriological innovation enabled a boom in hospital development as a whole, and brought public confidence in medicine to an unprecedented level.

Here we will examine some of the less often discussed factors in this area of investigation, touching upon conditions of spatial developments in hospital care through new sets of architectural ideals, and venture into the connections between these new ideals and the paralleled development in hospital practice of new cultural roles, new social patterns of behavior, and their position within early twentieth-century western culture.

TO READ A BUILDING

Buildings express meaning—just like spoken words or a text, they represent ideals and cultural contexts, and they can be interpreted. The prerequisite being that we hold some sort of information about its designated functions, the internal structuring of space informs us about social hierarchies, power and classification. These insights in turn acquire meaning through the subjects, i.e. the relevant historical actors who expressed themselves through these social means and experienced the effects of them. A new function and a new usage does not necessarily change the internal division of space, but invests it with new meaning. A building thus carries, through its continual redefinition by inhabiting subjects, a narrative of its ages.[1] The central architectural structure in the current analysis, the new women's clinic in Lund University Hospital, was opened in 1918, which makes it relatively close to us in time. The building still stands, and is still a part of Lund University Hospital, although not used for its original purpose since 1975 (now serving as a rehabilitation center), and there is ample text and pictorial material documenting its creation. Architect and social scientist Thomas Markus has reasoned around social practice, social relations and the subject as categories in a historical investigation in which the building stands as the central object of analysis. The creation of meaning in itself lies in the social practice (to build a house) as well as in the text (about the house). The construction of meaning and function lies with the subjects, who in themselves define, and are defined by, surrounding social relations, i.e. their culture.[2] Such a definition is slightly exaggerated, but on the whole quite accurate. The material world obviously does not carry any meaning in itself, but is composed of what would be empty structure were it not for the subjects continuously and actively investing it with meaning. Knowing this, it is of great importance to take note of the differences in perception experienced by socially divergent groups within the clinic, i.e. doctors, nurses/midwives and patients. These groups all experience the clinic in different ways in accordance with their respective social status. Through texts and architectural drawings we are able to map social power structures and relations between those subjects that used to move within the clinical structure, and furthermore, which groups controlled its construction and spatial disposition through their control of social and material resources. At the heart of this lies spatial subdivision for the purpose of classification. Who and what is excluded or included, and how? As an interpreter of the clinical space in Lund, I trust my knowledge of the social reality of the historical actors. This knowledge is acquired through texts from their hands, other texts about them and my own cultural closeness to them.[3]

The clinic carries cultural code in its design—it is made for the expression of a certain social hierarchy. The dominating group within this structure, the full owners of the local social code and symbolic capital,[4] can be categorized as "inhabitants," a term borrowed from Hillier/Hansen.[5] In a study of the clinic, doctors are the inhabitants. For the corresponding category the same authors use the term "visitor," i.e. an individual passing through for a limited time, thereby subjecting herself to external labelling beyond her control, and without full knowledge of, or control over, the local cultural/social coding. In the clinic, patients are visitors. The social coding and classification are comprised of ideas from within medicine, and clinical ideals as expressed through spatial structure and inhabitants. Nurses and midwives share some characteristics from each group, being as they were (and are) partly initiated inhabitants. However, they remain unable to control the full scope of symbolic and cultural coding, a position shared with the visitors. Parallels are possible; Hillier/Hansen speak of the attendants, or guards you encounter in museums as ". . . uniformed agents of the inhabitants . . . ,"[6] that is, representatives of the controlling social group, the inhabitants. Inhabitants are, in the case of museums, seldom visible amongst the exhibits, but fully control what and how exhibitions represent. The doctor-nurse relation is a similar one, where nurses serve as intermediaries and representatives of what will only fully be controlled by medical doctors.

THE BUILDING—WHEN AND HOW IT WAS CONSTRUCTED. BASIC ATTRIBUTES.

The Lund University Hospital's women's clinic was designed by the architect Salomon Sörensen in collaboration with Professor Elis Essen-Möller. The latter of these men had become the first professor of gynaecology and obstetrics at the Lund medical faculty in 1900.

Mentored and brought forward by the professor of surgery, Jacques Borelius, he soon showed himself to possess a somewhat prodigious talent and great networking abilities (see figures nr. 1 & 2). He spent twenty years in the older and smaller lying-in ward (to be described below), but was during that time able, through his friendly relations with Professor Borelius, to dispose of around twenty beds in the surgical clinic for obstetrical and gynaecological purposes. Essen-Möller then planned and obtained financing for the new women's clinic in the scarce wartime of 1918. This clinic, the first one of its kind in Sweden, was considered state of the art in the eyes of its contemporaries, and was as such comprised of three formerly separate units, namely: an obstetric ward, an obstetric/gynaecological surgical clinic and an outpatient clinic. Opened in 1918, it soon became outdated and was rebuilt and extended in the 1950s, and then—only twenty years later—taken out of its original use in the early 1970s (see figures nr. 4 & 5). It is built of red brick, in the shape of an irregular L (therefore lacking symmetry), and surrounding a semi-enclosed courtyard. It lacks the ornamental character of earlier hospital buildings, but it has not yet reached the square cubes of later hospital architecture, starting from the 1930s onwards (only fully realized in the massive hospital blocks of the 1970s). Its architectural style could very well be called a subtle jugendstil (art nouveau). The historian Anders Åman has put significant emphasis on the side corridor, contra central corridor as a definite style break in hospital architecture occurring in the 1920s—the central corridor being adopted after 1920.[7] The Lund women's clinic adheres to the older style in that it is indeed constructed with side corridors. However, other attributes point towards the above-mentioned "modern" architectural trends, as may be illustrated through a comparison with the Lund surgical clinic built in 1868. This older structure has a facade of heavy ornamental attributes, a cathedral-like rose window, and a symmetrical layout.[8]

Jacques Borelius wrote of the women's clinic and the ideals taken into consideration for its construction: "The aim is, by locating all sick beds in wards facing south and surgical wards with maternity wards facing north, to keep the latter isolated from the sick, and also to isolate the lecture rooms and residence halls."[9] Separated wards, free-flowing air and an abundance of space dominated the hygiene discussion of the time—in spite of newer bacteriological theories already being present. The exact amount of space required, measured in square metres per patient, is outlined in contemporary literature on appropriate hospital building standards.[10] Fear of sepsis and the

Figure 1. Professor of gynaecology and obstetrics Elis Essen-Möller (1870–1956). © Lund University Library.

Figure 2. Professor of surgery Jacques Borelius (1859–1921). Statue outside former surgical clinic, Lund. © Emma Shirran.

ongoing fight against puerperal fever were two probable causes for this slight obsession with airiness. The phenomenon could possibly be significant of a certain "resistance" in the introduction of new scientific ideas. This being the early days of the above-mentioned insights into bacterial micro-organisms, these insights were not yet fully integrated with scientific thinking, but rather merged with old ideas and strategies for the treatment of infection. Another major influence on the construction of the new women's clinic was a newly passed reform from 1907, which granted Lund Hospital a full right to give clinical teaching. This meant that medical students at Lund University no longer had to end their studies with a clinical internship at the Karolinska Institute (KI) in Stockholm. Therefore, a considerable part of the new women's clinic was built to fully accommodate the residential needs of these students, who had to live and work at the clinic for 4 months. Single bedrooms, a bathroom and a kitchen were built

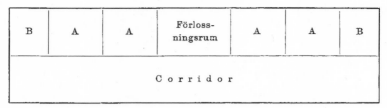

A = Rum för 2ne Patienter
B = —   — 1   Patient

Figure 3. Maternal ward of 1882, top floor. Illustration from Elis Essen-Möller, *Bidrag till förlossningskonstens och den obstetriska undervisningens historia i Skåne*, Lund, 1943, 195.

Figure 4. New Women's Clinic of 1918. Main entrance. © Emma Shirran.

Figure 5. New Women's Clinic of 1918. Eastern view of the west wing, candidate entrance to the left. © Emma Shirran.

for this purpose. Laboratories, a specimen museum and overnight rooms for nurses were also regarded as essential components of the new building. As we shall see, in the end product of Sörensen and Essen-Möller there was comparatively little room for the actual patients, and a lot more dedicated to the surrounding activities.

THE OLD LYING-IN WARD

For the sake of comparison, let us take a brief look at the predecessor to Essen-Möller's state-of-the-art modern clinic—the lying-in ward (henceforth, I shall use the Swedish equivalent of a lying-in ward, a *BB*, which is short for *barnbördshus*) built in 1882 (see figure nr. 3).[11] The construction of this ward was swiftly decided upon by the hospital's board of directors after a small but significant outbreak of puerperal fever in 1881, in the earlier *BB* on Paradisgatan. The building of 1882 had two floors, the bottom one dedicated to the living quaters of the head midwife and her maid, and the top one to delivery and lying-in confinement.[12] Electricity had not been installed. Water was heated over an iron stove in the delivery room. A total of sixteen women could be admitted, but during the first fifteen years of the twentieth century, the number of childbearing women who sought hospital help in Lund tripled (from 370 in 1900 to 1000 in 1915). This massive increase in demand put heavy pressure on the facilities.[13] Obstetric interventions with forceps and similar instruments took place by the meagre light of a gas lamp, and patients in need of surgery had to be carried down the stairs and over the courtyard to the surgical clinic, where gynaecology and obstetrics held a share of first twelve, and later twenty-two, beds. The *BB* of 1882 had neither lecture rooms nor offices for doctors. The Royal Medical Board, which inspected the facilities in 1902, did not find that any specific complaints could be made with regard to the maternity ward ". . . except possibly that the location of the delivery room, in the central axis and surrounded by lying-in rooms, might be slightly inappropriate."[14] This statement reflects upon the limited expectations concerning obstetric care at this time. When the clinic on Paradislyckan was extended and rebuilt in 1901–1905, there were plans for a small expansion of the *BB* that would have added twenty-five much-needed beds for gynaecological surgery (see figure nr. 8).[15] These plans were never realized. Instead, things stayed the same until the opening of Essen-Möller's new women's clinic in 1918. However—once circumstances changed, they changed radically. Gynaecology and obstetrics went from a minor unit within the hospital to a large separate clinic literally overnight.

TOOLS OF ANALYSIS

With the support of analytical tools from Hillier/Hanson, the women's clinic of Lund can be reconstructed as seen respectively from the perspective of the medical doctor, the medical student, the nurses/midwives and the patient. The objective here is to clarify the different degrees of accessibility for each group within the building, starting from a certain point in the facility by mapping out the possible ways to reach further into the building structure. It is not sufficient to limit the social categories to inhabitants (doctors) and visitors (patients), as there are two more significant groups with designated areas (and separate relations to space) within the building, namely nurses/midwives and medical students. This is not to cast aside the utility of "inhabitants" and "visitors" as categories, but rather to introduce shades of grey. The degree of access available to each of these categories in turn delineates to us a clearer pattern of social inclusion and exclusion at the clinic. A brief reference to distance as experienced by members of these social groups will add a dimension to the analysis, and show how access can be relative to distance, and how distance thereby affects the interaction of movements of individuals within a respective social category.[16] A prerequisite for this methodology has been complementary eye-witness sources regarding the original use of the building, sources that let us know what might not have been readable from the architect's original drawing. Furthermore, the internal structure and usage of a building is continuously renegotiable within its static architectural frames. A slight mutation within the residing symbolical capital (for example, a shift in priorities, or a complete new usage) could change its internal utilization drastically. This is true of Essen-Möller's women's clinic, and through text from the hands of first-hand "witnesses" we are informed of some internal alterations of space.

DEPTH VERSUS SHALLOWNESS—SPATIAL ACCESS IN RELATION TO POWER AND CONTROL

We should bear in mind the control over resources exercised by the medical community at this point. Elis Essen-Möller worked, as has already been mentioned, in collaboration with the architect prior to construction of "his" women's clinic. Behind Essen-Möller stood Jacques Borelius, not only professor of surgery, but also entrusted with the position of hospital director, member of the board of directors of Lund University, and holding a chair on the communal board of directors for the City of Lund, amongst other honorary duties. His networking capabilities can be regarded as a major driving force behind the hospital expansion of 1901–1905, and even more so during the second stage of development 1915–1918 (see figures nr. 8 & 9). His foremost protégé, Essen-Möller, was given full control over distribution of resources regarding the construction of a new state-of-the-art women's clinic. The hierarchical structuring—the inclusion/exclusion—of social categories within the clinic is a structuring as seen through the eyes of the dominant social class, a class in complete control of resources and therefore in possession of power (and the tools of power) through architectural layout. Power is viewed here as the ultimate result of control over resources.

In spatial structures, power is usually associated with depth of placement and limited access. The interaction between inhabitants and visitors takes place in shallow parts with clear delineation from those spaces to which inhabitants have exclusive access. However, there are exceptions to this rule. In one type of western institution the opposite seems to be true—inhabitants move freely in a shallow pattern with a constant high flow of visitors and inhabitants moving through, whereas visitors mainly inhabit inner delineated spaces. This is noted in Hillier/Hansen as a phenomenon true of the hospital. Such a "reversed building" is constructed so that ". . . patients [. . .] occupy the primary cells, while [. . .] doctors occupy the distributed system and move freely in it."[17] A placement within the clinical heartland endows the patient with a status of being monitored and controlled, and moreover kept separate from other subjects within her social group. By their shallow patterns of movement, doctors, and to some extent nurses, control the amount of interaction allowed to reach the deeply kept patients. The control of access marks a high value of power and is relative to the amount of social status held by the medical community. As this status rises around 1900, clinical departments are designed with the increasing tendency to isolate patients at the inner end of spatial structures.

INNER STRUCTURE OF THE WOMEN'S CLINIC

As seen in the architectural drawings, the clinic is outlined as follows (see figures nr. 6 & 7).

Although a seemingly massive structure in its total lack of pavilions, the clinic is on the ground floor a highly compartmentalized construction, dividing—at the same time as physically cutting off—the interacting social groups within. With its own entrance from the courtyard, and with its separate staircase leading upward through storeys above, completely separated from other parts of the ground floor, this makes the candidate dwellings separate and distinct, with the exclusive set of stairs acting as an umbilical cord to the wards above. To accommodate them during four months of service, six rooms, a kitchen and a bathroom were installed for the wellbeing of these students. Needless to say, these spatial circumstances point to the importance with which they were viewed, and to the weight their presence carried in the building—although still only beginners in their

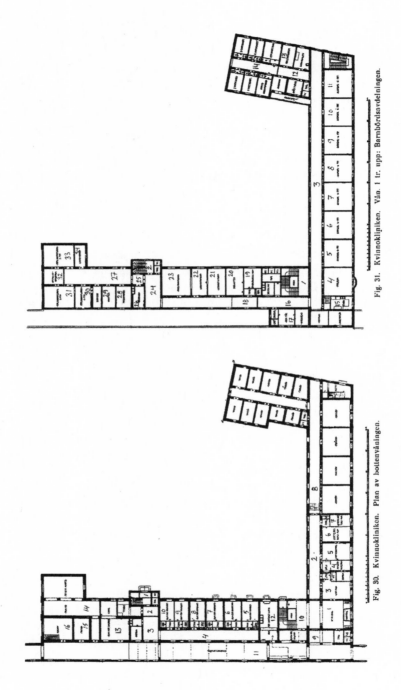

Fig. 31. Kvinnokliniken. Vån. 1 tr. upp: Barnbördsavdelningen.

Fig. 30. Kvinnokliniken. Plan av bottenvåningen.

44

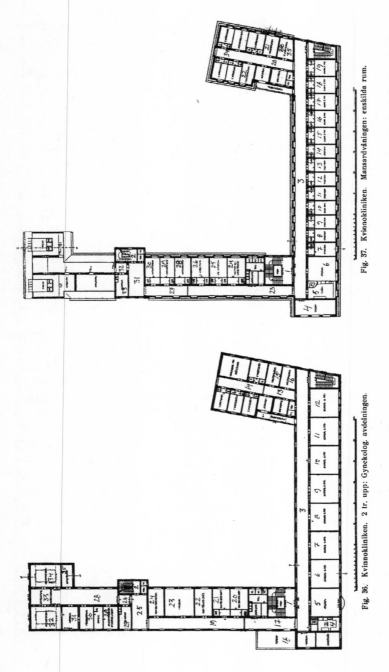

Fig. 37. Kvinnokliniken. Mansardvåningen: enskilda rum.

Fig. 36. Kvinnokliniken. 2 tr. upp: Gynekolog. avdelningen.

Figure 6. Floor plans of the new clinic 1918. In Jacques Borelius, *Malmöhus läns lasarett i Lund 1768–1918*, Lund, 1918. (Architects' original drawings are no longer available.) Numbers added by Emma Shirran. These plans are explained by room numbers (in relation to function and spatial availability) in figure nr. 7.

45

field, about to cross the threshold of the initiated medical community. The other part of the bottom floor is accessed through a larger vestibule, which leads straight to the outpatient department, intake for delivery and the junior doctor. Other floors are reached by means of a lift and a flight of stairs, facing the entrance vestibule. A corridor running along the west wing is accessible from the left side of the vestibule. The eastern wing of the bottom floor is used entirely for storage. A maternity ward is found one floor up, extending northward—located directly above the students' dwellings and in immediate connection with them through the staircase. The western corridor leads to a lecture room, a laboratory and a head doctor's office with its own adjoining library. Facing south and in connection with the lift and stairs are seven ward rooms, each holding six patients, a kitchen, a security office, and a day room for ambulant patients. The east wing contains a waste room, an isolation room, and rooms for nurses and midwives. The second floor has no apparent cut off in spatial communication lines, but is interconnected through doors and corridors. The third floor contains the gynaecological ward. Directly above the maternity ward and the student dwellings at the top of the west wing are two surgical theaters, linked through a sterilization room, and connected to a wash room, a bandage room and a dressing room for the operating surgeon and his assistant. These rooms can alternatively be reached via a corridor in connection with the student staircase. South of these stairs in the west wing are a room for patients who have just been operated on, a specimen museum, a room for the ward head nurse, and a room for the surgical nurse. The southern corridor on this floor is constructed like the one on the second floor, with a side corridor, a day room and a room for nurses/midwives. The next floor, the mansard floor, contains single and double rooms for paying patients. The upper part of the west wing holds the attic and, more importantly, skylight windows for the surgical procedures taking place beneath. The west corridor leads to the night nurse's room, a room for cleaning personnel, and a room for the ward head nurse. The south corridor has a balcony, described by Jacques Borelius as a ". . . roomy loggia with grand view over the Öresund."[18] (There was a balcony in the gynaecological/surgical ward; it was of the same size and facing west, but it was not described in as glamorous terms—Borelius called it a "terrace".) The mansard floor kitchen is larger, probably because of the greater amount of service required by paying patients. The east wing holds cleaning staff, nurses and an isolation room.

INTERNAL FUNCTIONS OF THE NEW CLINIC

One of this building's important functional areas, the delivery intake, was at the time of construction situated by the ground floor vestibule. Here, women were washed and shaved before being led by a nurse to the lift and taken to the second-floor maternity ward at the end of the west wing. "Those of you who have been at the old clinic [1918 version] can easily imagine how far it was for us to run from the delivery ward to the vestibule intake when the bell rang. Sometimes you got there just in time for the patient to go into final stage labour . . ."[19] Looking at the situation with the perspective of a nurse or a midwife, distances were considerable and practical management difficult. However, from a medical student's point of view, the construction of the ground floor with an exclusive staircase provided this group with *easy access and efficiency in relation to their task.* Since the student floor was completely separated by walls on the ground floor, medical students were guaranteed absolute access to the most efficient way through the spatial structure. The clinical "heart," i.e. the delivery room and the surgical theaters, were consequently located at great structural depth for a midwife or a patient, but at a superficial level for a student or a doctor. Furthermore, a majority of the nurses' lodgings were located at the end of the east wing, consequently as far as possible from delivery and surgery (at the end of the west wing). The head doctor's room was situated on the second floor closely adjacent to the student staircase, the neighboring laboratories and the lecture room—thus within close reach of the delivery rooms and the surgical theaters.[20] The head doctor's assistant had a room farther down the same corridor. The pattern of movement of the nurse was controlled by and centralized around the lift/stairs starting at the vestibule and going upward. That made the ward rooms and kitchens shallow, but put delivery and surgery at the deepest level. The exceptions were the head ward nurse and the surgical nurse (residing in the western corridor of the gynaecological/surgical floor), and the night nurses (in the western part of the mansard floor), but even then we are relatively deep in relation to the bottom floor vestibule entrance. The west wing, with laboratories, museum, the head doctor's room, and so on can be viewed as an insulating social "airlock," or controlling phase, between the core activities taking place at the end of the west wing and the more mundane practices connected with ward rooms, isolation and nurses' lodgings in the south corridor and east wing. This was especially true for delivered women on the second floor, as they were

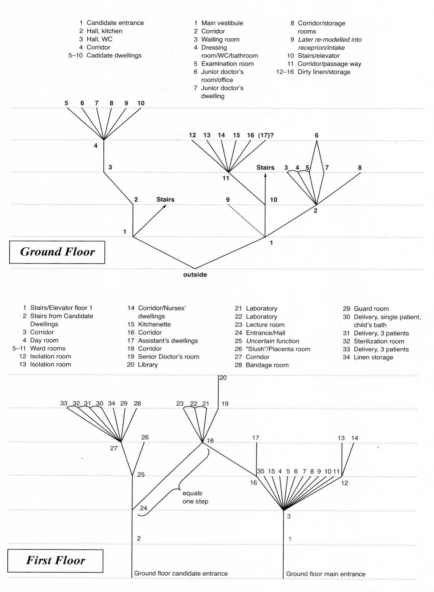

Figure 7. Graph for making visible the degree of accessibility as experienced by different groups within the hospital body. Every level (horizontal line) represents one step further into the structure. Note, for example, that the candidate dwellings were deeply located from the point of view of nurses, midwives and patients, but in a shallow position seen from their own perspective. This was thanks to their having their own entrance and staircase, providing easy access to all four floors. One can easily imagine the struggle for an on-call midwife, though, as she

1 Stairs/Elevator/Main entrance
2 Stairs to/from candidate dwellings
3 Corridor
4 Kitchenette
5 Day room
6–12 Ward rooms
13 Corridor
14 Assistant nurses'
dwellings/Assembly room
15 Isolation room
16 isolation room
17 Corridor
18 Terrace
19 Corridor
20 Ward nurse's room
21 Surgical nurse's room
22 Ward nurse's room
23 Specimen Museum
24 Recovery room
25 Hall/Entrance
26 *Uncertain function*
27 "Slush"
28 Corridor
29 Dressing room for Surgeon with
Assistant
30 Bandage room
31 Laundry
32 Surgical theatre
33 Sterilization room
34 Surgical theatre
35 Linen storage
36 Guard's room

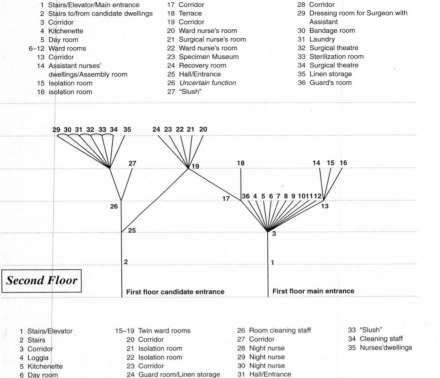

Second Floor

First floor candidate entrance

First floor main entrance

1 Stairs/Elevator
2 Stairs
3 Corridor
4 Loggia
5 Kitchenette
6 Day room
7–14 Private ward rooms
15–19 Twin ward rooms
20 Corridor
21 Isolation room
22 Isolation room
23 Corridor
24 Guard room/Linen storage
25 Ward nurse's room
26 Room cleaning staff
27 Corridor
28 Night nurse
29 Night nurse
30 Night nurse
31 Hall/Entrance
32 *Uncertain function*
33 "Slush"
34 Cleaning staff
35 Nurses'dwellings

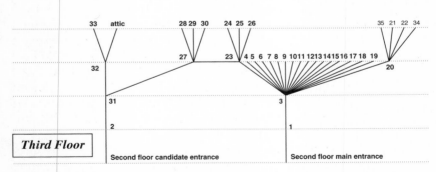

Third Floor

Second floor candidate entrance

Second floor main entrance

had to find her way down the structure, and then walk a patient in labor from the main entrance to the deeply located delivery rooms (at 30, 31 and 33, first floor). Regular wards were located at a relatively shallow level (for example 5–11, ground floor), whereas paying patients were kept on the top floor, at a deep level. Key practices—delivery rooms, surgical theaters, laboratories, etc.—were placed at a relatively deep level (for example 19–23, first floor and 30–33, first floor). © Emma Shirran.

brought from delivery through the west wing, passing on their way the head doctor, the laboratory, a lecture room and an assistant's room, and eventually ending up in the ward rooms of the south corridor.

The clinic has been rebuilt and internally re-disposed several times. The intake for delivery was, for example, eventually moved to the former students' entrance. In its original shape, it does tell us about the prevailing social hierarchies and ideals of early twentieth-century medicine. Above all it tells a story of gynaecology and obstetrics establishing itself as a separate and highly valued medical discipline, and of its being equipped with the symbolic and material resources needed to rule its own destiny.

CONCLUDING DISCUSSION

A study of the Lund University Hospital from 1900 to 1918 poses interesting questions regarding its rather sudden physical expansion, and internal reorganization. We see here a gradual formalization of hospital work, and the introduction of a clinical, disciplinary sub-division of specialities—all in just a couple of decades—which points to a sudden cultural turnaround in society's understanding of hospital care and medicine. The choice of maternity care as a subject for analysis was made for a number of reasons, the first being that women's clinical units at Swedish, and other western hospitals, had a sudden breakthrough around 1900. Gynaecology and obstetrics would now be spatially merged, and women would prefer hospital births in steadily increasing numbers. In part, this development can be attributed to the great innovation of bacteriology—which had a special significance for childbirth in its effect of dramatically lowering the high rate of puerperal fever that used to haunt maternity wards. However, to give new hygienic insights all the credit for this change would be a gross misconception. One of the more prominent professors at Lund Hospital during the nineteenth century, Carl Jacob Ask, studied with Lister in Edinburgh, and became thoroughly familiar with the ideas of aseptic methods in hospital care. Yet whatever knowledge he might have had, he did not put it to use in Lund. Eyewitnesses speak of him smoking a cigar during surgery, letting the sweat from his forehead dribble down into the wound of the patient (whilst commenting that his "sweat was sterile anyway"). The sterilizing instrument boiler bought during his residency spent its time locked up in a wardrobe.[21] The idea of what we think of as modern hospital care could only flourish in the right cultural *context*, regardless of the basic and groundbreaking scientific discoveries already present. This contextual milieu came about as the medical community grew stronger in its relation to science, and was granted control over necessary economical funds. Turn-of-the-century Sweden, along with many other parts of the western world, provided such a context. However, the Swedish situation in relation to other countries differed regarding the professional situation of Swedish midwives. As has been pointed out by Swedish historians Lisa Öberg, Christina Romlid and Lena Milton, Swedish midwives traditionally were educated to a high level, higher than their colleagues around the world.[22] They were early on licensed to handle instrumental births, otherwise exclusively practiced by (male) medical doctors.[23] For these professional women, the shift in social relations and power structures at the introduction of hospitalized childbirth entailed a dramatic change of status. Starting out as locally employed and largely self-sufficient, they gradually had to give way as birth was institutionalized. And although still working, they were now brought in to manage secondary tasks within the hospital. Their position became that of an intermediary between patient and doctor, a status emerging as clearly visible in their pattern of movement within the building.[24] A high level of education would provide no protection against professional degradation.

Expanded and fully developed medical services, headed by specialist medical doctors, were on a political level part of a plan to persuade people to accept new ideals of living, such as cleanliness and proper bodily care. This entailed the bringing of childbirth away from the private sphere and, through heavy medicalization, into public control. Childbirth as a cultural concept took on the shape of a great risk, an event that had to be placed under the supervision of medical professionals in a technocratic system of medical apparatus.[25] The modern maternity ward represents a new order. Its structure, organizational as well as physical, represents the symbolic and ritual expression of this new order (and/or these new ideas). The structural set up and design of Essen-Möller's clinic, put in the context of being the first *modern* women's clinic in Sweden, carries the above-mentioned symbolic and ritual values in its physical disposition, and so speaks to us about the social categories that used to inhabit it. The establishment of larger maternity wards in connection to surgical facilities and obstetric resources interestingly predates the actual willingness of women to give birth in hospital. Only after the careful medical establishment of gynaecology/obstetrics as a separate and prominent medical discipline and the building of larger maternity

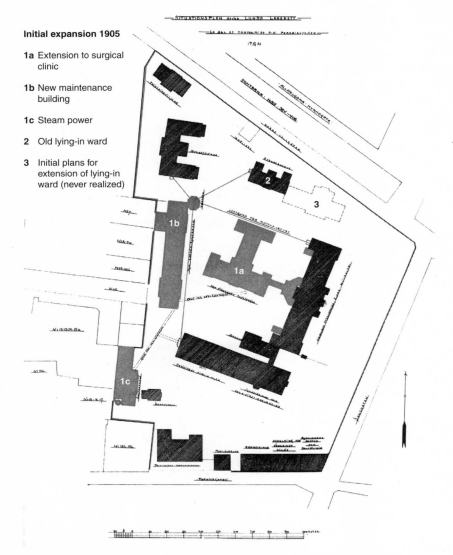

Initial expansion 1905

1a Extension to surgical clinic

1b New maintenance building

1c Steam power

2 Old lying-in ward

3 Initial plans for extension of lying-in ward (never realized)

Figure 8. Overview presented with Lund Hospital's yearly report 1905 (Lund University Hospital Administrative Archives, Lund). Also in Alfred Flaum, *Lasarettet i Lund 1768–1968*, Lund, 1968. Numbers and adhering descriptions added by Emma Shirran.

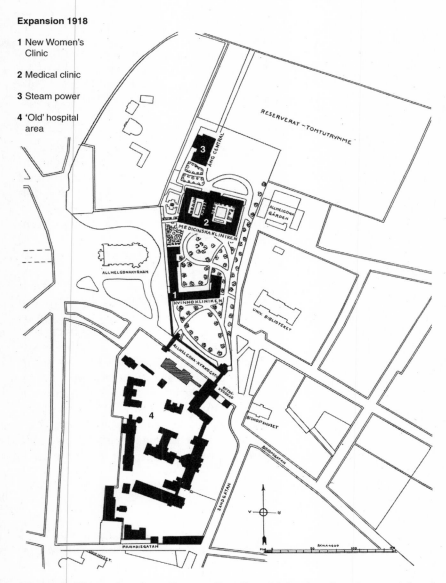

Expansion 1918

1 New Women's Clinic

2 Medical clinic

3 Steam power

4 'Old' hospital area

Figure 9. Illustration from Jacques Borelius, *Malmöhus läns lasarett i Lund 1768–1918*, Lund, 1918 (fig. 15). Numbers and adhering descriptions added by Emma Shirran.

53

wards within the hospitals—only then were women gradually convinced of the "necessity" of medical supremacy over childbirth. A major part of the complications of labor could for a long time be attributed to malnutrition and rickets, which deformed the female pelvis in such a way as to obstruct the emerging fetus. This then often resulted in prolonged childbirth, severe physical damage, and possibly a dead fetus. A subsequent infection and the consequent death of the mother were common results of such circumstances. One might argue, since health improved over all, and the problem of deformed pelvises gradually diminished during the early twentieth century, that the major reason for supervised hospital births would then have disappeared. Instead, ongoing cultural medicalization of birth has established it as a pathological process entailing great risk.

Medical supervision of birth, such as seen in the build-up of the Lund women's clinic, has become a natural choice for the majority of western women. In its disposition, the clinic resembles a standardized landscape, where a maximum organization of the social in relation to space has been achieved—"once we have experienced one, we know how to 'behave' in each of them because they seem to be organised following an invisible rationale . . ."[26] Our society has thus been fostered in the modern hospital's clinical practice. In the early twentieth century, gradually increasing medical specialization, as supported by a new scientific link with bacteriology, promoted the construction of a clinical medicine within new carefully laid out spatial structures. Parallel to, and intertwined with these developments, an initially hesitant public was convinced of the new medical supremacy—a change in social behavior that was, and is, most clearly spelled out in the medicalization of childbirth.

NOTES

1. Something similar to this has been expressed by Thomas Markus: "From the moment it is conceived, through its design, production, use, continuous reconstruction in respond to changing use, until its final demolition, the building is a developing story, traces of which are always present." Thomas A. Markus, *Buildings & Power: Freedom & Control in the Origin of Modern Building Types*, London/New York, 1993, 5.
2. See Thomas A. Markus, *Buildings & Power: Freedom & Control in the Origin of Modern Building Types*, London/New York, 1993, 8.
3. For a similar analysis, see Brandt/Sloane, "Of Beds and Benches: Building the Modern American Hospital," from *The Architecture of Science*, Cam-

bridge (MA) 1999, 281, "Ultimately, embedded in hospital design—in the nature of the physical plant and its aesthetic—are notions of normative doctor-patient relations, physician-staff relations, and medical and scientific authority, as well as specific explanatory models for understanding and treating disease."

4. Social code and symbolic capital refer to the shared and exclusive knowledge within a social group regarding the *implicit meanings* of certain behaviors and actions. The ability within the group to interpret this symbolic language serves to mark its boundaries against 'the other,' and thereby reinforce and build upon its internal image. In the case of doctors, examples of these 'others' would be physically neighboring social groups represented by nurses, other staff and patients; or in a broader perspective even members of the non-academic working class (which would of course include a large percentage of the patients).

5. Bill Hillier, Julienne Hanson, *The Social Logic of Space*, Cambridge, 1984.

6. Bill Hillier, Julienne Hanson, *The Social Logic of Space*, Cambridge, 1984, 183.

7. Anders Åman, *Om den offentliga vården: Byggnader och verksamheter vid svenska vårdinstitutioner under 1800- och 1900-talen. En arkitekturhistorisk undersökning*, Uddevalla, 1976, 274f.

8. Floors 1 and 2 hold two wards per wing, designed for ten patients each, and have single rooms at each end of the corridor. Office, examination room and operating theater are located in the central axis of the building. This according to an architect's sketch in Anders Åman, *Om den offentliga vården: Byggnader och verksamheter vid svenska vårdinstitutioner under 1800- och 1900-talen. En arkitekturhistorisk undersökning*, Uddevalla, 1976, 194f.

9. Jacques Borelius, *Malmöhus läns lasarett i Lund 1768–1918: De äldre lasarettsbyggnadernas historia*, Lund/Leipzig 1918, 45. Author's translation from the Swedish original.

10. See Gustav Birch Lindgren, *Svenska lasarettsbyggnader: Modern lasarettsbyggnadskonst i teori och praktik*, Stockholm, 1934, 43, which lays down 21 square metres of air per patient as a basic requirement. See also Anders Åman, Om den offentliga vården: Byggnader och verksamheter vid svenska vårdinstitutioner under 1800- och 1900-talen. En arkitekturhistorisk undersökning, Uddevalla, 1976, 188. Åman concludes that the demand for individual space in hospitals grew during the 19th century, and thereafter sank proportionally to the establishment of bacteriology.

11. The term "lying-in" is used here (and commonly elsewhere) for the earlier, simpler type of obstetrical ward of the nineteenth century, whereas a "women's clinic" signifies the new type of combined obstetric/gynaecological clinic as it emerged in the early twentieth century. These terms are thus respectively applied here to mark type, character and chronology of the ward or clinic in question. The Swedish terms "barnbördshus," or "BB," and "kvinnoklinik" bear the same meaning and relation.

12. No plan of the bottom floor is available at this moment; I am therefore unable to describe it in greater detail.
13. See Elis Essen-Möller, *Bidrag till förlossningskonstens och den obstetriska undervisningens historia i Skåne: Ett bidrag till Lunds universitets historia*, Lund/Leipzig 1943, 264 about the sudden flow of new patients.
14. *Berättelse till Kongl. Medicinalstyrelsen öfver af undertecknad* [R.A.Wawrinsky] *den 7 juni 1902 företagen inspektion af Malmöhus läns sjukvårdsinrättningar i Lund*, bilaga till lasarettsdirektionens protokoll från 4/8 1902. [*Report to Royal Medical Board regarding inspection of Lund Hospital on June 7'Th 1902*, Appendix to Lund Hospital Board minutes from meeting, August 4'Th, 1902.]
15. See Lasarettets årsredogörelse 1905 [Lund Hospital annual report, 1905] in Alfred Flaum, *Lasarettet i Lund 1768–1968*, Lund, 1968, 196; Elis Essen-Möller, *Bidrag till förlossningskonstens och den obstetriska undervisningens historia i Skåne: Ett bidrag till Lunds universitets historia*, Lund/Leipzig, 1943, 264; Elis Essen-Möller, *Anteckningar om artis obstetriciæ professionen i Lund 1783–1918*, Lund/Leipzig, 1918, 34.
16. An alternative approach is described by Hillier/Hansen as RA, Relative Asymmetry, to be explained as depth of placement of a certain space in a building divided by the total amount of space (of the building), where low value equals high flow and mix of people, and high value means depth and segregation. See Bill Hillier, Julienne Hanson, *The Social Logic of Space*, Cambridge, 1984, 108f and Thomas A. Markus, *Buildings & Power: Freedom & Control in the Origin of Modern Building Types*, London/New York, 1993, 14.
17. Bill Hillier, Julienne Hanson, *The Social Logic of Space*, Cambridge, 1984, 184. This anomaly seems to be valid for the more powerful of western societies, different types of hospitals and prisons.
18. Jacques Borelius, *Malmöhus läns lasarett i Lund 1768–1918: De äldre lasarettsbyggnadernas historia*, Lund/Leipzig, 1918, 49. Author's translation from original text.
19. From 'Svea Lundins minnen' [Excerpt from 'The memoirs of Svea Lundin'] i *Minnen från Gamla KK*, Lund 1977, 10. Author's translation from original text.
20. Thereby assuming that the resident doctor on duty made use of the students' staircase.
21. Quoted from an article by Gustaf Petrén, "Om sjukvårdsförhållanden och den kirurgiska verksamheten på Lunds lasarett på 1880-talet," from *Svenska läkartidningen*, nr 15, 16/4 1943, 996–1003.
22. Lisa Öberg, *Barnmorskan och läkaren: Kompetens och konflikt i svensk förlossningsvård 1870–1920*, Stockholm, 1996; Christina Romlid, *Makt, motstånd och förändring: Vårdens historia speglad genom det svenska barnmorskeväsendet 1663–1908*, Uppsala/Stockholm, 1998; Lena Milton, *Folkhemmets barnmorskor: Den svenska barnmorskekårens professionalisering under mellan- och efterkrigstid*, Uppsala, 2001.

23. Swedish midwives acquired the right to become certified in the use of obstetric instruments in 1829.
24. Interestingly, Swedish midwives have gradually regained some of their lost social status, and are today managing most normal births—a doctor only being called for in case of "complications." However, the vast majority of Swedish births are still handled in the hospital.
25. Granted, childbirth was already associated with risk, albeit from the late nineteenth century onward for a new set of reasons as formulated by the flourishing clinical system here discussed.
26. Miodrag Mitrasinovic, *Theme Parks*, Dissertation at the University of Florida, 1998:4. Mitrasinovic analyzes Disney's amusement parks as a form of heterotopian milieu absolutely connected to time—heterotopias of the moment.

A MACHINE TO WORK IN

The Ultracentrifuge and the Modernist Laboratory Ideal

SVEN WIDMALM

INTRODUCTION

In a secret report to Harry Truman in 1949, the Central Intelligence
Agency presented an overview of Swedish science, its strengths and
weaknesses. The report was meant to show whether there was reason
to fear leakage of sensitive scientific—in particular, nuclear—information from Sweden to the Soviet Union. According to the CIA,
there were no such risks. The Swedes were thought to be friendly towards the West and they had little interest in nuclear weaponry. In
short, they were harmless. This impression was strengthened by an
evaluation of the general level of scientific research in the country. It
was, according to the CIA, fair but not very high. In a few areas the
Swedes rose above average. Besides forestry research they were
prominent in "the development of new tools and new techniques in
the biochemical and physiochemical study of macromolecules and
high molecular weight materials":

> Physical chemists and biochemists throughout the world have
> adopted Swedish equipment and designs for investigations of pro-
> teins, cellulose, numerous high polymers, enzymes, and other com-
> plex chemical systems which are highly significant in biochemistry,
> physiological chemistry, textiles, plastics, and rubber.
>   A fruitful practice has been the building of research and teach-
> ing institutes around leading scientists. A good example is Fysikalisk-
> Kemiska Institutionen (the Physical Chemistry Institute) of the
> University of Uppsala which for the past two decades has attracted

and trained superior scientific talent from all over the world. Swedish scientists trained here have become leaders in other research establishments and foreign students at the institute have introduced Swedish methods and equipment to other countries.[1]

The (Theodor) Svedberg was not mentioned by name, but it was to his laboratory that the report alluded. The CIA noted a few details that will be of importance in this paper. It has often been said that Swedish research has been characterized by a university-based model of institutionalization that was adopted in the decades around 1900— in contrast to a system where autonomous institutes constituted a backbone of scientific research, as in France or Germany.[2] The case of Svedberg illustrates that this distinction is not so clear cut. A number of the more important research environments that were created in Sweden before the Second World War were, as the CIA suggested, research institutes created for particularly prominent scientists rather than university departments created to serve the needs of a scientific discipline. This was true of, for example, Herman Nilsson-Ehle's famous plant-breeding institute in southern Sweden (which doubled as the University of Lund's department of heredity research), and to some extent of Manne Siegbahn's department of physics at Uppsala University (dominated by his research program in X-ray crystallography). Svedberg's laboratory for physical chemistry, built around 1930, definitely had the character of a research institute—funded by government but also by private sponsorship from the Rockefeller Foundation and the Swedish Wallenberg Foundation.

As a matter of fact, most university chairs that were created in the natural sciences in the first half of the twentieth century were the result of donations or were personal professorships earmarked for prominent researchers, often designated as "geniuses."[3] There was a close relationship between the scientific profile of these prominent researchers and the work carried out at their departments or institutes. The new academic environments that were created in this period came to embody specific research programs. This was also true in a physical sense—through architecture and instrumentation. This was in contrast to the earlier situation in which university laboratories were designed to reflect the various aspects of a scientific discipline. Probably one of the first examples of this trend was Svante Arrhenius's Nobel Institute for Physical Chemistry, created in 1905 and inaugurated in 1909.[4] This institute was unusual in that it was not integrated with a university. Other Nobel Prize winners—Allvar Gullstrand in medicine and Hans von Euler-Chelpin in chemistry—were endowed with university institutes where they could direct work as they saw fit. Svedberg (after retirement) and Siegbahn (in the mid-1930s) eventually became directors of privately funded institutes.

Svedberg's laboratory was planned and equipped to suit the purposes of a research program that was directed towards first colloid chemistry and later protein chemistry. He said as much in 1923 when his pupil and assistant Yngve Björnståhl suggested that they should buy X-ray equipment: "we must specialize in colloid science at our little laboratory in order not to lose ourselves."[5] At this point in time it was unclear whether proteins were colloids. When Svedberg and Björnståhl collaborated a few years later in setting up a new laboratory, they continued, on a technologically more advanced level, to follow a path that originated in the early 1900s, when Svedberg started out in colloid chemistry, and which research at the Uppsala institute would follow for a long time, transforming colloid chemistry into biochemistry in the process. Svedberg and, not least, Björnståhl subscribed to a modernist ideal of scientific progress through rapid and constant change. But the example of their laboratory rather illustrates the transforming power of a kind of scientific conservatism (or tenacity).

One measure of Svedberg's success was, according to the CIA report, that his laboratory attracted many foreigners and that many of the researchers trained there became prominent scientists. In other words, the CIA noted that the laboratory functioned as a hub in an important scientific network. As we will see below, the network was a medium for technology transfer, even for the transfer of a peculiar scientific context. The transfer of technology was not automatic. Rather it was guided by Svedberg's research program, which came to influence the scientific environments where his technology was adopted.

Svedberg's laboratory was promoted as a center of modernist science where spatial restrictions that afflicted older scientific establishments had been replaced by an encompassing principle of flexibility. In such a laboratory, spatial restrictions on research would be minimized. In this paper I will show how the ideal of modernist science was expressed in the design of Svedberg's laboratory, and how it was adopted in later laboratory schemes in Sweden. I will also show that there was a contradiction in the modernist scientific ideal that became manifest when the ultracentrifuge was exported and incorporated into other environments.

BJÖRNSTÅHL'S LABORATORY

On 30 May 1942, the chemist Yngve Björnståhl arrived at a sanatorium near Ulricehamn, a small town in the southwest of Sweden. He had been ill for several years, with lung and heart problems. After two days he left the sanatorium, rented a boat, and rowed out on the lake Åsunden. He was known to be an accomplished oarsman, but the following evening the boat was found empty except for Björnståhl's hat and coat and a broken oar.[6] At the time of his apparent suicide, Björnståhl was 54 years old and unmarried. He worked at the laboratory for physical chemistry at Uppsala University but he did not have a tenured position. He was an associate professor (*docent*) and his stipend had just run out. His future must have seemed bleak professionally speaking, and his health was bad.

Svedberg spoke about Björnståhl after his death, emphasizing his critical astuteness and his gift for rationalization and technological development. He was "the most faithful caretaker of machines and instruments," fiercely loyal to the department, always emphasizing "rationalization and exactitude."[7] Björnståhl was, said Svedberg, theoretically gifted but "in spite of this—or perhaps in a deeper sense because of this—he was interested in rational laboratory apparatus and laboratory planning."[8] This interest had been given a free range when, around 1930, the new institute for physical chemistry was planned and built at Uppsala University. In the mid-1920s, Björnståhl had spent several years travelling in Europe and in the United States, visiting laboratories, investigating all aspects of laboratory planning.[9] He had the main responsibility for planning Svedberg's laboratory and in 1934 he published a book (in English) on its design. Svedberg commented on the fact that Björnståhl was later engaged for several other laboratory-building projects in Sweden and in other countries. "Björnståhl was rightly seen," he said, "as an almost infallible judge in such matters."[10]

In his book, Björnståhl gave an ideal typical expression of a modernist ideal of laboratory design: "Owing to the rapid development of science and technique, let us take comfort in the prospect that we shall soon witness the epoch when this laboratory may be considered primitive."[11] When he wrote those words, the Uppsala institute was heralded by some experts as the most modern facility of its kind in the world.[12] In fact, he had planned the laboratory so that it could *remain* modern as long as possible. This was the ambition behind what Björnståhl called "the fundamental principle in the new laboratory"—"that everything must be capable of easy alteration."[13] This "flexibility principle," as he also called it, penetrated the laboratory design from the smallest detail to the overall structure.[14] It constituted a bid for constant modernity.

Björnståhl underlined the modernity of his design by invoking the authority of Le Corbusier, the great modernist architect, who had said that an apartment house should be a machine to live in. Björnståhl noted that this opinion was still controversial, and he was doubtless referring to the reactions caused by the so-called Stockholm Exhibition of 1930. It represented the breakthrough of modernist architecture in Sweden and had caused an uproar among conservatives who claimed that the international style—functionalism, as it was called in Sweden—was ugly and un-Swedish. On the other hand, Björnståhl pointed out, opinion was unanimous that "a laboratory should be a machine to work in": "Suitability for its purpose must be the sole deciding factor for the choice of the design."[15] Hence, functionalism was the architectural style of science as it was the style of rapid change, of internationalism, of rationality, of modernity. Flexibility and standardization were his "ruling principles" of design, wrote Björnståhl, and these were also cherished by the architects of functionalism.[16]

In order to drive home his points, Björnståhl castigated older styles of laboratory architecture. A laboratory should not pretend to be a "castle, a renaissance palace, or a manor-house," he wrote, and continued: "the ginger-bread decorations that blighted the 19th century or the ornamental motives of l'art nouveau" must be avoided.[17] Discussing the roof of the building, Björnståhl pointed out that its design was "reminiscent of the movement 'The New efficiency' ['*Die neue Sachlichkeit*'] in that many exhaust pipes are run directly up through the roof, without any attempt at masking or hiding."[18] *Sachlichkeit* was reflected in the absence of halls, large staircases or other representative spaces—the building was designed solely for the use of those working in it, not for occasional visitors. This was typical of modernist architecture, as was the general lack of ornamentation: "The visitor to some degree gets the impression of an industrial establishment," Björnståhl proudly announced.[19] This impression must have been strengthened for those who probed deeper into the building, with its many machines and workshops and with its strict functionality and embodied division of labor. The offices were somewhat nicer, with oak parquet floors for instance, but there too modernism was exhibited as the furniture, designed by the staff, was made in "stained birch with a light cubist touch."[20]

This knowledge factory was a child of its time, but it also aspired to be flexible enough to keep up with the changing of the times. There are many details in the construction of the building that give evidence of this—and not only in the building itself but in the equipment, not least the furniture. Björnståhl devoted an immense amount of effort to the construction of furniture, standardized for efficiency and at the same time so flexible that it allowed for rapid rearrangement and use for diverse purposes. Most famous are the so-called Björnståhl shelves (service strips), later widely adopted in Swedish laboratories.

In older laboratories, work benches were fastened to walls and floors—partly because this arrangement improved stability, ever important when sensitive measurements were made. Such arrangements became inflexible, especially in a chemistry laboratory where outlets for water, gas, compressed air, etc. were fixed to the tables. As experimental equipment had to be readily accessible, often simultaneously from both ends of a table, moveable tables were often used for the experimental apparatus, whereas the fixed tables were not actually used for experimental work. The labs became crowded with furniture, inefficient and dirty.

In Björnståhl's laboratory such messiness would be avoided and it "should be possible to adapt any room to any purpose."[21] The solution was to use moveable tables for experimental apparatus, and shelves no more than 25 cm deep attached along the walls, above which were mounted gas taps and other fittings. The shelves were 85 cm from the floor, the same height as the tables, so that these could easily be attached to one another when needed. Under the shelves were piping and wiring—not hidden but exposed so that they were readily accessible when changes had to be made.[22] Thus "the whole room is available for an experiment instead of only the area of the fixed tables."[23] Even the lecture room was designed in this way, so that it could easily be transformed into a laboratory.[24] This was functionalism in pure form: building and furniture adapted to one another, serving the purposes of flexibility and efficiency.

The laboratory rooms exhibited these principles in other ways as well. The so-called standard-laboratory rooms were fairly large modules of 5.5×8 square metres, and several of them were divided in two by the use of concrete walls which, according to Björnståhl, could be torn down in only one day and at the moderate cost of 200 Swedish crowns.[25] The metal workshop in the basement was, it was often pointed out, central to the efficiency of the institute. There, much of the equipment was built or repaired. Equally important, equipment was constantly modified: "because improvements are developed so rapidly. It soon becomes obsolete; it must be modernized."[26]

The emphasis on constant change gives Björnståhl's laboratory design an almost incorporeal quality: nothing seems solid, everything seems always to be melting into something else. That is the typically modern perception of scientific development, expressed by Björnståhl through the medium of his building.

Another tenet of modern science was also embodied in the building: the reliance on expensive, complicated and cumbersome experimental apparatus. The basement, and to some extent the other floors too, housed some of the heaviest and most expensive scientific equipment available at the time: ultracentrifuges, a huge electromagnet, smaller centrifuges, high-voltage apparatus, and apparatus for extracting proteins from organic material. The building was made as much for the machines as for the scientists.[27] In fact, some of the staff were supposed to behave like machines: in the computing room tedious calculations and measurements were carried out in assembly-line fashion, partly with the help of calculating machines.[28] The building was in a sense a machine for machines to work in, and Björnståhl's comparison with a factory was therefore appropriate.

Much of the heavy equipment, and also the metal workshop, was situated in the basement. There were the ultracentrifuges, supported on pillars of concrete sunk several metres into the ground in order to prevent vibrations; there was also the electromagnet—so large that the ceiling had to be taken down and several other rooms used for housing the measuring equipment that was to be used with the magnet. The fact that these objects in themselves did not represent the ideal of flexibility is illustrated by the fact that the ultracentrifuge lab still remains as it was in the 1930s (now turned into a museum). Once put into place, these objects were not easily removed or put to other uses than those for which they were originally intended.[29]

In several ways, the institute was constructed to fulfil the needs of the machinery that it housed. The walls could have been built around a skeleton of reinforced concrete or steel, materials favored in modernist architecture. That, said Björnståhl, would indeed have been better from the point of view of flexibility, as it would have been easier to tear down walls or erect new ones. But, in order to prevent the propagation of vibrations from machines through the building, brick was chosen instead.[30] Ventilation was an interesting technical problem, treated lovingly by Björnståhl over many pages, but it was also a health issue. Here Björnståhl was adamant: though constant temperature and dry air were regarded as less than satisfactory from a health perspective, they had to be accepted because such conditions were demanded by the technical equipment: "the hygienic requirements must give way to laboratory needs," he wrote, violating yet another tenet of functionalism, with its emphasis on health and hygiene.[31] Likewise, the staff had to be satisfied with a minimum of windows and with aesthetically unappealing wall paint—all because of the peculiar demands of their co-inhabitants, the machines.[32] The lack of large windows, unsuitable in a building where you wanted to be able to control the temperature, made the building's exterior look anything but functionalistic in style.

Björnståhl hence subscribed to a modernist architectural ideal, the scientific interpretation of which was expressed by the flexibility principle and a strong emphasis on standardization (e.g., the system of laboratory modules). At the same time, however, the building was characterized by traits that reflected the special needs of its machine inhabitants and that were not compatible with the flexibility principle or with modernist ideals of architecture. This did not make the flexibility principle any less attractive to laboratory builders. As we shall now see, it soon became a tenet of belief in modernist laboratory architecture in Sweden.

IMPACT OF THE MODERNIST LABORATORY IDEAL

Björnståhl may not have invented flexible laboratory design but he was perhaps one of the first to have used it for an important laboratory.[33] And he was influential. His book was very much in demand among foreign and domestic laboratory planners; he himself participated in the designing of several other laboratories, and his principles of good laboratory planning were adopted in other laboratory projects in Sweden.[34]

Descriptions of laboratory buildings in the house organ of the functionalists, *Byggmästaren* ("The Master Builder"), reveal a general acceptance of Björnståhl's principles by the 1940s. In 1941 the Director of the Swedish Academy of Engineering (*Ingenjörsvetenskapsakademien*, IVA) Edy Velander, published an article on "The research institute as an architectural problem" in which he emphasized the flexibility principle as well as the inter-disciplinary character of modern research. Velander contrasted the free spirit of research with the realities of inert industrial development:

A research laboratory must never become a rigid frame that stifles life within it; it must live with research, change, develop. In a factory one strives for uniformity, standardization at least with regard to work procedures. And this is also true of industrial laboratories and testing sites for monitoring manufacturing, that are to be found here and there in a modern industrial plant. With research it is rather the opposite. It strives for change, for new ideas, new methods, new products, and impatiently it rattles both the spiritual [*ideella*] and material chains.[35]

According to Velander, the greatest authority on laboratory design was Svedberg.[36] A few years later, Svedberg himself wrote an introductory essay to a series of papers in *Byggmästaren* on laboratory projects—most of them in the planning stage rather than finished buildings. Svedberg's point of departure was the fundamental tenet of modernist architecture: "the function should be the guiding principle of the design."[37] Svedberg emphasized flexibility and standardization. Like Björnståhl, he stressed the importance of standardized furniture and well-organized workshops and other auxiliary functions.

In general, the laboratory articles in the "Master Builder" emphasized the principles that had been codified by Björnståhl: flexibility, standardization, the modular system. Some architects were specialized in laboratory design. Gunnar Forzén collaborated with Björnståhl in the building of the Department of Physiological Botany at Uppsala University and wrote a general article on the principles of laboratory design; the office of Ahrbom and Zimdahl (Helge Zimdahl, a former editor of the journal, was highly regarded by Svedberg's group) was responsible for most laboratory buildings that were presented in *Byggmästaren* in 1945.[38] They published a short general discussion that fully endorsed the modernist principles of laboratory building. According to Ahrbom and Zimdahl, the architectural problem of laboratory design was characterized by the need to constantly adapt to "the nature of research, which in its turn is constantly changed and renewed."[39] The demand for flexible designs was described as the most characteristic aspect of laboratory architecture, necessitating peculiar technical solutions such as the module system or Björnståhl shelves.[40]

The flexibility principle was also underscored by Forzén: "The primary goal is to design buildings and fittings so that they may easily be adjusted to the changing nature of work and unpredicted but constantly arising changes."[41] Forzén, along with several other authors, emphasized the Björnståhl shelves that seem to have achieved almost emblematic status.[42] The ideal, aesthetically speaking, was a "restrained and naked beauty."[43]

The modernist ideal expressed through these laboratory descriptions was summarized by Forzén, who wrote that a laboratory must be designed as a "perfectly functioning provisional solution [*provisorium*]."[44] But there was a tension between functionality and flexibility. The kind of technology developed by Svedberg's group and institutionalized in their laboratory was complicated and especially designed for certain kinds of measurements. When the technology was to be exported, it became obvious how much it relied on a meticulously designed spatial, organizational, and scientific context. If architectural design manifested the dream of constant change, the reality of technology transfer revealed a paradoxical contradiction inherent in this modernist vision.

CONTEXT TRANSFER: THE MIGRATION OF THE ULTRACENTRIFUGE

In 1933, Arthur Sproul McFarlane, head of the biochemical laboratory at the Glasgow Royal Cancer Hospital, wrote to Svedberg, asking if he could come to Uppsala and work with the ultracentrifuge. McFarlane was primarily interested in using the apparatus to determine the sizes of viruses. He arrived in Uppsala in September and stayed for a few months. Almost a year later, he wrote from London that the Lister Institute for Preventive Medicine, where he was now working, was interested in buying a centrifuge of its own.[45] Apparently McFarlane had by then, thanks to his experiences from Uppsala, gained the status of an expert on the new technology. His lectures on the centrifuge at the institute drew large crowds from all of London: "I anticipate that when the centrifuge comes I will be asked to perform miracles with it!"[46]

Within a few years, two centrifuges (a smaller equilibrium centrifuge and a larger high-speed centrifuge) had been purchased from Uppsala and installed at the Lister Institute. At first glance, this seems like an example of run-of-the-mill technology transfer: a Brit travelling to Sweden, learning the technology and importing it to England. A closer look at the transfer process reveals that it was more complicated, and that it gives valuable insights into the relationship between a scientific technology and its context.

Svedberg strove to influence the implementation and use of centrifuge technology in a way that may be captured using the term *context transfer*. Importing the centrifuge was not enough to make it work, Svedberg pointed out. The context of use had to be imported with the apparatus: for example, the organization of work, the research program, to some extent the laboratory setup. As we have seen, Svedberg's laboratory was described as a paragon of modernity because it was flexible and easy to alter. But the transfer of centrifuge technology reveals limitations of flexibility that affected not only material and organizational but also intellectual aspects of technology use.

The transfer of centrifuge technology from Uppsala to London was part of the Rockefeller Foundation's program of supporting a "new biology."[47] Svedberg had encouraged McFarlane to seek economic support from the Foundation for the purchase of a centrifuge, and in 1934 McFarlane reported that the Lister Institute had been visited by Daniel O'Brien from the Foundation and he seemed to endorse the idea as long as the centrifuge was made accessible to researchers from other British institutions.[48] Svedberg, who had recently been given extended financial support from the Rockefeller Foundation, wrote encouragingly: "We seem to be in the sun both you and I now."[49] He described ongoing work on a new rotor that it would be possible to run at a speed of 150,000 rpm—to McFarlane the prospect of getting such an apparatus to his own laboratory was "almost too good to be true."[50]

McFarlane was as yet something of an underling at the Lister Institute and his contacts with Svedberg were informal. The official negotiations concerning the purchase of a centrifuge were handled by Svedberg and McFarlane's boss. J. C. G. Ledingham. The latter contacted Svedberg in July 1934 and told him that the Rockefeller Foundation seemed willing to finance a "Svedberg centrifuge" for the Lister Institute, with the object of creating a biophysical department there. Ledingham regarded McFarlane as an obvious candidate for directing the new department, which should be equipped with "the most refined instruments."[51] In order to accomplish this, help from Svedberg was needed.

Svedberg did all he could to encourage these plans. He mentioned that he and his co-workers had helped build experimental apparatus for other laboratories on several occasions, in particular an ultracentrifuge for Du Pont.[52] He endorsed the suitability of McFarlane for leading such work as was planned at the London institute. In particular, Svedberg rejoiced in the fact that centrifuge-based research would be extended to the domain of medicine: "It has always been my dream to be able to do something towards the development of methods for medical investigation."[53]

In November 1934, McFarlane wrote to Svedberg that he would soon hear more from Ledingham regarding the centrifuge but asked him not to mention that he was being given information about the developments directly by McFarlane. The reason was that he was not playing an official part in the negotiations that went on with Svedberg and the Rockefeller Foundation. The board had decided that the Lister Institute would pay the running costs of the centrifuge, including the salaries of one full-time technician, and one scientific director of centrifuge work—McFarlane. All parties expected the ultracentrifuge to become a very useful tool for research in various areas of medical significance—the study of vitamins, of viruses, hormones and so on.[54]

By the middle of the month, Ledingham gave Svedberg a more detailed account of the centrifuge plans. Among other things, it was planned to mount larger cells, made of metal, on the rotor in order to be able to centrifuge larger samples—not to analyze them optically, as Svedberg did, but in order to extract various phases of the sample, e.g. to purify protein: "I shall be very grateful if you will give me your opinion as to the practicability of including in the velocity centrifuge and in the equilibrium centrifuge cells capable of holding [. . .] somewhat larger quantities of fluid [. . .] in addition to the standard small cells with which you have worked and which, of course, we should also desire to have."[55]

Svedberg was skeptical: "one could hardly tell offhand what difficulties might arise from cells of the type you indicate."[56] Furthermore, he admitted to being "a little suspicious of such qualitative and semi-quantitative methods" as Ledingham had proposed, but he indicated that there was a possibility that the centrifuge might be adapted to the technical demands of these methods. But he was careful not to raise expectations. Many "years of hard work" lay behind the development of centrifuge technology and in Svedberg's experience "even a slight change may cause much unforeseen trouble." He therefore proposed that the Lister Institute should install the ultracentrifuge without making changes to its technological specifications and that McFarlane should visit Uppsala in order to investigate the possibility of making such changes in the future.

To McFarlane, Svedberg expressed his opinion about Ledingham's plans more candidly:

He states that they want chiefly to conduct types of experiments, for which our ultracentrifuges are not at all worked out. We have not and are not interested to supply machines for quantitative [*sic*, should be "qualitative"] and semi-quantitative studies of the kind he suggests. I have tried—for your sake—to give my answer (cop enclosed) a form as sympathetic as possible, but I cannot write entirely against better judgement. [...] In my opinion we should avoid to complicate the wuestions [*sic*] of installing ultracentrifuges of our type in your Institute by asking for accomplishments which have not been sought for when constructing the machines.[57]

According to Svedberg, it was impossible to predict how the proposed changes of the ultracentrifuge's design would affect the functionality of the apparatus. He repeated that the matter should be investigated by McFarlane himself in collaboration with Svedberg and his team at the Uppsala laboratory.

McFarlane had not opposed the biomedical investigations that Svedberg criticized, as he believed he might have imperilled the whole scheme by doing so. They were important not only to Ledingham but to many other potential users of the machine. Besides, he risked being accused of wanting to monopolize the ultracentrifuge for his own research on serum proteins. But he thought the leadership of the Lister Institute would accept a more limited use of the ultracentrifuge once Svedberg made clear his objections.

The status of Svedberg's technology at the place of reception, in London, was apparently changing during the process of negotiation. Originally, the ultracentrifuge was seen as a concern not only of researchers at the Lister Institute but in London more broadly. Svedberg's more restricted view of the uses to which the machine might be put made it more exclusively a resource for McFarlane and his researchers: "I am personally indebted to you once more, for clearing the air here in no uncertain manner and incidentally improving somewhat my own position if, and when, the centrifuge arrives. My one regret, frankly, is that it should have only been possible to offer so little in the way of encouragement to those other workers here who have shown considerable interest in, and enthusiasm for, the whole project."[58]

The transfer of this particular piece of scientific technology would hence not automatically benefit researchers in several fields. On the contrary, the technology was so *inflexible* that it would bring about a concentration of resources in a fairly limited number of areas.

Ledingham eventually agreed that this had to be accepted. He wrote that the institute would order "replicas" of Svedberg's machines and that it was a good idea to let McFarlane return to Uppsala in order to discuss possible future modifications of the apparatus.[59]

In January 1935, McFarlane wrote to Svedberg that the Rockefeller Foundation had granted £3000, as expected, and that he thought he could convince the board of the institute to put aside an equal amount for a new centrifuge laboratory. He saw himself as the future leader of this outfit: "Needless to say, I am very excited at the idea of having such a small centrifuge 'station' of my own."[60] Immediately a telegram arrived from Uppsala, congratulating "the centrifuge station master."[61] Svedberg, who had already sent architectural drawings of his own laboratory, now sent corresponding drawings of the laboratory under construction at Du Pont. We have seen that the transfer of centrifuge technology involved the transfer of a research style. It would now become clear that it also involved a transfer of laboratory configuration.

The correspondence between Uppsala and London turned towards matters of laboratory planning. Svedberg pointed out that the centrifuge and its spatial surroundings could not really be separated: "As you know it is somewhat difficult to draw the line between the centrifuge and the other parts of the laboratory."[62] McFarlane aimed for a design that was suitable for the particular requirements of the serum work he planned:

> As I mentioned to you once before I consider that in the serum runs it is important that the operator should observe rather constantly from the camera what is happening in the cell. With pathological serum containing three or four components considerable skill may be developed in taking the exposures at the times of best separation of each component before it reaches the bottom of the cell, and well chosen exposure times greatly facilitates the subsequent graphical analysis of the curve. Following out this idea I propose to have the metal panel in two halves, one on each side of the camera, and to arrange that as many operations as possible can be performed from a raised chair in front of the camera.[63]

Centrifuge and laboratory were to function as one unit. The wish to integrate functions included the observer, who appears rather as a component of the technical equipment. The overriding goal was to make the integration of apparatus, spatial arrangement, and human observer such that the program of serum analysis could be pursued with maximum efficiency. Svedberg was happy about this. He did not oppose the idea of letting the demands of machinery and of a rather narrow research program dictate the design.[64]

In March 1935, however, McFarlane sent plans of the laboratory, explaining that they were now urging a more flexible use of the machine.[65] Again, Svedberg reacted with consternation, explaining that the setup of the instruments would not work as planned. The drawings showed a deplorable lack of understanding of the technical requirements for working with the ultracentrifuge. Svedberg recommended that McFarlane go back to the drawing table, but that he should take a detour via Uppsala:

> Many a thing that you may regard merely as a matter of taste, is, we think, of primary importance for the investigations to be carried out in the laboratory. After going over the various problems again and again, we have come to the conclusion that the only rational solution would be for you to come over here for, say, a week so as to be able to discuss the plans thoroughly with us. I cannot take the responsibility of recommending the arrangement which you have just outlined with just a few minor changes. We all feel that the planning has to be completely reconsidered.[66]

McFarlane was shaken by the harsh criticism. However, he could not travel to Uppsala immediately as his wife was soon to give birth.[67] Meanwhile, Svedberg sent detailed criticisms of McFarlane's laboratory scheme, written by Kai O. Pedersen, who was in charge of the day-to-day running of the Uppsala centrifuges: "While you were over here you were so extremely busy with your investigation that you found but little time to get acquainted with the principles of the various machinery and the lack of information in this respect is plainly visible in your plans."[68] Svedberg wished McFarlane could visit Uppsala in mid-April, when John Philpot was there in order to partake in the dismantling and reassembly of a complete ultracentrifuge in preparation for installing such an instrument at the Department of Biochemistry in Oxford.[69] Svedberg made it clear that he did not believe McFarlane had grasped the full significance of the need for detailed knowledge of the machine in order to make a successful transfer of the technology. Ledingham supported the idea, declaring that the laboratory would not be built until the plans had Svedberg's "entire approval."[70]

The child was born at the beginning of April but it was a difficult delivery and McFarlane could not leave for Uppsala until the end of the month and then only for a short stay.[71] But this seems to have been sufficient for work in London to continue with Svedberg's blessing. During the following months, Svedberg and Pedersen guided McFarlane through the different stages of planning and procurement of everything that was needed for the laboratory.[72] Sometimes apparently trivial problems caused difficulties. This was true of the difference in metrological systems between England and Sweden. Svedberg wanted drawings on a scale 1:20, which the construction firm in London did not have—they had to be made especially for the Swede.[73] A more difficult problem concerned the steel beams that had to be of metric dimensions. Eventually they were ordered from Sweden.[74] This illustrates the environmental replication that characterized the transfer of technology from Uppsala to London—making it in effect a transfer also of context.[75] During the process, McFarlane seems to have totally agreed to Svedberg's demands. A typical comment was: "I intend to copy your arrangements in the closest detail."[76]

When work in London neared completion, McFarlane was again called to Uppsala. This time he would have to stay for several weeks, participating in the dismantling and reassembly of a centrifuge.[77] McFarlane complained: he was very busy and did not want to leave his wife and new-born child for such a long period. But at the same time, he stressed that he would abide by Svedberg's instructions: "I recognise the great importance of this visit and the folly of detracting from its value by undue haste. I will therefore confidently leave the decision to your better judgement and will expect you to let me know in due course when you would like me to make the journey."[78]

Eventually the transfer of instrument and context was successful. In 1936 the centrifuge was installed at the Lister Institute and it seems to have functioned satisfactorily thereafter, with only small modifications. It was used mainly for virus research.[79]

CONCLUSION

The vision of progress through the intellectual pursuit of truths about nature and associated technological development has held a powerful sway over the modern mind. But, as historians of technology have shown, machines are not entirely flexible, they are embedded in sociotechnical systems that develop momentum and become rather inert.[80] Efficient at what they do, their functionality is difficult to change. Large investments in heavy equipment that depend on close ties between science and industry open new avenues for research but simultaneously limit or close alternative possibilities.

The only protection against stagnation under such circumstances is a constant growth in funding, and since the end of the Second World War that has indeed been a prerequisite for scientific success in areas of high-tech research. When increased funding is not available, decline threatens, as in recent times, in some areas of physics. In circumstances such as these, with a closer and closer symbiosis between science and technology, it is not surprising that the distinction between the two, which Svedberg was at pains to uphold, is currently collapsing.

I would suggest that such a collapse is a logical consequence of the self-contradictory nature of the modernist ideal of science: large-scale technology is simply at odds with intellectual flexibility. According to the cherished cliché of the linear model, technology is science-dependent. But twentieth-century big science became technology-dependent to such a degree that the raison d'être of research was gradually identified with technological development.[81]

This problem was already visible in Björnståhl's laboratory design. The use of advanced and costly equipment made the laboratory dependent on industrial relations. It is enough to take a glance at the description of the great electromagnet to get a vivid impression of how close this dependence was:

> The material for the house of the electromagnet has been put at our disposal through the generosity of *Mr. Axel Ax:son Johnson*, Stockholm, and *Avesta järnverks Aktiebolag, Avesta, Sweden* has spared no efforts in order to produce a steel with suitable properties. [...] The cost of the copper tubes has been defrayed by *Finspongs Metallverk, Finspong, Sweden*. [...] The poleshoes are made of a cobalt-iron alloy, containing 34 per cent cobalt from *Fagersta Bruks Aktiebolag, Fagersta, Sweden*. [...] The magnethouse rests on a roller device which rests on a turn table donated by *A.-B. Svenska Kullagerfabriken, Göteborg, Sweden*.[82]

The institute was a node in an industrial network by virtue of its equipment and also because of Svedberg's many industrial activities, which included turning the institute into a laboratory for the development of synthetic rubber during the war. He was an ardent promoter of collaboration between science and industry—cooperating with the cellulose industry, brewing companies and so on, and helping to establish research laboratories in industry.[83] If he strikes us as a prime example of that very modern type of scientist who promotes high-tech in science and the application of science in industry, it is perhaps because he was so very much an *American* type of scientist. It is often said that Swedish academics switched their cultural allegiance from Germany to the United States after the Second World War. Svedberg did this as early as the 1920s, if not before, and from around 1930 the American connection grew very strong indeed, which is probably one reason why the CIA gave him such high marks in their presidential report.

The move towards industrialized research, American style, which, with hindsight, was implicit in the Uppsala laboratory, guided its design as much as Björnståhl's flexibility principle. The fact that things were adjusted so as to optimize the working conditions of experimental apparatus is in itself unremarkable: such had been the guiding principle of laboratory architecture since the mid-19th century. What made the architectural adaptation to experimental demands extreme, by older standards, was the sheer size of the apparatus and the fact that much of the problem of disturbance was caused by the scientific equipment itself. Earlier, laboratory designers had attempted to protect the interior of a lab building against the disturbing influences of industrial society without; now industrial society had moved into the building itself, though Svedberg and Björnståhl tried as best as they could to harness the beast in the basement. In order to do this, they had to adapt not only the basement but other parts of their laboratory as well, and also their working routines, to the demands of high-tech experimental equipment.

As we have seen, the transfer of this equipment to another location demanded a transfer of context, including organization and to some extent research style. The severe restrictions imposed on science by technology and, indirectly, industry made the idea that flexible spatial arrangements would promote flexibility of intellect seem phoney, like the ornamentation so abhorred by functionalists.

NOTES

1. *An Estimate of Swedish Capabilities in Science*, Presidential Report (secret) published by the Central Intelligence Agency, 9 Aug. 1949, p. 18. Copy in President's Secretary's Files, Box 257, Intelligence File, OSI Reports 1949 (OSI 1/1949), Harry S. Truman Library, Independence, MO. I am grateful to Kalle Grandin for kindly lending me a copy of this publication.

2. Thorsten Nybom, *Kunskap, politik, samhälle: Essäer om kunskapssyn, universitet och forskningspolitik, 1900–2000* (Stockholm: Arete, 1997), ch. 1.
3. Sven Widmalm, "The Old Production of Knowledge: The Academic System of Science in Sweden, 1880–1950," in Tore Frängsmyr and J.L. Heilbron (eds.), *The Structure of Knowledge: Classifications of Science and Learning Since the Renaissance* (Berkeley: Office for History of Science and Technology, 2001), 117–51.
4. Sven Widmalm, *Det öppna laboratoriet, Uppsalafysiken och dess nätverk, 1853–1910* (Stockholm: Atlantis, 2001), ch. 6.
5. Svedberg to Björnståhl, April 11, 1923, Uppsala University Archives at Uppsala University Library, The Svedberg papers (UUATS), F4 CA: 11.
6. Undated and unsigned notes in pencil on Björnståhl's last days, in Archives of the Uppsala University Department of Physical Chemistry (AUUPC), E1:1 (folder, Yngve Björnståhl).
7. The Svedberg, "Yngve Björnståhl," obituary in pencil, signed but not dated, in *ibid.*
8. *Ibid.*
9. Letters from Björnståhl to Svedberg 1927–29, in UUATS, F4 CA: 11.
10. Svedberg's obituary, cited in note 7.
11. Yngve Björnståhl, *The New Laboratory of Physical Chemistry at Uppsala University* (Lund, 1934), iv.
12. According to Harold Urey, quoted in *Svenska Dagbladet*, Feb. 2, 1935, Svedberg's laboratory was the best in the world.
13. Björnståhl, 136.
14. *Ibid.*, 240.
15. *Ibid.*, 12.
16. *Ibid.*, 13. On modernist architecture in Sweden around 1930, see Eva Rudberg, *Stockholmsutställningen 1930: Modernismens genombrott i svensk arkitektur* (Stockholm: Stockholmia förlag, 1999). For an extremely influential contemporary statement on modernist architecture in Sweden, see Gunnar Asplund et al., *acceptera* (Stockholm: Tiden, 1931).
17. Björnståhl, 12.
18. *Ibid.*, 18.
19. *Ibid.*, 18.
20. *Ibid.*, 244.
21. *Ibid.*, 25.
22. *Ibid.*, 135–37.
23. *Ibid.*, 166.
24. *Ibid.*, 230, 240.
25. *Ibid.*, 46.
26. *Ibid.*, 254.
27. The experiences of planning an ultracentrifuge laboratory are summarized in The Svedberg et al., *The Ultracentrifuge* (Oxford: The Clarendon Press, 1940), 183–88 (this section written by Svedberg, Kai O. Pedersen and Gustaf Boestad).

28. Sven Brohult and Nils Gralén, "The Institute of Physical Chemistry at Uppsala," in Arne Tiselius et al. (eds.), *The Svedberg 1884 30/8 1944* (Uppsala, 1944), 623–38, on p. 631.
29. Boelie Elzen, "Two Ultracentrifuges: A Comparative Study of the Social Construction of Artefacts," *Social Studies of Science* 16 (1986), 621–62.
30. Björnståhl, 21.
31. *Ibid.*, 49.
32. *Ibid.*, 24–26.
33. According to Peter Galison, the flexibility principle became generally adopted after the Second World War in connection with the adoption of factory-style research, first in physics. Peter Galison, *Image and Logic: A Material Culture of Microphysics* (Chicago: University of Chicago Press, 1997), 827–28; Peter Galison and Caroline A. Jones, "Factory, Laboratory, Studio: Dispersing Sites of Production," in Peter Galison and Emily Thompson, eds., *The Architecture of Science* (Cambridge, Mass.: The MIT Press, 1999), 497–540, on p. 499. On the flexibility ideal in current laboratory architecture, see Robert Venturi, "Thoughts on the Architecture of the Scientific Workplace: Community, Change, and Continuity," in *ibid.*, 385–98, on pp. 388–93.
34. An American overview of laboratory planning from 1950 expresses similar ideals to those of Björnståhl and describes them as universally accepted. Flexibility was stressed and Björnståhl shelves—here called "service strips"—were highly recommended. Charles Haines, "Planning the Scientific Laboratory," *Architectural Record*, July 1950, 107–127.
35. Edy Velander, "Forskningsinstitutet som arkitektproblem," *Byggmästaren* 1941, 16, 195–96, on p. 195.
36. *Ibid.* Velander did not mention Svedberg by name but it is clear that he was talking about him.
37. The Svedberg, "Laboratoriebyggen," *Byggmästaren* 1945, 22, 415. Svedberg was advising the editor of *Byggmästaren* regarding suitable laboratories to present in the special issue. Leif Reinius to Svedberg, Feb. 12, 1945; Svedberg to Reinius, February 13, 1945; UUATS, E 1:7.
38. Sven Brohult to Svedberg, July 10, 1944, UUATS, E 1:7.
39. Nils Ahrbom et al., "Laboratoriebyggnader," *Byggmästaren* 1945, 22, 421–422. The article summarizes five short descriptions of laboratory buildings designed by the firm. On Zimdahl's status as a laboratory architect, see Sven Brohult to Svedberg, July 10, 1944; UUAPC, E 1:7.
40. Cf. the more detailed description in Bertil Sjögren, Nils Ahrbom and Helge Zimdahl, "Astra centrallaboratorium i Södertälje," *Byggmästaren* 1945, 23, 443–52, esp. pp. 444, 447.
41. Gunnar Forszén, "Laboratoriebyggnaden och dess inredning," *Byggmästaren* 1941, 16, 197–210, on p. 197.
42. Forszén, "Laboratoriebyggnaden," 205. Cf Forszén, "Svenska forskningsinstitutet för cement och betong vid Kungl. Tekniska högskolan i Stockholm," *Byggmästaren* 1945, 23, 453–58, on p. 458; Forszén, "Medicinsk-kemiska och farmakologiska institutionen i Uppsala," *Byggmästaren* 1945, 22, 426–27, on

p. 427; Melchior Wernstedt, "Svenska textilforskningsinstitutet, Göteborg," *ibid.*, 438–41, on pp. 439–40; Sjögren, Ahrbom and Zimdahl, 444.

43. Forszén, "Laboratoriebyggnaden," 200.
44. Forszén, "Laboratoriebyggnaden," 207. Cf. Lennart Tham, "Siporexfabrik- ernas centrallaboratorium, Södertälje," *Byggmästaren* 1945, 22, 442; Gustav Holmdahl, "Lantbrukshögskolans laboratorier, Ultuna," *ibid.*, 429–30, on p. 429; Gustaf Birch-Lindgren, "AB Bofors laboratorium, Bofors," *ibid.*, 432–34, on p. 434; Sjögren, Ahrbom and Zimdahl, 444.
45. McFarlane to Svedberg, Jan. 23 & Sept. 1, 1933; July 25, 1934, UUATS, F4 CA: 19. Cf. Angela N. H. Creager, *The Life of a Virus: Tobacco Mosaic Virus as an Experimental Model, 1930–1965* (Chicago: University of Chicago Press, 2002), ch. 4. On Svedberg and McFarlane, see especially Boelie Elzen, *Scientists and Rotors: The Development of Biochemical Ultracentrifuges* (Enschede, 1988), 97, 324–26.
46. McFarlane to Svedberg, July 9, 1937, UUATS, F4 CA: 19.
47. Lily E. Kay, *The Molecular Vision of Life: Caltech, the Rockefeller Foundation, and the Rise of the New Biology* (New York: Oxford University Press, 1993); Robert E. Kohler, *Partners in Science: Foundations and Natural Scientists, 1900–1945* (Chicago: University of Chicago Press, 1991). On Svedberg's contact with Rockefeller and Weaver, see also Elzen, *Scientists and Rotors*, 101–107.
48. McFarlane to Svedberg, Sept. 29, 1934, UUATS, F4 CA: 19.
49. Svedberg to McFarlane, Oct. 8, 1934, UUATS, F4 CA: 19.
50. McFarlane to Svedberg, Aug. 27, 1934; Svedberg to McFarlane, Oct. 8, 1934; McFarlane to Svedberg, Oct. 11, 1934; UUATS, F4 CA: 19.
51. Ledingham to Svedberg, July 27, 1934, UUA, TS, F4 CA: 18.
52. The Du Pont centrifuge was a success technically speaking but fell into disuse as the company management discouraged fundamental work for which the machine was mainly intended. Elzen, *Scientists and Rotors*, 311–21.
53. Svedberg to Ledingham, July 31, 1934, UUA, TS, F4 CA: 18.
54. McFarlane to Svedberg, Nov. 2, 1934, UUATS, F4 CA: 19.
55. Ledingham to Sveberg, Nov. 12, 1934, UUA, TS, F4 CA: 18. Cf. Elzen, *Scientists and Rotors*, 326.
56. Svedberg to Ledingham, Nov. 17, 1934, UUA, TS, F4 CA: 18.
57. Svedberg to McFarlane, Nov. 17, 1934, UUATS, F4 CA: 19.
58. McFarlane to Svedberg, Nov. 20, 1934, UUATS, F4 CA: 19.
59. Ledingham till Svedberg, Nov. 21, 1934, UUA, TS, F4 CA: 18.
60. McFarlane to Svedberg, Jan. 20, 1935, UUATS, F4 CA: 19.
61. Copy of telegram to McFarlane Jan. 22, 1935, signed by Svedberg, his wife Jane, and some of the personnel at the laboratory, including Svedberg's secretary Astrid Hedenius. UUATS, F4 CA: 19.
62. Svedberg to McFarlane, Jan. 29, 1935, UUATS, F4 CA: 19.
63. McFarlane to Svedberg, Feb. 11, 1935, UUATS, F4 CA: 19.
64. Svedberg to McFarlane, Feb. 15, 1935, UUATS, F4 CA: 19.
65. McFarlane to Svedberg, March 11, 1935, UUATS, F4 CA: 19.

66. Svedberg to McFarlane, March 19, 1935, UUATS, F4 CA: 19.
67. McFarlane to Svedberg, March 21, 1934 [sic, should be 1935], UUATS, F4 CA: 19.
68. Svedberg to McFarlane, March 26, 1935, UUATS, F4 CA: 19.
69. The Oxford machine was installed in 1936 and technically it was a success. When Svedberg visited the inauguration ceremony he was awarded an honorary doctorate. Elzen, *Scientists and Rotors*, 326–29.
70. Ledingham to Svedberg, April 6, 1935, UUA, TS, F4 CA: 18.
71. McFarlane to Svedberg, April 7, April 15 (telegram) 1935, UUATS, F4 CA: 19.
72. E.g. McFarlane to Svedberg, May 19, 1935; McFarlane to Pedersen, June 8, 1935; UUATS, F4 CA: 19.
73. McFarlane to Pedersen, June 8, 1935; McFarlane to Svedberg, June 18, 1935; UUATS, F4 CA: 19.
74. McFarlane to Svedberg, June 19, 1935, UUATS, F4 CA: 19.
75. For this purpose, Svedberg also used "stereo slides" of his laboratory, which he lent not only to McFarlane but also to those responsible for the centrifuges being built in Oxford and at Du Pont. Svedberg to McFarlane, June 22, 1935, UUATS, F4 CA: 19. Bruno Latour has famously pointed out that the success of modern laboratory science can be interpreted in terms of a transformation of social order in the image of the laboratory. My argument is less broad but nevertheless important for understanding the influence of laboratory science: that its impact rests on an ability to multiply sociotechnical settings. Bruno Latour, "Give me a laboratory and I will raise the world," in Karin Knorr-Cetina and Michael Mulkay, eds., *Science Observed* (London: Sage, 1983), 141–170.
76. McFarlane to Svedberg, Jan. 1, 1936, UUATS, F4 CA: 19.
77. Svedberg to McFarlane, Feb. 19, 1936, UUATS, F4 CA: 19.
78. McFarlane to Svedberg, Feb. 22, 1936, UUATS, F4 CA: 19.
79. Elzen, *Scientists and Rotors*, 326.
80. Thomas P. Hughes, "The Evolution of Large Technological Systems" in Wibe Bijker, Thomas P. Hughes and Trevor Pinch (eds.), *The Social Construction of Technological Systems: New Directions in the Sociology and History of Technology* (Cambridge, Mass.: The MIT Press, 1987), 51–82.
81. For a broad discussion on this theme, see the contributions in Karl Grandin et al., eds., *The Science-Industry Nexus: History, Policy, Implications* (Sagamore Beach, MA: Science History Publications/USA, 2004).
82. Björnståhl, 196.
83. Sven Widmalm, "The Svedberg och gränsen mellan teknik och vetenskap," in Widmalm (ed.), *Artefakter: Industrin, vetenskapen och de tekniska nätverken* (Hedemora: Gidlunds, 2004), 149–87.

PART II

Crossing Meso-Places

Timber-floating in the 1930's on lake Sommen in southern Sweden. Photography from the personal collection of Christina Garpevik.

A Worthwhile Road?

Attaining the Science City
of Stockholm

JENNY BECKMAN

In 1916, the "Science City" was presented to the world. In a lavish brochure, printed on fine paper and bound with golden tassels, eight scientific institutions were displayed in large photographs. Monumental buildings turned their brick faces to the sun, sculptured boars reared their heads, pine trees shaded picturesque terraces planted with rare flowers. There were captions stating the names of the institutions in four languages; but there was no text.[1]

What was this "science city" that merited such extravagant presentation and such scant commentary? Structurally, it might be said to be a scattering of buildings at Frescati, a rural suburb of Stockholm. Administratively, it was, for a while, the official designation of this part of the city. In the imagination of its prospective inhabitants, it was "a centre of science, which almost certainly has few equals in Europe, and should prove very appealing to the science-minded public."[2]

The subject of this paper is the construction of the Science City of Stockholm, as a place and as a concept. The conception of the Science City is closely connected to the debate surrounding the relocation plans of the Swedish Museum of Natural History (SMNH). In the early years of the twentieth century, museum officials decided to abandon the old building in central Stockholm and move to a new site in the rural suburb of Frescati. Depending on the perspective, the move can be viewed as a success or as a failure: a success in terms of funding and space for the large new buildings; a failure in terms of geographical and social distance from colleagues, the political and financial authorities, and the public.

In a matter such as the moving of the museum, the concrete spatial conditions are easily described as determinative. The size of the collections required more space; the dimensions of the new buildings made the move from the constraints of the inner city a necessity; the topography of the new site forced the buildings into a certain shape. However, every planning stage was characterized by a multiplicity of alternatives. Every question of function, location, and design presented museum officials with choices, which were determined by their conceptions of economy, city planning, research interests and audiences, rather than by geography and architecture alone. Thus, space should not be viewed as conclusive to the issue of the new museum. The spatial dimension was important for the design, use, and effect of the institution, but these were not fully determined by it.

Similarly, the spatial set-up of the museum may provide an understanding of its function as well as of the objectives of its designers, but again a partial one. The fact that a building was constructed in specific circumstances does not necessarily imply that these circumstances form an indissoluble part of the building, nor that they are automatically recreated through its structure and setting. Architectural historian Thomas Markus has pointed out that even a building as charged with meaning as a church can be redefined, and function in ways and situations quite different from the circumstances of its initial construction.[3] However its location, structure, and design provide clues for investigating those circumstances. A building—or a landscape—is "much more than a stage set or background" for a social drama played out in it.[4] Buildings and landscapes mediate the social situations and ideals that contributed to their present form. Considering this spatial feedback loop, an investigation of the localization of the SMNH is a way of studying the social function and position of the museum in an actual as well as a projected sense.

Recent interest in space as an analytical tool in the history of science may be regarded as an instance of the focus on the material culture of science that has been prominent in historical research.[5] Encouraged by geographers and architectural theorists, historians have widened their traditional preoccupation with time to include space as an analytical category.[6] But the concept also lends itself easily to metaphorical interpretations, illustrating power relations and hierarchies. Thus, "space" is not simply a material category containing museums, laboratories, open doors and locked rooms, but a socio-cultural one consisting of conventions, habits, and rules for navigating the corridors of power in senses other than the physical.[7]

To deal with the multiple meanings of the category, space explorers have experimented with a number of concepts to turn it into a practical tool. Time geographers describe the *constraints* influencing the way actors move through space and time.[8] A related way of dealing with the ambiguity of space is to look at it in terms of *access* and *accessibility*. These terms address the material as well as cultural and socio-economic dimensions of spatial conditions. The accessibility of a place or a context is affected by distances and locked doors, as well as by working hours, education, and economic resources.

In this paper I will link different conceptions of the Science City, as they were formulated by several officials of the Swedish Museum of Natural History, to questions of accessibility. The images of the Science City articulated over the decades reflect the changing geographical, economic, and organizational circumstances of the Swedish Museum of Natural History and related institutions in the city of Stockholm at the turn of the twentieth century. But they also indicate ideas about the function and purposes of these institutions, their audiences and relations. Physical access to the SMNH, in terms of opening hours, entrance fees, train fares, and infrastructure, is one side of the story. But a crucial aspect of the function of the Science City is its meaning. Relocating to Frescati, the SMNH was not moving into a void, but into a landscape with its own history and connotations. The tale of the Science City is as much a story of continuous efforts to redefine Frescati, as one of bricks and mortar.

VISIONS OF THE SCIENCE CITY

The Swedish Museum of Natural History was formally created by royal decree in 1819 as three large collections were combined: the royal collection described and catalogued by Linnaeus in the 1750s and '60s, the collection of the Royal Academy of Sciences, and a private collection of primarily zoological specimens. It was put under the guardianship of the Academy of Sciences, and spent most of its first century of existence sharing a small house on Drottninggatan in central Stockholm with the offices of the Academy of Sciences itself.[9]

In the course of the nineteenth century, this building was extended several times. Applying to Parliament for a radical enlargement in the 1850s, museum officials claimed that all existing species would surely be found within the foreseeable future, so that after this last one, no more building projects would ever be necessary. The result, several times as large as the original building, seemed to satisfy every need the Museum and the Academy could possibly have.[10] But in 1878, little more than a decade after the inauguration of the extended museum building, Academy officials felt obliged to go back on this promise. The new building had begun to seem too small to house both the growing collections of the Museum and the offices of the Academy of Sciences. By the early twentieth century, modest references in the museum guidebook to lapses in the systematic order had escalated to explicit complaints about the lack of space and apologies for the presence of rhinoceroses and alligators in the cloakroom.[11]

However, this time Parliament was not prepared to listen. Growing concerns for the national infrastructure—most importantly railways and schools—made them disinclined to keep feeding the ever-hungry museum funds for more space. Moreover, the extension site the museum had in mind was next to the old building on Drottninggatan, in a part of town that was becoming increasingly valuable as the city expanded and the population grew. Why, city and state officials asked, should they waste this valuable site on a museum, when it could earn them a great deal of money on the booming property market? Several members of Parliament expressed considerable reluctance to spend "millions" on a new building in the inner city, and argued that, instead, very much "less expensive land should be purchased in the immediate vicinity of Stockholm."[12]

To museum officials, this was not an appealing prospect. Apart from the lack of space, the site at Drottninggatan was everything a public-minded scientist could wish for. In 1910, people taking a Sunday stroll down the street from Observatory Hill—itself the site of one of the city's oldest scientific institutions—would pass the Royal Institute of Technology on the right and Stockholm University College on the left, followed by the Swedish Museum of Natural History and the Academy of Sciences, and in a side street, the Pharmaceutical Institute. Further on was the old site of the Nordic Museum of Scandinavian ethnology (Nordiska museet), which was in the process of moving to the royal island of Djurgården, two of the largest and most prestigious secondary schools, and the city offices of the Academy of Agriculture. At Drottninggatan, the SMNH was located in a cluster of public and scientific institutions, as well as in a commercially dynamic part of town.[13]

But after spending twenty-five years vainly trying to realize their building plans, museum and Academy officials radically changed their strategy. In order to get Parliament to agree to the extensions, they had to trade location for space, and move the entire museum and the Academy of Sciences to a cheaper and bigger site—the rural suburb of Frescati, north of Stockholm. The final decision was made in 1904, and twelve years later the new museum opened in its new location.

In campaigning for the idea of Frescati as an attractive site for the museum, museum officials had to deal with existing connotations of Frescati. The status of the area was complicated legally and administratively as well as in the social life and imagination of the people of Stockholm. It was—and is—part of Kungliga Djurgården, the Royal Deer Park, expropriated by the Crown during the Reformation, and later fenced in to the keep the royal deer safe from wolves and poachers. The gatekeepers often kept inns (legal or illegal) as well as gates, so the former hunting grounds became popular with revellers, and figured frequently in 18th- and 19th-century art and poetry. The name Frescati was a relic from a royal trip to Italy in the 1784, after which three different parts of Djurgården were named Tivoli, Albano, and Frescati—rather unaccountably spelt with an "e"—and their care and beautification assigned to royal favorites. Favorites and caretakers changed through the centuries, but the romantic status of Djurgården as a place of amusement and recreation for all sections of society persisted.[14]

With the new Swedish constitution of 1809, all Crown lands were turned into state property—except for Djurgården, which remained under the disposition of the Regent, his to keep and to control during his reign, but not for profit: the yield was only to be used for the care and improvement of the area itself. Neither wholly public nor wholly private, it was semi-protected, and semi-official, and could be used as an arena to play out royal whims as well as public projects.[15] In the early years of the Bernadotte dynasty following the new constitution, hunting was supplanted by military installations and exercise grounds; towards the end of the century charitable and scientific institutions such as museums, gardens and a teaching hospital were favored; and the Olympic Stadium and tennis courts of the early twentieth century show the influence of Gustav V, an avowed sports fanatic.[16] The uses of Djurgården thus reflected the interests of the monarch, as well as changing ideas about the role of government in public life.[17]

Different parts of the extensive grounds came to be associated with different activities. The southern part of the area—the island of Djurgården—remained a place of recreation, for some in mansions erected by royal favorites on royal ground, and for others at the restaurants, exhibitions and open-air museums established around the turn of the twentieth century. The northern part, further removed from the city and more rural, developed in a slightly different direction. In 1814, the Experimental Farm of the Royal Academy of Agricultural Sciences was placed here by royal decree, to conduct modest agricultural experiments and to serve as an example to farmers all over the country. This pastoral aura was reinforced towards the end of the century, when the growing city started to encroach on the centrally located Botanic Garden and the director decided to move it somewhere quieter and more spacious. The chosen location was Frescati, divided from the Experimental Farm by the main road north and the narrow-gauge tracks of a suburban railway.[18]

These two institutions, though green and pastoral, provided the core for the argument on the part of SMNH officials that rural Frescati was, in fact, *scientifically central*. A further attraction in the area was the maceration building where the museum's whale exhibits were prepared—banished to the sea-shore in 1885 by the city health authorities because of the terrible smell of putrefying whales. If the Academy of Sciences and the Swedish Museum of Natural History, in turn, moved their main buildings here, the area would serve as a focal point for scientific Stockholm. In this context, the Science City was conceived.

The image of the Science City went through several changes during the twenty years from conception to stabilization. When the plan was first launched in 1903, the city of Stockholm was still in a stage of violent growth. The most dynamic expansion was in the north-east, where land prices were rising as fashionable new blocks rose out of former swamps and military exercise grounds. Crowded by the growing city, the military decided to seek wider horizons for their cannon. To fund the move, they would give up their land in Djurgården for urban development, and a state committee was appointed to determine the fate of the old exercise grounds. Their proposal was presented in 1902 and revealed a grid of solid city blocks extending all the way north to the proposed museum site in Frescati.[19] Under this scheme, the Science City would turn into a city borough, in a development similar to what had happened to the Natural History Museum in London when the South Kensington area suddenly boomed.

On the face of it, the Kensington area shared many of the characteristics of Djurgården. Its situation relatively far from central London suggested reasonable property prices, and if not actually owned by the royal family, it was enthusiastically promoted by Prince Albert as a site for exhibitions and public projects. But when the Natural

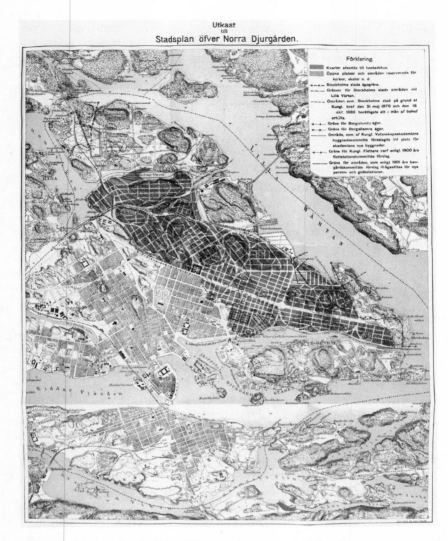

Figure 1. The proposal of the 1902 committee to extend the city to cover most of Djurgården. From *Underdånigt betänkande om förslag angående försäljning af Norra Djurgården m. m. afgifvet af den af kungl. maj:t för sådant ändamål tillsatta kommittén* (Stockholm, 1903).

History Museum finally opened in 1881, it found itself not in a peripheral suburb, but in the middle of an expansive, as well as expensive, urban development, where institutions of art and science such as the South Kensington Museum and the Imperial Institute as well as an attractive middle-class clientele, were establishing themselves.[20]

In Stockholm, however, the plans to urbanize Djurgården were never realized. The complicated legal situation and the pastoral aura surrounding Djurgården proved too difficult to overcome, and in the following years it was put under even more protective legislation. In 1913, a second committee was appointed to explore the future of the area, but in the context of new ideas about city planning and nature conservation, rather than the massive urban development schemes of the previous decade. Though the proposal expressed no disapproval of building projects that were already under way, a large section of Djurgården—including Frescati—was designated a "natural park": neither as domestic as an urban park, nor as wild as a national park.[21] Any further development of the Science City concept would take place on garden terms.

In this new situation, and deprived of their chance of an urban setting, officials at the SMNH were ready to exploit the potential correlation between the conservation ideals expressed in the Djurgården legislation, and scientific practice at their own institution. The importance of having an institution of research into Swedish nature situated in such exemplary surroundings echoed through Parliamentary proposals and committee reports, as well as museum speeches and documents.[22] The director of the Department of Vertebrate Zoology was in fact a member of the second committee, and stressed the importance of infrastructure, housing, and public projects even in a "natural park." In this context, the Science City could use the natural history connotations of its institutions as an asset, and emerge as a sort of biological garden city.

Here, too, there were international parallels. In Berlin, the Botanic Garden moved from expansive Schöneberg to rural Dahlem in 1897, as urban growing-pains struck the German capital. Under the aegis of Friedrich Althoff, the Minister of Education, Dahlem was designed as a "German Oxford," with a number of state institutions— research institutes, scientific state agencies, and teaching hospitals— surrounded by middle-class residential areas. Though hindered by war and changing university politics, Dahlem eventually did develop into a flourishing garden city of science.[23]

The Berlin success was not to be repeated in Stockholm. Despite the construction of a few villas for administrators at the Experimental Farm, Frescati remained rural and lacking in infrastructure. As museum officials had to reconcile themselves to the idea that there were no prospects for *any* housing development in Frescati, be it professorial villas or city blocks, a third vision of the Science City was articulated in the late 1920s. This suggested turning the area into an unequivocally public space, a giant showcase for the Academy of Sciences and its related institutions. An expanded museum would include a new wing for the ethnographic collections, and it would be connected to the Botanic Garden—with a large new greenhouse after the fashion of Kew or the Copenhagen Botanical Garden—by a tree-lined avenue with fountains and herbaceous borders. A more exclusive aspect of science was represented by the Nobel research institutes for physics, chemistry and physical chemistry, the Nobel institution even then developing into the massively public phenomenon it was later to become.[24]

This vision, too, faded under the pressure of the restrictive Djurgården policy. It was not revived until several decades later, as Frescati began to play a role in the planning for university expansion in the 1950s. Until then, the Science City remained, to all intents and purposes, a peripheral and exclusive cluster of research institutions in the biological sciences.

ATTITUDES TOWARD THE PUBLIC

Most of the visions of the Science City presented in the early twentieth century emphasized the research orientation of the institutions concerned. In particular, the Swedish Museum of Natural History, whose location problems were at the heart of the proposed Science City, emerged as an institution devoted to research in systematics, rather than to educating visitors in natural history. But not all Museum officials shared this view. It was particularly problematic for the Department of Ethnography. For most of the nineteenth century, the ethnographic collections were part of the Department of Vertebrate Zoology, but they were hardly the most valued part. Despite constant growth from expeditions and donations, and various efforts to turn them into an independent museum—together with collections owned by other individuals and institutions—the collections were not on permanent display, but surfaced in temporary exhibitions during

Figure 2. The vision of a future Science City as presented by Axel Anderberg in 1928. The SMNH has been enlarged and joined, to the right of the courtyard, by a new Ethnographic Museum; and two new Nobel institutes and a greenhouse have been added. From Jonsell, Bengt (ed.), *Bergianska botanister: Bergianska stiftelsen och dess professorer under första seklet* (Stockholm, 1991), 108–109.

the 1870s and 1880s. In 1899, they were finally separated from the vertebrate collections, and the archaeologist Hjalmar Stolpe was given
the directorship of this tentative new museum department.[25]

Stolpe started to organize an ethnographic exhibition in a temporary building across the street from the main building of the museum.
But, almost immediately, he was faced with the prospect of moving
his fledgling displays to Frescati, with the rest of the museum. And
while his colleagues were all strongly in favor of the move, Stolpe
had other ideas. He rejected the practical arguments that the new
site would be cleaner, safer and less vulnerable to fires. But his most
forceful objections concerned the effect of the move on museum visitors. The peripheral position would make the museum inaccessible to
the public. The distance would require a bigger investment of both
time and money from prospective visitors. Tourists coming from the
provinces to visit the capital might not have either the time or the in-
clination to abandon the attractions of the inner city in order to visit
the museum. Most importantly, in Frescati the SMNH would lose all
the random visitors, all those people who simply happened to pass the
door and decided to enter. Instead, the museum would be dependent
on the "mass migration of school children under teacher's orders"—
but Stolpe did not want his exhibition to be a mere appendage to the
education system.[26]

Stolpe valued the display function of the museum much more
than his colleagues. The Department of Ethnography was small and
neglected, and ethnography itself a young science, dependent on its
public for funds as well as legitimacy.

> The negligible, all too inadequate funding of the Department of
> Ethnography, the increasing expense of the material, the urgency of
> completing the collections before the material ceases to accumulate
> as a result of the extinction or cultivation of the primitive peoples;
> all these force the Department of Ethograhy to depend primarily
> on the interest of the visiting public for its development.[27]

The very presence of the department of ethnography in a museum of natural history, an institution of some scientific standing, also
lent it an aura of academic respectability, so although Stolpe was reluctant to move away from the city, he was even less eager to sever
the connection with the museum. "Before the science of ethnography
is more firmly established in this country, complete independence and
the resulting isolation would be a fateful gift."[28] Consequently, Stolpe

found himself in the unenviable position of requiring administrative unity with colleagues whose ideas about the location and function of the museum were unacceptable to him.

Stolpe's concern for his audience also found more tangible expression. Access to the SMNH remained limited for most of the nineteenth century. During the early years of its existence, admission to the museum had been difficult both to arrange and to afford—although a few free tickets were graciously distributed to the grammar schools of the city for the edification of the students. All collections were nominally open to the public, but in fact only the zoological part of the museum was available on a regular basis, that is, 2 hours 3 days a week. As public funding for the museum increased, in the form of new chairs and architectural additions, so did parliamentary calls for greater public access. Ticket prices plunged in the 1860s, but although the opening hours were more generous, they remained limited and slightly erratic. Until 1904 only paying visitors were counted.[29]

Under Stolpe and his successors, several steps were taken to increase access to the ethnographic collections. The department was kept open to the public on a regular basis, and remained accessible despite increasing accommodation problems as the rest of the museum began the move to Frescati. However, Stolpe's successor Hartman managed to introduce increased opening hours in 1912: in addition to the few hours in the afternoon that the main museum building was open, the ethnographic collections were accessible two evenings a week, when prospective visitors would have finished work. This was made possible by the introduction of electricity in the ethnographic building, which increased opening hours in wintertime. In contrast, visitors to the display areas of the main museum had to make do with natural light, even in the new Frescati buildings.[30]

The ethnographers' motives were partly crass: unlike Sundays, evening hours at the museum were not free of charge. But unlike some of his museum colleagues, Stolpe also had experience of large exhibition projects, as a way of increasing funding for and interest in new fields. While several of the other museum departments were to remain indefinitely guideless, guidebooks to temporary exhibitions organized by the Department of Ethnography as well as a guide to the main ethnographic collections—by then in urgent need of succour in their crowded and dilapidated old building—appeared in the 1910s and 1920s. But despite these measures on the part of Stolpe and his successors, his very success in getting his own way in the building battles eventually proved disastrous for the Department of Ethnography.

It remained part of the SMNH, and was also allowed to continue in the old building after the move to Frescati was effected. But the Academy of Sciences ceased to take any significant active interest in the Department, and its fortunes deteriorated steadily until it finally closed its doors to the public in 1921.[31]

A diametrically different picture of the attitude to the visiting public emerges from the story of the Stockholm Botanic Garden. Formally, the Botanic Garden was an independent foundation managed, like the SMNH, by the Academy of Sciences. In practice, its ties to the museum were strong, since the directorship of the Garden automatically devolved on the professor of botany at the museum. Its relocation problems—predating those of the SMNH by two decades—provided a model for the discussion of the museum move.[32]

According to the city plan of 1879, the growing capital would increasingly encroach on the site of the Botanic Garden. Several streets and avenues were to be run through it, and in order to make the best of the situation and avoid expropriation, the newly appointed professor of botany Veit Brecher Wittrock decided to move the entire garden to a more peaceful location. Permission being granted by His Majesty, 7 hectares of first-class inner-city land, was sold in 1884 for just over a million *kronor*. The following year, 32 hectares of wooded hills and pasture in Frescati were purchased for less than a quarter of that sum. The proceeds were to be used to pay off old debts after several decades of financial difficulties, as well as for the laying out of the new garden. On the new site, the Academy of Sciences planned not only to carry on with the horticultural school and the market garden as stipulated in the instructions for the Botanic Garden, but also to establish a botanic garden of a scientific nature, in addition to, and not to the detriment of, prior activities.

Wittrock's plans for the scientific section, launched in 1891, were grandiose. All categories of plants were to be represented: the garden was to contain algae ponds, lichen beds, mosses and fungi. Phanerogams were to be presented in truly systematic order—mixing annuals and perennials to the glory of systematics and the despair of the gardeners—as well as in phytogeographic groups. The most magnificent project of all was the construction of an artificial alpinetum, a gigantic rockery for mountain plants from all over the world. Representatives of the alpine flora of every continent were to be planted on replicas of famous peaks, constructed with rocks and clay: accordingly, North American plants would flourish on a miniature Mount Tacoma, their Swedish counterparts on Åreskutan.[33]

Although the knowledge-seeking public appeared from time to time in Wittrock's description of his plans, his main interest was clearly the research part of the new garden. This orientation became even more obvious in October 1895, when the garden—and Wittrock personally—was targeted for attack in the press. Under the motto ("home-made, but true"): *O science, what stupidity and childishness flourish under thy venerable name!*, an anonymous attacker going by the name Vertumnus condemned the Frescati garden. Vertumnus berated Wittrock for exploiting the staff beyond their normal duties, for mistreating the gardeners, and for completely lacking any talent for "practical horticulture."[34] The main target, however, was Wittrock's so-called scientific activities. Apparently it was far from obvious what the function of the Stockholm Botanic Garden should be. In the 1784 will of Peter Johan Bergius, a doctor and member of the Royal Swedish Academy of Sciences, the Stockholm property called Bergielund had been bequeathed to the Academy of Sciences for the establishment of a market garden and a horticultural school, "for the good of the Country and the benefit of the Public." The director, bearing the title of professor, was to give classes primarily in horticulture, but also in natural history. This already ambiguous purpose of the garden became even more difficult to interpret after the garden moved from its central location to Frescati in the late 1880s.

Not very surprisingly, it was the giant rockery that most enraged Vertumnus. In 1895, blasting in the garden hills had begun to provide the vast amounts of rock needed for the alpinetum; but the only result so far were huge and shapeless piles of gravel and rocks in the north east corner of the garden. These "toy mountains" were expensive and ugly, scarred the original hillsides, and were not even suited for the growing of alpine plants. How could Wittrock spend tens of thousands on them, when the market garden lacked even a reliable water supply? The market gardeners were already severely put upon, drafted into scientific service among the drying mosses and wilting beds of mixed perennials and annuals, when they should have been tending to their fruit trees.

Vertumnus also deplored the lack of greenhouses in the garden. A tropical greenhouse would not only be of scientific value, but more importantly, it would be attractive to the public, thus furthering an "active interaction with the interests and education of the public," which would benefit scientists and visitors alike. Wittrock's total disregard for public interest was thus detrimental to his own scientific interests, as well as being contrary to the aims of the donor. As interpreted by Vertumnus, the "public benefit" stipulated in the will indicated that the garden should be an institution of civic education.

Perhaps not very surprisingly, the battle of the mountains touched on other, and more private, issues than science and public utility. Hiding behind the pseudonym of Vertumnus was a disgruntled former subordinate of Wittrock's at the newly founded Stockholm University, whose animosity had been enlisted in a feud on an international scale over the appointment to the botany chair at the University of Stockholm.[35]

But professorial battles and academic intrigue apart, the episode of the toy mountains reflects an attitude toward the public role of the garden that differed markedly from that of Hjalmar Stolpe. To Wittrock, the peripheral location of the garden was an advantage: it would less easily be confused with a public park, and the absence of cafés nearby would further discourage the public from venturing into the garden. The small tropical greenhouse for water-lilies that was eventually constructed in 1900 was ostensibly intended for research, rather than for the entertainment of the visiting public.

Wittrock's attitude toward visitors was not entirely representative of his colleagues at the SMNH, many of whom devoted considerable effort to building pedagogic exhibitions and writing guidebooks for the new museum. Nevertheless, the conditions in Frescati were hardly ideal for encouraging visitors.[36] The pastoral fields of the nearby Experimental Farm of the Academy of Agriculture were a pleasing enough prospect, but the gardens planned for the museum's surroundings were a long time in the making, particularly when food shortages turned the grounds into potato fields in 1917. The lack of artificial lighting in the exhibition halls precluded extensive visiting hours, especially in winter, and difficulties with the management of the museum café discouraged long visits. But the most serious problem was transportation. Located several kilometres beyond the last tram stop, the museum could only be reached by a small suburban train that catered mainly to the affluent garden cities of the north. Faced with a train fare almost as expensive as the museum entrance fee, most visitors chose to walk, and the records reveal a close correspondence between the number of visitors and the weather. Even in the 1940s, the poet Tomas Tranströmer, then a young and ardent amateur entomologist, would take the tram as far as the city limit and walk the remaining kilometres to the museum. He recalls biting winds, constantly running nose and eyes: "The road was always a little longer than I imagined."[37]

MEANING AND ACCESSIBILITY

A "Science City" does not necessarily imply exclusivity: a case in point is the Cité des Sciences et de l'Industrie at La Villette, Paris, a giant center of public education and entertainment that opened in 1986. But for most of the twentieth century, the Frescati project remained a remote collection of research-oriented institutions. By moving away from the inner city, the Swedish Museum of Natural History affirmed its dedication to research rather than public education. In several tangible ways, the museum was less accessible in its new location.

The restricted opening hours and the poor transportation combined to make a visit to the museum an expensive and complicated affair. Lack of funds and inadequate organization delayed the garden plans and the establishment of a café, obstructing the transformation of the museum grounds from a building site into a beauty spot worthy of a weekend excursion. In other ways, too, the move failed to facilitate access to the SMNH. Advocates of the move had argued that pedagogy could compensate for distance: if the new exhibitions were arranged as instructively and as neatly as modern museum practice dictated, "the public will find that 'the road is worthwhile' and that distances that used to be considered vast, are in fact small."[38] But although the pedagogic efforts of museum officials intensified—exhibitions were rearranged and enlarged and guidebooks were added—their main audience remained the rather exclusive segment of the population that was receiving secondary education in systematics and the finer points of biology. The exhibitions still harmonized with higher education rather than elementary schooling or the image of the natural world presented in other popular fora. In this sense, accessibility proved more than simply a physical problem.[39]

The museum officials themselves hardly considered the situation of the new museum ideal. Forced to abandon, in turn, the visions of the Science City as a bustling city borough, a smiling garden city, and a magnificent exhibition ground, they concentrated their energies on improving public transportation to the SMNH. But even in these efforts, the research bias was evident: rejecting as unrealistic the prospect of extending the tram lines to Frescati, they strove to reduce the transportation costs of the museum staff rather than consider the problems facing prospective visitors.[40]

Ironically, the Science City proved difficult to establish among research colleagues and city officials as well. In 1926, the Science City had achieved the distinction of becoming the official designation of

Riksmuseets
Buffé

Belägen vid första järngrinden
(Huset med stenpelarna)

Fullständig Konditoriservering

Servering av smörgås och smörgåsbrickor
Öl till spisande gäster

Obs. Billigt och gott!

PLANRITNING
ÖVER
NATURHISTORISKA RIKSMUSEET

Museets visningstider:

Riksmuseets skådesamlingar hålles öppna för allmänheten *alla dagar*, mellan kl. 11—3. Onsdagar och lördagar är museet öppet avgiftsfritt mellan kl. 12—3 samt *söndagar* mellan kl. 1—3. Inträdesavgift för de dagar och tider museet icke är fritt öppet är 50 öre för vuxna, och 25 öre för barn under 15 år, skolor, korporationer och studiegrupper kunna beviljas fritt tillträde efter härom gjord anmälan till intendenten genom uppsyningsmannen, telefon 85978. Resande som icke kunna passa ovannämnda visningstider hänvisas till uppsyningsmannen för överenskommelse.

BUSSTRAFIKEN
Riksmuseet — Jarlaplan och vice versa.

Omnibussar avgå från Jarlaplan till Riksmuseet var 10:e minut och från Riksmuseet till Jarlaplan var 10:e minut.
Bussar till och från Engelbrektsplan var 15:e minut.
Turistbuss; biljettpris o. d. efter särskild taxa beroende på bussens storlek och vägsträckan.

STOCKHOLMS LÄNS OMNIBUSSAKTIEBOLAG
Telefoner: Roslags-Näsby 243, 278

Figure 3. Timetables and refreshments were as important to museum visitors as floor plans and guidebooks. From "Planritning över Naturhistoriska riksmuseet" (s.l., s.d.). [Sv. Museer Kaps. Sthlm, Uppsala universitetsbibliotek].

the Frescati area, as a Stockholm counterpart to the *Quartier Latin* or *Cité d'Université* of Paris.[41] But this proved a fleeting glory, as the City Planning Committee reversed their decision only eight years later:

> The motive behind this is, on the one hand, that the name 'Science City' has not been widely adopted in Stockholm, and on the other hand, that it is rather unjustified considering that the scientific institutions of Stockholm are not exclusively located there; but are to be found in other parts of the city, particularly in Vasastaden, where a special "science city" has developed around Observatory Hill.[42]

This "science city" around Observatory Hill was precisely the part of the city that the SMNH and the Academy of Sciences had abandoned in order to gain funding and space at Frescati. Not only had the Academy and SMNH officials failed to establish themselves as a Science City, but they had managed to leave an actual Science City behind.

The failure of the Science City may be interpreted as an unsuccessful attempt to redefine the meaning of Frescati, from remote and rural to central and scientific. After the initial failure of the far-reaching urban plans of the military committee of 1902, the very pastoral aura of Frescati was enlisted to turn it into a scientific garden city. However, the aura of Frescati was not the only factor in this process. The character of the area around Drottninggatan, with its agglomeration of academic institutions, remained as scientific after the move of the Academy and the museum, as Stockholm University College, the Institute of Dentistry, and the Stockholm School of Economics rushed in to fill the space vacated by other institutions.

Although the Science City of Frescati initially failed to take root, it takes on a different character in the long-term perspective. When Stockholm University College began expanding beyond the limits of its inner-city site, city officials proved unwilling to provide the needed space in the vicinity of Drottninggatan—just as they had done in the case of the Academy and the SMNH almost a hundred years earlier. After years of rather acrimonious debate, it was decided that Stockholm University (having shed its administrative connection to the city of Stockholm and turned into a state university) should move to the Frescati area as well. The move was initiated in the mid-1960s, and is only now being completed, as the physicists and the far-away astronomers have been brought into the fold, and moved into the newly constructed Physics Centre. And in the same way that the University gradually expanded into the old institutional buildings in the city center as other institutions moved out in the early 20th century, today it has incorporated many of the Frescati buildings and institutions. The Institutes of Forestry and Veterinary Science currently accommodate psychologists, economists and mathematicians, and large parts of the Botanic Garden have been absorbed by the Botany Department.[43]

As the University tries to strengthen its ties to other research institutions in Stockholm—the Royal Institute of Technology, a thirty-minute walk away through the woods or a short underground journey, and the Karolinska Institute, quite close as the crow flies but located on the other side of a lake—the Science City proves to be not only well established, but spreading well beyond its original limits. It has lent its name to a foundation, *Stiftelsen Vetenskapsstaden*, whose mission is to promote scientific expansion and interdisciplinary contacts in the area.[44] The problems of infrastructure that haunted the Science City in the early twentieth century have, to some extent at least, been alleviated through the development of better transportation, student housing, and the establishment of canteens, cafés, and convenience stores in the area.

Ironically, as the Science City is beginning to savour the joys of urban development, the old recreational aura of Frescati has come back to haunt it. The ghosts of eighteenth-century shepherds and shepherdesses linger among the ancient oak trees, along with the rare insects inhabiting the bark of those trees, inspiring the creation of a "National City Park." This is a novel legal concept designed to protect the natural and cultural heritage of the area.[45] In its mediation between ideas of conservation and of scientific development, it recalls many of the sentiments of the 1913 committee that formulated the equally indefinite concept "natural park." Again, a strict enforcement of this law would make further expansion of the Science City difficult, though several construction projects have been completed despite protests from conservationists. And again, representatives of the institutions involved—the University, the Academy, the Botanic Garden and the SMNH—have tried to turn the difficulty into an advantage. In 1998 they presented Frescati as "the Garden of Science" (*Vetenskapens lustgård*), with obvious Edenic associations.

As a marketing concept, the Garden of Science evokes the spirit of rational recreation, as the Victorians would have put it. Citizens and city dwellers are invited to pursue their interest in science and education among the flowering lawns, the cafés, and the venerable public institutions of Frescati. (Although the six-lane motorway cutting through the area may undermine the pastoral impression somewhat.) But more importantly, it suggests a strengthening of the alliance between academics and city officials in the promotion of Stockholm as a city of science. The story of the SMNH and the Science City illustrates the conflicted nature of this relationship. The twentieth century is characterized by a series of breakdowns in communication between academics and national and regional authorities: the refusal of Parliament to accommodate an expanding Museum of Natural History in Drottninggatan at the turn of the century; the failure to develop Frescati as an academic area and the renewed allocation of resources to Drottninggatan in the 1920s; and finally the reluctance to supply the resources required for university expansion in the inner city.

The Garden of Science, on the other hand, combines the traditional ideals of the pastoral production of knowledge with the modern politics of regional development. Promoters of universities as engines of economic growth delight in the bucolic terminology of research intitutions, and campuses and science parks continue to multiply.[46]

There are many parallels between the Garden of Science and the recreational Science City envisioned by Axel Anderberg in 1928. Both

are attempts to turn the Science City into a success, despite its initial
character as an emergency solution. Both are also attempts to reconcile the different groups with different interests in the area. The holiday visitors picnicking on the grass (abhorred by Professor Wittrock
in the 1890s), the school children visiting the SMNH (provoking am-
bivalence in the heart of Professor Stolpe), the scientists picking up a
cup of coffee on the way from one research institution to another—all
are welcome in the Garden of Science. As are industrialists and policy makers who wish to explore the economic potential of science.

In the short term, however, both are failures. The golden-tas-
selled brochure of 1916 failed to establish the Science City as a concept and as a scientific center, and Anderberg's fountains and avenues
were never built. Its modern counterpart, the website of the Garden
of Science, is now down.[47] But although the Science City as originally
envisioned did not materialize, the meaning of Frescati is changing.
Transportation, urbanization, and legislation are making it pastoral
and picturesque, rather than remote and rural. But, as Simon Schaffer reminds us, "[p]lans and networks will not alone provide historians of science with the key to science's local and spatial powers [. . .]
[I]nterpretation demands an account of the varying cultural narratives in which the design acquires its meaning."[48] In the context
of contemporary policy discussions about research and regional development, the rhetoric of space increasingly centers on economics
rather than accessibility. And perhaps, in the union of economic
regeneration, research, and recreation, the Garden of Science may
bloom again.

NOTES

1. *Vetenskapsstaden* (Göteborg, 1916).
2. Handlingar angående K. Vetenskapsakademiens, Naturhistoriska Riksmuseets
   och Vetenskapsakademiens Nobelinstituts byggnadsfråga III (Stockholm,
   1904), 223.
3. Thomas A. Markus, *Buildings and power: Freedom and control in the origin
   of modern building types* (London, 1993), 5ff. The redefined religious building is an example cited from the work of historian of architecture Paul
   Frankl.
4. Bill Hillier, *Space is the machine: A configurational theory of architecture*
   (Cambridge, 1996), 397.
5. For comments on the relations of the history of science to material culture
   and space as analytical tools from a historian interested in both traditions,

see Peter Galison, *Image and logic: A material culture of microphysics* (Chicago, 1997); idem & Emily Thompson (eds.), *The architecture of science* (Cambridge, MA, 1999).

6. Important examples and influences have been provided by the geographer David Livingstone and the architectural theorists Sophie Forgan and Thomas Markus. Sophie Forgan, "The architecture of display: Museums, universities and objects in nineteenth-century Britain," *History of science* 32 (1994), 139–162; Sophie Forgan and Graeme Gooday, " 'A fungoid assemblage of buildings': Diversity and adversity in the development of college architecture and scientific education in nineteenth-century Kensington," *History of universities* 13 (1994), 153–192; idem, "Constructing South Kensington: The buildings and politics of T. H. Huxley's working environment," *British journal for the history of science* 29 (1996), 435–468; David N. Livingstone, "The spaces of knowledge: Contributions towards a historical geography of science," *Environment and planning D: Society and space* 13 (1995), 5–34; Markus, op. cit.

7. An attempt to distinguish these perspectives on space is made in Adi Ophir and Steven Shapin, "The place of knowledge: A methodological survey," *Science in context* 4 (1991), 3–21.

8. For a brief outline of time geography, see Torsten Hägerstrand, "What about people in regional science?" (1970), in Gösta Carlestam and Barbro Sollbe (eds.), *Om tidens vidd ochtingens ordning: Texter av Torsten Hägerstrand* (Stockholm, 1991), 146ff.

9. The early history of the SMNH is recounted in *Naturhistoriska riksmuseets historia: Dess uppkomst och utveckling.* Utgifven med statsunderstöd af Kungl. Vetenskapsakademien (Stockholm, 1916); the period 1866–1925 is investigated in Jenny Beckman, *Naturens palats: Nybyggnad, vetenskap och utställning vid Naturhistoriska riksmuseet, 1866–1925* (Stockholm, 1999). The papers of the SMNH are scattered. Most are in the Proceedings of the Royal Swedish Academy of Sciences; some are in the central archives of the SMNH; yet others are in the departmental archives of the SMNH, many of which have not been catalogued. The papers relating to the move of the SMNH are incomplete. The proceedings of the Building Committees are divided between the Archives of the Royal Swedish Academy of Sciences (Handlingar angående K. Vetenskapsakademiens och Naturhistoriska riksmuseets byggnadsfråga 1899–1903, Handlingar angående K. Vetenskapsakademiens och Naturhistoriska riksmuseets byggnadsfråga 1903–1906); and the archives of the Department of Vertebrate Zoology, SMNH (Handlingar rörande museibyggnaden); some are missing. Official letters and memorials are in the National Archives, Ministry of Education and Ecclesiastical Affairs; and in the Proceedings of the Royal Swedish Academy of Sciences. Parts of the early proceedings were printed, and wherever possible I have quoted the printed material: *Handlingar angående K. Vetenskapsakademiens, Naturhistoriska Riksmuseets och Vetenskapsakademiens*

Nobelinstituts byggnadsfråga I (Stockholm, 1902); *Handlingar angående K. Vetenskapsakademiens, Naturhistoriska Riksmuseets och Vetenskapsakademiens Nobelinstituts byggnadsfråga II* (Stockholm, 1903); *Handlingar angående K. Vetenskapsakademiens, Naturhistoriska Riksmuseets och Vetenskapsakademiens Nobelinstituts byggnadsfråga III* (Stockholm, 1904); *Nya handlingar angående K. Vetenskapsakademiens och Naturhistoriska Riksmuseets byggnadsfråga I* (Uppsala, 1906); henceforth referred to as *Handlingar I, Handlingar II, Handlingar III*, and *Nya handlingar*.

10. Letter from the Royal Swedish Academy of Sciences to the Swedish Government, 11 June 1856, MS Utgående skrivelser B1:9, *Archives of the Royal Swedish Academy of Sciences*.

11. Interestingly, the complaints were at their most explicit after the decision to move the museum had already been made. Cf. *Handledning vid beseendet af zoologiska samlingarna uti Riksmuseum*, 18th edition (Uppsala, 1900), 15; and *Handledning vid beseendet af zoologiska samlingarna uti Riksmuseum*, 22nd edition (Uppsala, 1908), 2–3, 19.

12. Proceedings of the Swedish Parliament, *Andra kammarens protokoll 1884*, nr 39, 31, 40.

13. For a more detailed description of the Drottninggatan area, see Beckman, *Naturens palats*, ch. 3.

14. The literature on Djurgården is voluminous. A relatively concise history is Peter Lundevall, *Djurgården—kungens och folkets park: Djurgårdsmarkens förändring sedan medeltiden fram till vår tid* (Stockholm, 1997), where Djurgården is referred to as the most thoroughly surveyed and described green area in Sweden (18). Classic works are Staffan Tjerneld, *En bok om Djurgården under 300 år* (Stockholm, 1980), and Gunnar Bolin, Nils Östman and Tor Hedberg, *Djurgården förr och nu* (Stockholm, 1925). A useful, if controversial, account of the history of urban planning in Stockholm is Ingemar Johansson, *Stor-Stockholms bebyggelsehistoria: Markpolitik, planering och byggande under sju sekler* (1987; Stockholm, 1991).

15. Lundevall, 30; Tjerneld, 29.

16. Tjerneld, 26.

17. Svenbjörn Kilander, *Den nya staten och den gamla: En studie i ideologisk förändring*. Studia historica Upsaliensia 164 (Stockholm: Almqvist & Wiksell, 1991); Torbjörn Nilsson, *Elitens svängrum: Första kammaren, staten och moderniseringen 1867–1886*. Acta universitatis Stockholmiensis (Stockholm: Almqvist & Wiksell, 1994). On increasing government involvement in matters of education and public culture, a classic study is Gunnar Richardson, *Kulturkamp och klasskamp: Ideologiska och sociala motsättningar i svensk skoloch kulturpolitik under 1880-talet* (Göteborg: Akademiförlaget, 1963).

18. For the history of the Experimental Farm, see Ulrich Lange, *Experimentalfältet: Kungl. Lantbruksakademiens experiment- och försöksverksamhet på norra Djurgården i Stockholm 1816–1907* (Stockholm, 2000); Erland Mårald, *I mötet mellan jordbruk och kemi: Agrikulturkemins framväxt på Lantbruk-*

sakademiens Experimentalfält 1850–1907 (Stockholm, 1998); for the history of the Botanic Garden, see below.

19. *Underdånigt betänkande om förslag angående försäljning af Norra Djurgården m. m. afgifvet af den af kungl. maj:t för sådant ändamål tillsatta kommittén* (Stockholm, 1903).

20. Nicolaas A. Rupke, "The road to Albertopolis: Richard Owen (1804–92) and the founding of the British Museum of Natural History," in Rupke (ed.), *Science, politics and the public good: Essays in honour of Margaret Gowing* (London, 1988).

21. *Betänkande angående Djurgårdens bevarande såsom park avgivet av särskilt tillkallade sakkunniga* (Stockholm, 1917).

22. The Parliamentary debates are reprinted in the proceedings of the Stockholm City Council: Bihang nr 169, *Stockholms stadsfullmäktiges handlingar 1918*, "Handlingar i det till stadsfullmäktige remitterade ärendet angående Kungl. Djurgårdens i Stockholm bevarande såsom park," 6ff.; and restated at the inauguration of the SMNH in 1916, *Kungl. Vetenskapsakademiens årsbok 1917*, 140.

23. Michael Engel, *Geschichte Dahlems* (Berlin, 1984); idem, "Dahlem als Wissenschaftszentrum," in Rudolf Vierhaus and Bernhard vom Brocke (eds.), *Forschung im Spannungsfeld von Politik und Gesellschaft: Geschichte und Struktur der Kaiser-Wilhelm-/Max-Planck-Gesellschaft* (Stuttgart, 1990).

24. The plan is reprinted in Bengt Jonsell (ed.), *Bergianska botanister: Bergianska stiftelsen och dess professorer under första seklet* (Stockholm, 1991), 108–9, 115. The original seems to be missing, but a copy of it, along with a site plan, is in the Archives of the Royal Academy of Sciences.

25. The struggle over the power and place of the ethnographic collections is described in Olof Ljungström, *Oscariansk antropologi: Etnografi, förhistoria och rasforskning under sent 1800-tal* (Hedemora, 2004).

26. Stolpe's views on the moving plans are presented in *Handlingar II*, 122–128; also Hjalmar Stolpe, "Hvad är och hvad bör ett etnografiskt museum vara?," *Hvar 8 dag*, 19 April 1903.

27. *Handlingar II*, 126.

28. Ibid., 128.

29. On changing attitudes to visitors to the SMNH, see Jenny Beckman, "The Swedish Museum of Natural History and the 'Linnaean tradition,' " in Marco Beretta (ed.), *From Private to Public: Natural Collections and Museums* (Sagamore Beach, 2005).

30. See yearly reports of the Department of Ethnography in *Kungliga vetenskapsakademiens årsbok* 1903–1924. On electricity in the new museum, see Axel Anderberg, "Riksmuseets nya byggnader," in *Naturhistoriska Riksmuseets historia*.

31. *Handlingar II*, 165–175; Eric von Rosen (ed.), *Museet i packlårar: Pressuttalanden om Riksmuseets etnografiska avdelning med anledning av dess lokalfrågas framläggande inför Riksdagen 1930* (Stockholm, 1931).

32. On the history of the Botanic Garden, see *Bergianska botanister.*
33. Veit Brecher Wittrock, "Om planen för Bergielunds botaniska trädgård samt om trädgårdens tillstånd 1891." *Acta Horti Bergiani* 1:2 (1891); Robert E. Fries, "Några drag ur den Bergianska trädgårdens historia 1885–1914," *Acta Horti Bergiani* 6:1 (1918). Rock gardens were fashionable features of botanic gardens in the late nineteenth century; the trend established by Berlin botanist Adolf Engler and magnificently realized among the old battlements in the new botanic garden of Copenhagen, where it served as an inspiration for Wittrock. C. Hansen Ostenfeld, *Botanisk Have gennem 50 aar: 1874–1924.* Festskrift udgivet af Københavns universitet i anledning af Hans Majestæt Kongens fødelsdag 26. September 1924 (Köpenhamn, 1924).
34. "Vertumnus," "De Wittrockska leksaksbergen vid Bergielund: En sorglustig episod ur den Bergianska stiftelsens modärna krönika," *Nordisk Revy* 1895, 746–752, quotation 746; "Bergen på Bergiilund," *Stockholms Dagblad* 17 October 1895; "Bergen på Bergiilund," *Stockholms Dagblad* 22 October 1895; V. B. Wittrock, "Om Bergielund: Ett genmäle," *Stockholms Dagblad* 24 October 1895; "Obefogade angrepp mot vetenskaplig institution," *Svenska Dagbladet* 24 October 1895; "Vertumnus," "De Wittrockska leksaksbergen vid Bergielund, jämte andra hittills otryckta bidrag till den Bergianska stiftelsens modärna historia," *Nordisk Revy* 1895, 825–835.
35. Letter from Nordal Wille to Wittrock, 27 October 1895; Gustaf Lagerheim to Wittrock, 11 November 1895, *Archives of the Royal Academy of Sciences.*
36. A detailed account of the infrastructural problems at Frescati is in Beckman, *Naturens palats,* ch. 4.
37. Tomas Tranströmer, *Minnena ser mig* (Stockholm, 1993), 17.
38. *Handlingar I,* 53.
39. This argument is developed more fully in Jenny Beckman, "Nature's palace: The construction of the Swedish Museum of Natural History," *History of science* 42 (2004), 85–111.
40. The application for subsidies is in a letter from Einar Lönnberg to the Royal Academy of Sciences, 7 September 1917, submitted to the Government 12 September 1917. Konseljakt no. 30, 9 November 1917, *Ministry of Education and Ecclesiastical Affairs, National Archives.*
41. Proceedings of the Stockholm City Council: Stadskollegiets utlåtande nr 352, *Stockholms stadsfullmäktiges handlingar 1926,* 1684; beslut fattat 6 December 1926. Protokoll, yttranden och motioner, *Stockholms stadsfullmäktiges handlingar 1926,* 180–181.
42. Proceedings of the Stockholm City Council: Stadskollegiets utlåtande nr 15, *Stockholms stadsfullmäktiges handlingar 1934,* 108; beslut fattade i Stadsfullmäktige den 22 januari 1934. Protokoll och motioner 22 januari, *Stockholms stadsfullmäktiges handlingar 1934,* 16.
43. Fredric Bedoire and Per Thullberg, *Stockholms universitet 1878–1978* (Stockholm, 1978); Thomas Hall (ed.), *Frescati: Huvudstadsuniversitet och arkitekturpark* (Stockholm, 1998).

44. http://www.vetenskapsstaden.se/, September 16, 2004.
45. Miljöbalken (SFS 1998:808), chapter 4, paragraph 7.
46. There is a growing literature that touches on pastoral ideals in education and research; see Claes Caldenby, *Universitetet och staden: Inför fältstudier!* (Göteborg, 1994); Thomas Bender (ed.), *The university and the city: From medieval origins to the present* (Oxford, 1988); Martin Trow and Torsten Nybom (eds.), *University and society: Essays on the social role of research and higher education* (London, 1991); Lawrence Stone (ed.), *The university in society. Volume II: Europe, Scotland, and the United States from the 16th to the 20th century* (London, 1974); Paul Venable Turner, *Campus: An American planning tradition* (Cambridge, Massachusetts, 1984); Herman van der Wusten (ed.), *The urban university and its identity: Roots, locations, roles* (Dordrecht, 1998). A more analytical discussion is provided in Simon Schaffer, "Physics laboratories and the Victorian country house," in Crosbie Smith and Jon Agar (eds.), *Making space for science: Territorial themes in the shaping of knowledge* (London, 1998), 149–180.
47. http://www.vetenskapenslustgard.org/, March 29, 2005.
48. Schaffer, 150.

THE BOUNDARIES OF NUCLEAR POWER

Security and Exclusion at Reactor FR-0

MAJA FJÆSTAD

The question leading to this article was formulated in my mind when, on a visit to the Swedish nuclear site of Studsvik, I stood wondering in front of the concrete walls of the former experimental reactor FR-0: Were the thick walls there to keep the dangers of the former reactor in—or to keep me out?

Therefore, the main purpose of this article is to discuss the implications surrounding the subject of nuclear safety. The safety boundaries of nuclear power have always been a difficult issue. From the very first nuclear chain reaction, with insufficient protection against radiation, to today's fear of terrorist attacks on nuclear power plants, the safety of nuclear power has been a topic of intense discussion. How has that impinged on the view on nuclear power itself? How has safety-consciousness affected scientists working on nuclear power? And what are the reasons for constructing boundaries around a scientific instrument? These are issues that I tentatively discuss in this article.

More specifically, I examine the security and the boundaries of a specific reactor, FR-0, at Studsvik, near Stockholm, Sweden. FR-0 was an experimental fast reactor, and was hoped to be the first step in a Swedish fast-breeder power program. I will discuss several aspects of the boundaries of the reactor, from spatial boundaries to social and professional ones. FR-0 was sited by the sea, far from populated areas, 100 km south of Stockholm. I will contrast this with Sweden's very first nuclear reactor, R1, which had been placed in the center of the Swedish capital. At the same time as the exclusion and safety of these reactors are discussed, a sketch of the Swedish nuclear power program during the 1950s and 1960s will be presented.

Several studies of the laboratories and the spatial prerequisites for scientific activities have been conducted in recent years. How the researchers interact and communicate in the architecture of universities and laboratories has been described by, among others, anthropologists, as is discussed in the introduction to this volume. In this article I point out the tension between the traditional academic openness of scientific milieus and the stringent safety and security considerations of a nuclear site. I will tentatively discuss how geographical isolation and high security might affect scientific activities.

A NEW FIELD OF KNOWLEDGE

The world's first steps towards the development of nuclear power were taken in the shadow of the Second World War, in the secrets of the Manhattan Project. A controlled chain reaction had to be obtained in order to understand the properties of an atomic bomb and produce fissile material. The first nuclear reactor was put in operation on December 2, 1942, under the supervision of the Nobel Prize-winning physicist Enrico Fermi, a historic moment that very few knew about at the time. The reactor, CP-1, was constructed in a squash court under the stadium of the University of Chicago, and was one of the events leading to the atomic bombs over Hiroshima and Nagasaki. Although the Manhattan Project also depicted the possibilities of atomic energy for civilian use, the project was conceived for military purposes, and nuclear energy never lost its association with the devastating bombs.[1]

The atomic bombs also made it clear to the rest of the world that something new had been discovered. The first impulse to the Swedish nuclear program came in the fall of 1945 from the Supreme Commander of the Swedish Armed Forces.[2] A "Swedish Atomic Energy Commission" was set up, with the intention of studying both nuclear weapons and reactors. Later, in 1947, it was decided that the development of nuclear reactors would be handled in a separate, partly state-owned and partly private, company. The Swedish name of this company was "AB Atomenergi," which will here be called "The Swedish Atomic Energy Company." In 1950, the physics department of the Defence Research Institute was transferred to this new company. Young men could do their military service here. The small, but growing, company was housed in different parts of Stockholm.

The physics department was placed close to the Royal Institute of Technology, in what was called "The City of Science" (see Jenny Beckman's article in this volume). The idea was to bring knowledge-intensive companies and activities together, in a 1950s version of a modern "science park." Here the Royal Swedish Academy of Engineering Sciences provided space and laboratory equipment for small companies and research institutes.

THE FIRST SWEDISH REACTOR

In 1949, the company made the official decision to build a low-power reactor. The choice of fuel was natural uranium moderated by heavy water. It was decided to place the reactor in a rock shelter under the company's office in "The City of Science." This was only a couple of kilometers from the very center of Stockholm, but the risks were not considered large.[3] The reactor came to bear the pragmatic name R1 from "Reactor 1."

The new and exciting reactor attracted talented young men who had just graduated as Masters of Engineering or Science. Working

Figure 1. The placement of reactor R1 in a rock shelter. The reactor was located 20 meters below ground and was reached with an elevator.

with the reactor conferred high status, and the social environment of the reactor was one of self-sacrifice, discipline, and masculinity.[4] Working shifts of 27 hours was not unusual.[5] Even though they worked for an industrial company (albeit partially government owned), the young men were given the opportunity to write dissertations and acquire doctorates.[6] This led employees to stay with the company for several years, and the academic publications also facilitated contacts with international organizations and universities. But how important really was the proximity to the academic milieus? It is of course difficult to say. The connection with universities was vital in that the industrial researchers in contact with professors could write academic articles and defend dissertations, but other than these rather formal contacts, I can see very little evidence that there was a close intellectual communication between the academic and the industrial researchers.

R1 started on July 13, 1954, and became a source of national pride, a symbol of the progress of Sweden and an important triumph for the Social Democratic Party. The King attended its grand opening ceremony, and each year's Nobel Prize-winner in physics came to visit.[7] Postcards of the reactor were printed, and it was described in popular magazines.[8] The glamorization of the reactor was, of course, an advantage to the company in attracting competent personnel. Although there was no real resistance to the reactor, the Swedish Atomic Energy Company kept an eye on public opinion. For example, it was stated in the discussion of certain modifications that it was important for it not to appear from these modifications as if the reactor had become more dangerous.[9]

The boundaries of this first reactor are interesting. Safety measures were of course taken, even though this was a time when the optimism about nuclear power was greater than the fear of it. The placing of a reactor in a rock shelter was for reasons of safety, but not only safety from the reactor, but also from possible attacks or bombs from a foreign power in case of war. Even though the reactor was a high-tech symbol and the subject of excited newspaper articles, its existence and location were not well known to its neighbors in the fashionable district of Östermalm. In this case, the boundaries were informal: the existence of the reactor was neither secret, nor very well known among those uninterested in scientific and technological marvels. Also, the information secrecy surrounding its activities was tight, largely due to the possibility of military development of Swedish nuclear weapons. Measures such as the classifying of most of the documents are indicative of another type of security, in which it is important to keep boundaries around certain information.

A NEW REACTOR SITE

In the mid-fifties, a drastic shift was made in the future development of Swedish nuclear reactors. A new reactor-site was needed for the building of more reactors, this time preferably far from populated areas and close to water for cooling. The country was scoured for a suitable place for nuclear activities. In 1955, a piece of land was found and bought by the Atomic Energy Co. near Nyköping, some one hundred kilometers south of Stockholm. The new site, named Studsvik, was by the sea, far enough away from the closest town, but not too far from the capital for a bus connection to be established between Stockholm and Studsvik. A security area was created around the Studsvik site, with a rule that there would be no settlement within a radius of 2 km.[10] The site itself was fenced and all visitors had to pass a guard, show an ID and have a host for the visit. No cameras were allowed. The staff picked up their dosimeters at the entrance. The increased security, compared to R1, was partly due to the fact that the new reactors were more powerful, but probably also because the attitude toward safety and public awareness had changed.

On this site, the next reactors in the Swedish development were constructed. In 1959, a heavy water zero-power reactor was finished and named R0, and a year later the material-testing reactor R2 was put in operation. FR-0, which I will discuss later in the article, was completed in 1964.

Even though Studsvik met the formal requirements, the transfer from Central Stockholm was not easy. It had been seen as advantageous to have a nuclear reactor in the capital, for example by companies that could buy nuclear isotopes from it.[11] The employees and their families were encouraged by the company to move from Stockholm to the smaller towns close to Studsvik, but this was not always popular.[12] The big city, the universities and the glamour and pioneering spirit associated with the first reactor were not altogether easy to abandon.[13]

The Atomic Energy Company moved from the inner city, with its proximity to useful knowledge institutions and other advantages, to the countryside, far from any population it might hurt. By the time this happened, the company had grown considerably, and maybe was not quite as dependent on being physically close to the universities. It can be discussed whether this gave the company a more independent identity. The practical, technological activities of atomic energy were not always considered to have the proper academic character of theoretical science, and therefore were not to be associated with universities. Indeed, it was a long time before the academic institutions began to do research and education in reactor or nuclear science. The established professors were not very open to the new field. Only when the researchers who had been employed by R1 transferred to the universities was knowledge of the new phenomena brought to the academic sphere, by them personally.[14]

Another reason for moving was the growing awareness of the dangers of nuclear power, as mentioned above. It was seen as impossible to have a reactor in the inner city. This tendency can also be seen abroad, where nuclear sites are placed in unpopulated areas, as often with the National Laboratories in the United States.[15] The Swedish historian Jonas Anshelm has pointed out that the first apprehension of the danger of nuclear power and radiation appears in Swedish newspapers in the second half of the 1950s.[16] Doubts about nuclear safety were expressed in, for example, the journals of the workers' union, which raised questions about occupational safety.[17] The shifting views on the danger of radiation are very likely to have contributed to the choice of a remote site.

FR-0 AND THE DANGEROUS NUCLEAR POWER

At Studsvik, several reactors were constructed. One of them was FR-0. FR-0 was a prototype of what is called a fast breeder reactor. The word "breed" was used because the reactor produces more fuel than it consumes; it seemed as if the reactor bred its own fuel. A breeder reactor has a core of plutonium and uranium-238, surrounded by a mantle of uranium-238. The velocity of the neutrons is not, as in a regular reactor, reduced by a so-called moderator, but the neutrons are left at high speed, i.e. fast reactor. The neutrons emitted transform the uranium into plutonium, which can then be processed in a reprocessing plant and used as fuel in other reactors. The ability of such a reactor to produce more nuclear fuel than it consumes promised cheap and reliable energy and the possibility of using uranium more efficiently. This was an important promise at a time when anxiety about lack of uranium was widespread.

This idea was present from the very beginning of nuclear reactors. The first breeder reactor was built as early as 1946 in Los Alamos,

New Mexico, and was called Clementine.[18] The world's second breeder reactor, EBR-I, started in 1951 at Argonne National Labs in Idaho. It was the first nuclear reactor in the world to actually produce electrical energy, which was used to illuminate the reactor hall. The successor EBR-II was started in 1962, and in the following year a commercial breeder plant called Enrico Fermi was built in the United States.[19] Optimism about breeder reactors was also great in Europe. Britain was early in breeder development. The British fast reactors ZEPHYR and ZEUS were started in 1954 and 1955. The larger British Dounreay reactor was put in operation in 1959. Meanwhile, the Soviet Union started its first fast reactor in Obninsk in 1956.

There were also several reasons for a small country like Sweden to invest in breeder reactors. The breeders would fit in well with the Swedish heavy water reactors, since these produced plutonium that could be used as fuel in the breeder reactors. There were also plans for a waste-fuel cycle with a reprocessing plant. The plant would be working on the waste of both the heavy-water reactors and the breeder reactors. It could also be used for extracting plutonium for possible Swedish nuclear weapons. Another reason for building Swedish breeder reactors was national independence. The Swedish uranium supplies were of low concentration and could only be mined very slowly. Therefore, it was important to have reactors that used as little fuel as possible.[20]

The next step towards industrial breeder reactors was to build a research reactor. The researchers wanted to apply and adjust mathematical models as well as to study the properties of fast neutrons.[21] Another reason was that the neutrons in an atomic bomb are fast, and therefore a breeder reactor could bring knowledge relevant to the production of nuclear weapons.[22] The military was also engaged in building a fast reactor. A study group was formed in the mid-1950s, and the prototype reactor FR-0 was put in operation in 1964.[23]

FR-0 was constructed of two halves that were put together to achieve a critical amount of uranium. Its fuel was 20% enriched uranium that was borrowed from the United States.[24] The size of the reactor was governed by the amount of uranium that it was possible to borrow.[25] Knowledge and inspiration from abroad were necessary, and FR-0 was built to resemble the reactors VERA in Britain and ZPR-II in the USA.

The reactor was placed in a cubic concrete building with walls 1.2 meters thick; the building is described by one of the former reactor researchers as a bunker.[26] The thick concrete walls were a

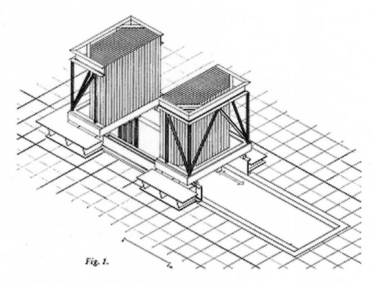

Fig. 1.

Figure 2. FR-0 was made in two halves that could be put together to start the reactor. Picture source: *Reaktorn* no. 4/61.

replacement for the reflector, a neutron shield, which usually surrounds a reactor. Placing the reflecting property in walls instead of a concrete shield made it possible for the researchers to approach the reactor in experiments. The walls also made the building pressure-resistant and almost hermetic. The building was connected to a laboratory where another reactor, R0, was placed.[27] To be able to supervise the laboratory, it was desirable to have only one entrance, but for practical reasons there was also an entrance for delivery vehicles.[28] Connected to the reactor hall were service facilities with an operating room, a fuel store and offices.[29] The entrance to the reactor was through a pressure-regulating lock controlled from the operating room to supervise who did enter the reactor. The operating room had always to be manned. The fuel was also thoroughly monitored; both a safety door and an armored door had to be passed. No water or sewage pipes were allowed to pass through the fuel room, due to the risk of unintended criticality and hence an uncontrolled chain reaction if the room was filled with water. The ventilation was only run when the reactor was not operating.[30]

What made the safety of this reactor especially crucial was the high enrichment of the fuel. There was also an awareness of the speed

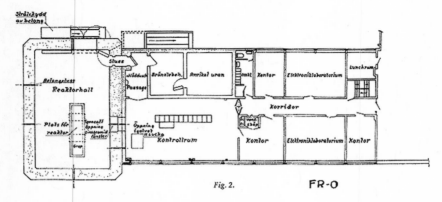

Fig. 2.   FR-0

Figure 3. Plan drawing of FR-0. It shows how the reactor hall was connected to offices and how the operating room ("Kontrollrum") had to be passed to reach the reactor. Picture source: *Reaktorn* nr 4/61.

of the processes in a fast breeder reactor. The design of the reactor hall was described as adapted to a worst-case scenario.[31] The most likely accident was considered to be an explosion, with showers of radiation. The hall was built to withstand an explosion equivalent to 10 kg of TNT-explosives.[32]

Another important consideration in the construction of this reactor was flexibility. The FR-0 hall was not intended only for this specific reactor, but was also a place for future fast-reactor experiments.[33] The walls had plugged openings that could be opened if in the future it was decided to do experiments outside the reactor hall.

We can note several differences and similarities between R1 and FR-0. One difference, of course, was that R1 was built in a rock shelter in a city and FR-0 in a concrete bunker in the countryside. Both of the reactors were pioneers—R1 being the first Swedish reactor and FR-0 the first fast reactor—but their pioneering status was different. FR-0 was just a part of a larger nuclear site, and did not receive as much attention as R1. R1 was also constructed in a spirit of great enthusiasm, when the fears and dangers of nuclear power were no greater than the wish to build a reactor in "The City of Science." Ten years passed between the building of these reactors, and the boundaries of FR-0 must be seen as more rigid.

FR-0 was the first step towards a new and unknown technology, and the designers of the reactor gave safety issues special attention. It was of course important for the company to take care—but conspicuous caution might also alert the public to the fact that these activities really were dangerous.

FR-0 also came to be the last of the line. For a number of reasons, fast breeder reactors never developed industrially in Sweden. The technical difficulties, for example cooling, were not solved as easily as had been expected. That made the fast breeder reactors very expensive. Concerns about plutonium handling and non-proliferation were raised. The price of uranium did not continue to rise as expected, largely due to new deposits being found, particularly in Africa. FR-0 was closed in 1971, and its anticipated sequel, FRX, was never constructed.

Science at FR-0

The scientific activities carried on in the FR-0 building mainly concerned the use and investigation of fast neutrons. The researchers mapped neutron spectra and tested different mathematical models for describing neutron movement.[34] It was also important to try out the control and safety systems, since these differed from those of the previous reactors.[35]

As a latecomer, it is difficult to tell how the scientific activities at FR-0 were shaped by the spatial conditions. It is likely, though, that the high level of security left its mark on them. There was also, as mentioned earlier, a military interest in FR-0 since the military could study fast neutron movement there. The National Defence Research Institute had several men stationed there who participated in the scientific work and did research for Ph.D. projects. The secrecy that prevailed for military and security reasons contrasted notably with the academic freedom of the universities, where open international publication is a part of the working process. There was at this time severe criticism of the secrecy of the Atomic Energy Company. This was even discussed in the Swedish parliament. In April 1967, a member of parliament questioned whether it was at all appropriate to carry on scientific research at a company that restricted what employees were allowed to say about their activities.[36] The fact that researchers were bound by professional secrecy was criticized in a motion in parliament in 1968.[37]

It must also have been quite noticeable to the researchers that they were far from the academic milieus where they had their background. There was an ongoing discussion on how to reconcile academic publication with internal reports to the company, and the possibility of doing Ph.D. work at a company. It was important to maintain contact with the universities. This may in some way be seen as a quest for scientific legitimacy despite the fact that activities at FR-0 were more affected by policy and technology than the pure research at universities.

THE BOUNDARIES OF A SCIENTIFIC INSTRUMENT

The discussion of the connection between location and science at FR-0 leads on to a question about the boundaries of these activities. The FR-0 reactor was a scientific instrument, but if we compare it to another type of big scientific instrument like a particle accelerator there are several differences in how the boundaries around the instrument are formed. This reactor was owned and run by a partly private company and subject to strict international non-proliferation regulations. Other scientific instruments are usually found in universities, without the secrecy and classification that surrounded FR-0. The boundaries around an accelerator, for example, are informal—not everyone knows where it is and how it works, people do not simply just walk in through the imposing doors of a university for the purpose of getting a glimpse of an accelerator. The boundaries of a reactor, on the other hand, are very much physical, and they have become more and more strictly controlled as awareness and fear of the dangers of nuclear power have grown. The security around a nuclear reactor is intended to protect the outside world from a meltdown or an accident, but also to protect the reactor from intruders who might use its dangerous potential as a weapon. The boundaries of FR-0 were thus very physical—in terms both of thick walls and a safety area around Studsvik. They were also of a legal nature, since access to the Studsvik site was controlled by a guard. ID was required, and it was more difficult for a foreign citizen to enter. There was also a boundary around FR-0 in terms of personal surveillance from the person in the operating room.

Laboratories might be seen as privileged places: places that through their distinctiveness and seclusion signal that the knowledge produced is different from everyday knowledge.[38] FR-0 was a very privileged place, which can also be seen as an expression of power. The functioning of power, surveillance and exclusion has been discussed among others by Michel Foucault in *Discipline and Punish* (in French 1975). Foucault discusses among other things the prison and its purpose of protecting the outer world from the disturbing people who offend against the general norms. In all places of exclusion, such as the quarantine of lepers, the penitentiary or the psychiatric asylum, the controlling authorities create a division between normal/abnormal places.[39] Foucault uses the example of the Panopticon, an architectural solution that allows one person to supervise all the prisoners in a prison.[40] The constant visibility becomes a functioning of power. There are differences and similarities between Foucault's prison and the first Swedish fast reactor. Both are "abnormal" places that contain danger. Both are by necessity embedded in an authoritarian system. The threat from outside intruders is more important for the reactor, but neither completely absent in the prison. However, the contents of the reactor building are abnormal in a high-status manner, whereas the prisoners are outcasts of society. The very thing being monitored, the reactor, is powerful in itself, since it forces people to adjust to its dangers.

The reactor is isolated from society by its thick concrete walls because of its dangerous nature, but that also excludes the public from its privileged knowledge production. The power of the reactor lies in the fear it inspires in people. The power does not emanate from a single person—the power exercised by the person in the operating room, who chooses whom to let in, is merely an authority arising from the necessity of surveillance.

This leads to a discussion of the *social* boundaries of a reactor. A high-status profession such as reactor physicist is one requiring a high level of education and enjoying social status. In those days, the profession was dominated by men. The pictures show serious men in white coats. The laboratory was obviously not a place for everyone. There are thus also boundaries around the profession, and the connection between science and professionalization is a broad discussion in sociology. Thomas F. Gieryn introduces the concept of "boundary work" to describe the efforts to demarcate science and the scientific profession.[41] The very legitimacy of science rests in the possibility of distinguishing between science and non-scientific activities. Gieryn emphasizes that science and policy are mutually dependent, but also dependent on not overlapping. Politicians need scientific answers to gain the authority to make certain statements, and scientists need to show their usefulness to society by contributing with what appear to be objective facts in support of political activities. But scientists must not jeopardize their detached position by allowing a confusion of science and politics. At FR-0, the traditional neutral position of science is not self-evident. Nuclear power was a highly political field, and the Atomic Energy Company did not offer the scientific legitimacy of a university. The security around the reactor made it different from an academic laboratory and the neutrality the latter was able to offer its inhabitants.

But if the reactor is a politically colored place rather than an impartial laboratory—is a democracy of the reactor possible? Obviously, not everyone could visit the reactor, even though it was publicly funded. The general public was excluded from the reactor, and there has also been a discussion of whether in the early years the people were excluded from decisions about nuclear power. There was also great confidence in the experts and the nuclear engineers, and nuclear power was seen as a technological issue. A change in this view took place in the 1970s when some political parties began to question nuclear power on the grounds that it was dangerous and destructive, and also that it created nuclear waste to be dealt with by future generations who did not have a political voice in the present. The shift from a technological to a political and democratic question has been described by Swedish historian Annki Schagerholm and sociologist Per Lindqvist.[42] We see here how the *political* boundaries of the reactor were renegotiated. It was decided in 1979 to hold a national referendum to decide Swedish nuclear energy policy, and this took place in 1980. It was decided to phase out Swedish nuclear power by the year 2010. The boundaries of nuclear power were thus opened to public opinion.

Let us conclude by dwelling for a moment on the reasons for putting up boundaries around a scientific instrument—why are experiments physically confined? One reason may be to gain power and professionalization. Another reason may be safety—dangerous experiments should be undertaken in remote areas. A further aspect of safety is to protect the experiment itself from intruders who might harm or damage it. To withhold the secrets of the experiment from presumptive commercial interests can be seen as another type of safety. These last two aspects of safety could be considered to point back at the professional confinement: this experiment is so important and valuable that we must protect it. In the confinement of FR-0, all these aspects are interwoven.

We have seen how the walls of a reactor building that demarcated the scientific activity and protected the outer world can be associated with political, social and professional boundaries. A scientific room is not just a room but contains other meanings, and an activity that needs to have such a high level of security cannot avoid being affected itself by the security measures. FR-0 was a scientific workplace with certain conditions and in the same manner nuclear power must be understood in a context of the safety that both protects and excludes it.

FR-0 TODAY

It is a day in May 2004, which is going to be the day I make the acquaintance of the walls of FR-0. Early in the morning, I drive the 108 km from Stockholm down to Studsvik. I have reported my visit to the librarian, who stands as host on the temporary permit I am given by the guard. The guard also checks my ID and asks if I have a camera or a GSM with a camera: I am not allowed to take that in. I walk into the site and I am surrounded by rather ugly buildings. Today, Studsvik is a company that sells nuclear-related services to nuclear power plants and to the health industry. Due to layoffs, several of the offices are completely empty, and parts of the site look like a ghost town. There are some reactors still running, but not FR-0. I am excited to see the bunker of FR-0 that I have been told about. And indeed, even today a visit shows me an ugly concrete hovel. I stop by the gray, box-like structure, which is overgrown with ivy and framed by a picturesque setting of spring flowers. The walls are indeed impressively thick.

The reactor building is locked with a padlock, and it is not easy to find someone to open it. No one seems to know where the key is. Obviously, access to FR-0 is still not very easy, but for different reasons. The issue is solved when someone goes and fetches the janitor, who

Figure 4. The FR-0 building today. Photo: Ingrid Wahlgren, Studsvik AB.

Figure 5. By the entrance to FR-0. Photo: Ingrid Wahlgren, Studsvik AB.

lets me in. Inside its concrete walls I feel rather intimidated, but also struck by the thought that it is hard to imagine that this building once held a highly scientific activity. Now, it looks more like a lumber shed, furnished only with shelves holding the remains of the company's venture into heat technology with biofuel. The building that was once a security precaution and an obstacle to intruders has lost its power.

NOTES

1. *Controlled Nuclear Chain Reaction: the First 50 Years* (Illinois, 1992).
2. The general information about the Swedish nuclear program can be found in, for example, Karl-Erik Larsson, "Kärnkraftens historia i Sverige" [The History of Nuclear Power in Sweden], *Kosmos* 64 (1987) or Stefan Lindström, *Hela nationens tacksamhet: Svensk forskningspolitik på atomenergiområdet 1945–1956* [The Whole Nation's Gratitude: Swedish Research Policy in the Field of Atomic Energy 1945–1956] (Stockholm, 1991).
3. Karl-Erik Larsson, "Kärnreaktorn R1—ett stycke högteknologisk pionjärhistoria" [Nuclear Reactor R1—A Piece of High-Technology Pioneering History], *Daedalus* (1989), p. 109.

4. Maja Fjæstad, *Sveriges Första Kärnreaktor: från Teknisk Prototyp till Vetenskapligt Instrument* [Sweden's First Nuclear Reactor: From Technical Prototype to Scientific Instrument]. SKI-rapport 01:1 (Stockholm, 2001), p. 32.

5. Interview with Karl-Erik Larsson 9/5 2000.

6. Karl-Erik Larsson, *Vetenskap i kärnkraftens skugga* [Science in the Shadow of Nuclear Power] (Stockholm, 2000), p. 45.

7. Interview with Karl-Erik Larsson 9/5 2000.

8. "Den svenska atomreaktorn" [The Swedish Atomic Reactor], *Teknisk tidskrift* 28 June 1955 (signature SHI), and for example "Sverige får atomreaktor om några år" [Sweden Will Have an Atomic Reactor in a Few Years], *Svenska Dagbladet* 22 September 1949, "Teknikens jättar och pygmeer" [Giants and Pygmies of Technology] *Svenska Dagbladet* 24 September 1952, "Stockholms uranmila färdig i bergvalv" [Stockholm's Uranium Pile Ready in Rock Vault], *Dagens Nyheter* 8 August 1953 (signature "answer"). (From the archive at Tekniska Museet, 2590:a.).

9. "Studiegruppen för R1:s ombyggnad" [Study Group for the Rebuilding of R1], protocol nr 1/1961 25/2 1961. The archive of Studsvik, centralarkivet, Sigvard Eklunds arkiv, skåp 4, holder "R1".

10. "Till Delegationen för Atomfrågor" [To the Atomic Energy Delegation] 7 May 1962. The Studsvik archive 23:01 AE RFK FR-0.

11. Interview with C. G. Österlund 3/7 2000.

12. Karl-Erik Larsson, "Kärnkraftens historia i Sverige" [The History of Nuclear Power in Sweden], *Kosmos* 64 (1987), pp. 135–136.

13. Maja Fjæstad, *Sveriges första kärnreaktor: Från teknisk prototyp till vetenskapligt instrument* [Sweden's First Nuclear Reactor: From Technical Prototype to Scientific Instrument]. SKI-rapport 01:1. (Stockholm, 2001), p. 50.

14. Maja Fjæstad, *Sveriges Första Kärnreaktor: från Teknisk Prototyp till Vetenskapligt Instrument.* [Sweden's First Nuclear Reactor: From Technical Prototype to Scientific Instrument] SKI-rapport 01:1 (Stockholm, 2001), p. 51.

15. Peter J. Westwick, *The National Labs: Science in an American System* (Cambridge, Mass., 2003), chapter 1.

16. Jonas Anshelm, *Mellan frälsning och domedag: Om kärnkraftens politiska idéhistoria i Sverige 1945–1999* [Between Salvation and Doomsday: On the Political and Intellectual History of Nuclear Power in Sweden 1945–1999] (Eslöv, 2000), p. 45.

17. Ibid., p. 46.

18. Pershagen, Jirlow, Lundell, Vieider, *Snabba bridreaktorer* [Fast Breeder Reactors] (Stockholm, 1982), p. 19.

19. *Controlled Nuclear Chain Reaction: The First 50 Years* (La Grange Park, 1992), Chapter 2.

20. Maja Fjæstad, "Drömmen om bridreaktorn" [The Dream of the Breeder Reactor] in: *Daedalus 2003* (Stockholm, 2003).

21. AB Atomenergis verksamhetsberättelse [Annual Report of the Swedish Atomic Energy Company] 1966, p. 3.

22. Interview with Bengt Pershagen 17/1 2002.
23. Pershagen, Jirlow, Lundell, Vieider, *Snabba bridreaktorer* [Fast Breeder Reactors] (Stockholm, 1982), p. 27.
24. Letter from H. Brynielsson to Ministry for Foreign Affairs 14 March 1960. The Studsvik archive 24:27 Handlingar rörande R0-reaktorn FR-0 [Documents concerning the R0-reactor FR-0]. Also interview with Eric Hellstrand 27/6 2002.
25. Per Lindberg, "Snabba nollan kritisk" [Fast Zero Critical], *Reaktorn* nr 1/64, pp. 7–10.
26. Telephone interview with Bengt Pershagen 26/3 2003.
27. I have not been able to find a drawing of the reactor, probably due to confidentiality. The descriptions here are based on newspaper articles and interviews.
28. Robert Vestergaard, "Om snabba reaktorer och FR-0-laboratoriet" [On Fast Reactors and the FR-0 Laboratory]. *Reaktorn* nr 4/61, pp. 10–12.
29. "Preliminär beskrivning av FR-0-anläggningen och dess säkerhetsprinciper" [Provisional Description of the FR-0 Plant and Its Safety Principles]. Robert Vestergaard 16.11.60. The Studsvik Archive 23:01 AE RFK FR-0.
30. "Preliminär beskrivning av FR-0-anläggningen och dess säkerhetsprinciper" [Provisional Description of the FR-0 Plant and Its Safety Principles]. Robert Vestergaard 16.11.60. The Studsvik Archive 23:01 AE RFK FR-0.
31. "Preliminär beskrivning av FR-0-anläggningen och dess säkerhetsprinciper" [Provisional Description of the FR-0 Plant and Its Safety Principles], p. 8. Robert Vestergaard 16.11.60. The Studsvik Archive 23:01 AE RFK FR-0.
32. Robert Vestergaard, "Om snabba reaktorer och FR-0-laboratoriet" [On Fast Reactors and the FR-0 Laboratory]. *Reaktorn* nr 4/61, pp. 10–12.
33. "Säkerhets- och förläggningsfrågor rörande snabba reaktorn FR-0" [Safety and Siting Problems concerning the Fast Reactor FR-0]. I.Wensfelt 8.2.1961, p. 2. The Studsvik Archive 23:01 AE RFK FR-0.
34. AB Atomenergis verksamhetsberättelse [Annual Report of the Swedish Atomic Energy Company] 1966, p. 3.
35. "Synpunkter på behovet av en snabb nolleffektreaktor" [Observations on the Need for a Fast Zero Effect Reactor] E. Hellstrand March 1957. The Studsvik Archive 24:27 Handlingar rörande R0-reaktorn FR-0 [Documents concerning the R0-reactor FR-0].
36. Riksdagens protokoll fre 7 april 1967 AK [Riksdag Records, Fri. 7 April 1967, Lower House], Hr Ståhl (fp)
    p. 92 "Vi kan inte ha vetenskaplig forskning i ett bolag vars ledning utan inskränkningar kan mörklägga vad den anser bör mörkläggas med följd att svenska folket blir mycket oinitierat" [We cannot have scientific research in a company whose management can conceal whatever it considers should be concealed with the result that the Swedish people remain highly uninformed].

p. 93 "Jag tillåter mig här i kammaren nämna att någon dag efter atom-
diskussionen vid fjolårets riksdag utfärdade ledningen för AB Atom-
enenergi ett påbud till sina anställda, att ingenting om verksamheten i
bolaget fick yppas till utomstående utan föregående tillstånd av bo-
lagsledningen" [I permit myself here in the House to mention that a day
or so after the atom debate at last year's Riksdag the management of the
Swedish Atomic Energy Company issued an order prohibiting its employees from saying anything about the activities of the company to third
parties without the prior consent of the company management].

37. Motion i Andra kammaren nr 1307 år 1968 [Motion in the Lower House no.
1307, 1968].
38. See for example Adi Ophir and Steven Shapin, "The Place of Knowledge: A
Methodological Survey," *Science in Context* 4:3 (1991), especially pp. 10–14.
39. Michel Foucault, *Discipline and Punish: The Birth of the Prison* (1975), English translation (Harmondsworth, 1979), p. 199.
40. Ibid., p. 201.
41. Thomas F. Gieryn, "Boundaries of Science," in Sheila Jasanoff et al., *Handbook of Science and Technology Studies* (Thousand Oaks, 1994), p. 434 ff.
42. Per Lindquist, *Det klyvbara ämnet. Diskursiva ordningar i svensk kärnkraft-
spolitik 1972–1980* [Fissile Material. Discursive Orders in Swedish Nuclear
Power Policy] (Lund, 1997), for example p. 12. Annki Schagerholm, *För het
att hantera: Kärnkraftsfrågan i svensk politik 1945–1980* [Too Hot to Handle:
the Nuclear Power Question in Swedish Politics 1945–1980] (Gothenburg,
1993), for example p. 5.

CONTROLLING SPACE

Scientific City Planning in Sweden between 1930 and 1970

PER LUNDIN

One should not need to take more than a glance at the older districts of our cities to be convinced that development by itself does not lead to good results. In spite of the existence of certain regulations for the settling of districts in olden times, the result has been something that can only be characterized as chaos. A jumble of houses. Cramped, dark backyards. Buildings of strange, impractical shape. Every plot built on with no thought of the neighbours. A case of dog eat dog.[1]

Uno Åhrén, 1943

Looking at Swedish city planning during the course of the 20th century, one could argue that there is a relation between knowledge and power, where scientific knowledge was used to survey, structure and categorize—i.e., to understand—space. Visions of rational spatial order were then imposed on the city, and space thus became a place where power relations were established, exerted, and manifested.[2] The aim of this article is to examine this process in order to describe and analyze how a scientific conception of space came to prevail between 1930 and 1970. The article considers the implications of a scientific city planning on the spatial structure of cities. It discusses whether knowledge-based planning implied a new kind of power relation, and if so, the various aspects this assumed.

Two phases are distinguished. The first one is the establishment of a modernist city planning ideal in Sweden during the 1930s and the 1940s by a heterogeneous group of planners (architects, city planners,

The author thanks Isabelle Dussauge, Hjalmar Fors, Anders Houltz, Anna Orrghen, and Anna Storm for their valuable comments on the original draft of this article.

and traffic engineers). They carried out reforms that legalized and institutionalized an overarching modernist planning, which contributed to an increasing spatialization of the city. The second phase is the rise of the Swedish "car society" during the 1950s and the 1960s. Planners combined new ideas on traffic engineering with the institutional framework and shifted the city planning discourse toward a concept of a "car city."

The argument presented here is that a group of planners gained a position as providers of expert knowledge by claiming the objectivity, rationality, and universality of science. On the basis of the epistemological benefit of *reductio ad simplicitatum*, they were able to establish a scientific approach to city planning.[3]

In the following pages, I will examine the planners' arguments, strategies, and methods of gaining a position as seemingly neutral providers of expert knowledge. How did they acquire *the right to speak*?[4] How did they become acknowledged as experts by the community?

FUNCTIONALIST CITY PLANNING: THE CITY AS A MACHINE

The Swiss architect Le Corbusier, the German architect Ernst May, and others had proclaimed a new modernist architecture and city planning ideal in the 1920s: functionalism. The ideal functional city was divided according to use and different parts were designed to fulfil specific functions, such as providing for housing, business, entertainment, and communication.[5] The ideas were quickly adopted by a number of young Swedish architects at the end of the 1920s.

The functionalist vision of the city may be seen as an expression of the widespread rationalizing spirit that followed in the wake of Frederick Winslow Taylor's efforts to improve the efficiency of work and its organization. His ideas gained a foothold in Sweden during the 1910s and 1920s. At the same time, industry and the public sector began to attract increasing political attention. In the 1920s and 1930s, the political focus shifted and Taylor's logic of efficiency began to permeate the social side of society, including housing and education. The rationalizing spirit was politically manifested by the Social Democrats in the idea of society as a home for all, known as a *folkhem* (people's home). The ideological goals of justice and equality could be achieved through reforms in housing and education. Meanwhile, the Social Democrats gained political power in 1932, and retained it until 1976.[6]

The Swedish functionalist architects published the manifesto *Acceptera* (Accept) in 1931, declaring, "We can do no more than face reality and accept it in order to control it."[7] With this, they introduced the notion of the inevitable influence of technological change into the realm of architecture and city planning.

The machine became a metaphor for the city. In 1929, the author and social scientist Stuart Chase compared the city to a *mega machine*,[8] and the authors behind *Acceptera* declared that "the irresistible machine culture conquers the world."[9] I argue that the introduction of the machine metaphor is important for an understanding of how the city was separated in its uses. The city was a machine and its parts were to be designed to perform specific functions, i.e., the provision of housing, business, industry, entertainment, and communication.

There are reasons, therefore, to linger for a while around the use of the machine as a metaphor for the city. As Jacques Derrida has noted, no metaphor is innocent—there is always a strategy behind the use of metaphors. Metaphors are more than mere poetic or rhetorical embellishments. They structure our thinking as well as our actions, and may thus even create realities.[10] Consider the metaphor "the city is a machine." It indicates quite another conception of the city, than, for instance, the metaphor "the city is a jungle." I would like to emphasize the abstracting power of the metaphor. Because of the high level of abstraction in metaphors, experts may use them to seize and incorporate new problems into their domains of competence. The experts' use of metaphors may be seen as rhetorical strategies for extending the boundaries of their legitimate domains by arguing that the new *problematique* resembles similar tasks that have earlier been successfully handled by the expert group.[11]

Following this line of thought, the machine was more than a way to describe the city for the functionalists: the well-greased machinery, its components performing well-defined tasks with high precision, was also a model for how the city *should* function. The City Engineer and head of the Stockholm City Planning Office, Albert Lilienberg, said in 1927: "The city should thus afford room for housing of different kinds [. . .] for lines of communication [. . .] This and other things should be satisfied in the city plan in such a way that the whole city organism works with as little friction and as high precision as possible."[12] Similarly, the Swedish architect Gunnar Sundbärg wrote in 1928, in the spirit of Le Corbusier: "The framework of the modern city must be formed entirely in accordance with the laws of modern traffic, a traffic that is mechanical and whose be all and end all are speed and flexibility. The infinitely differentiated traffic systems of the city should function, from the thickest arteries to the thinnest capillaries, in their every detail as a perfect machine; the city must be a machine."[13]

Paradoxically, the organism and machine metaphors seem interchangeable. One should note that the "city *organism*" should work with "as little *friction* and as high *precision* as possible," and that the city's traffic system "from the thickest *arteries* to the thinnest *capillaries*" should work as a "perfect *machine*." One possible explanation of this connotative connection between the organism and the machine is probably the old Cartesian notion of the body as a machine.[14]

When William Harvey presented his discoveries about the circulation of blood in *De motu cordis* in 1628, he revolutionized the understanding of the body. It has been argued that these ideas eventually led to a new understanding of the city; in the 18th century, Enlightenment planners applied the organism metaphor and spoke of the heart, lungs, arteries and veins of the city. Harvey believed that "blood is life itself," and that the heart was no more than a machine for circulation. The movement became an end in itself.[15]

Here is the essence of the two metaphors. A machine is essentially the physical embodiment of a process that occurs in time, and once the machine stops it has no meaning. Likewise, an organism, as understood since Harvey, presupposes a constant circulation of blood driven by the beats of a heart. Once the pulse stops, it ceases to be an organism. It dies.

The metaphorical theme may thus be elaborated further. Hugo Nicolaus Pallin, Professor of Roads and Transportation at the Royal Institute of Technology (Kungl. Tekniska högskolan) in Stockholm during the 1930s, discussed the general laws of traffic in his lectures and postulated: "Traffic is movement."[16] Combining the metaphors with the postulate and applying them to the city, the meaning of the metaphors is that the flow of traffic must never stop, otherwise the city will die. The question of traffic becomes a question of life and death. Both metaphors inseparably combine form and movement, which is precisely why they are used in this context.[17] If the machine is movement, the metaphor "the city is a machine" implies traffic as the city's *primus motor*. We have seen above how Lilienberg and Sundbärg articulated this idea.

In an analysis of the functionalistic visions of the city by the architectural historian Per Råberg, the street grid took over the symbolic function that architecture (that is, the ornamentation) had once filled.[18] The internationally renowned architect Gunnar Asplund discussed the architectural conception of space in his inaugural lecture in 1931 for the chair in Architecture at the Royal Institute of Technology: "Our understanding of the city is not manifested until we move within and take in the art, shape, and meaning of the whole structure. *Life, the very idea of movement, has gone into our perception of space.*"[19] Asplund's concept of space was shared by the art critic Gotthard Johansson, one of the most important Swedish voices of the functionalistic movement. He wrote in 1931 that the character of the street environment had changed radically with the growing traffic: "The street is no longer a lounge. There movement is the supreme ruler. There, people, cars, buses, trams are crowded, there, shop windows, traffic lights, signs shout their 'look out' message. There, the agitation that always accompanies business rules. The rushing, roaring traffic, the noise, the flows of people give the street a new character."[20]

I would like to take Råberg's analysis a step further and argue that the movement—the traffic—was the central element in the functionalistic planning paradigm, and from there, the step to describing the city in terms of traffic flow was not a big one.

In 1932, the architect and manager of the Tenants' Savings and Building Society (Hyresgästernas Sparkasse- och Byggnadsförening, HSB), Sven Wallander, wrote: "So comes our time with its pulsating life," and continued, "the growing population need transport between themselves and the harbours, between the factories and the department stores, between housing and offices, between housing and the places of entertainment. The need for good traffic routes [. . .] makes itself felt."[21] In Wallander's eyes, the circulation of traffic gave life to the city. Traffic was seen as an autonomous force, and, as we shall see, the functionalists' understanding of technological change as autonomous was important in their appropriation of the car.

Another reason for paying attention to the metaphor is that the behavior of a machine—its dynamics—can be described by general laws. Hence, to say that the city is a machine is to say that it can be *determined*, or that it is possible to *forecast*. In that sense, the machine metaphor was the raison d'être for the emerging scientific city planning.

It was a mechanistic view of society that put the technician in the center, i.e., the machine should be handled by the mechanic, thus emphasizing the technician's active role in society.[22] The architect and

leading functionalist theorist, Uno Åhrén, discussed the relation between architecture and democracy, and concluded that "the socially
aware technician" should plan and take responsibility for society's development.[23] Another term used during the 1930s was social engineer.[24] The machine metaphor was an argument for a technocratic
society, a society ruled by technicians. Furthermore, it was an argument for a *scientification* of city planning, and this forces a closer examination of the scientific approach to city planning.

SCIENTIFICATION OF CITY PLANNING

In the light of the discussion of the machine metaphor, there are two
things to note in order to understand the emergence of scientific city
planning; the metaphor implies on the one hand a city whose behavior is *intelligible*, on the other the traffic as its *primus motor*.

The rationalizing spirit that began to have an influence on the social side of society in the 1920s and the 1930s forms a background to
the architects' shift in interest from aesthetics to housing questions.
Historically, academics have depicted Swedish functionalist architects
as radical voices not only for a new architectural and city planning
paradigm, but also for a new type of society. Some even claim them to
have had a crucial role in the establishment of the Swedish welfare
society.[25] The picture is most likely exaggerated.[26] However, the architects did articulate the dominating ideas of the time and evoked a
public response that had no parallel among other intellectual groups
during the 1930s.

To the functionalist planners, city planning was above all a social,
economic, and practical problem. Åhrén later characterized their
breakthrough in the following words: "Shallow aestheticism was abandoned."[27] Instead, he emphasized that planning should be rational,
methodical and scientific; the planner should "study the mathematics,
structural mechanics, logic of city planning."[28] Åhrén argued for the
necessity of a scientific method when he wrote in 1928: "It is indeed
strange that a field of human activity in which the basic assumptions
are to such a high degree rationally comprehensible and measurable
has hitherto to such an extent avoided becoming a science."[29]

Research was regarded as the road to the knowledge necessary
for city planning, and attention was paid to social sciences such as geography, economy, statistics, and sociology. Wallander, for instance,
found city geography appealing: "The city geography [. . .] is to bring
order to this muddle, to investigate all the different factors that give

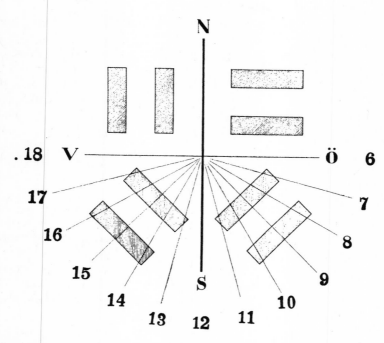

Figure 1. The scientific approach to city planning illustrated by the architect Gunnar Asplund's treatment of daylight conditions for housing. Source: Per G. Råberg, *Funktionalistiskt genombrott: Radikal miljö och miljödebatt i Sverige 1925–1931* (1970), 2nd rev. ed. (Stockholm, 1972).

rise to traffic in towns, to locate the places from which it originates, to find the cause of it [. . .] It is to give us in statistical numbers all the material with which the city planner is then to create and work."[30] The planning of the city should be implemented on the basis of scientific surveys,[31] or as Le Corbusier expressively put it: "Statistics help to formulate the problem."[32] A way of scientifying a complex problem was to *reduce* it to a number of measurable parameters, i.e., to quantify it.[33] Methods and measures such as population statistics and forecasts were introduced. The process of quantification implied that non-measurable qualities, for example aesthetics, convenience, and safety, were excluded (or simply vanished) from the planning discourse. The traffic engineer, an actor who entered the stage in the 1950s, as we will see below, even reduced the city to a two-dimensional diagram of the measurable traffic flow.[34] By analogy with the machine and the organism metaphors, circulation or flow became the central element of cities.

The process of establishing a scientific approach to city planning may be called *scientification*, and stands out as a central strategy in establishing a planning discourse. Scientification and the notion of the city as a machine are closely linked, as both assume an intelligible city.

The discourse led to a body of practice that consolidated a scientific city planning. The practice was that the group of planners established and manifested their approach to knowledge. An important part of the practice consisted in forecasting, and behind the concept of forecasts we find the assumption that it was possible to shape the city's development.

As mentioned above, the Social Democrats had gained political power in 1932. The functionalist planners had close links with leading Social Democratic politicians, some were even active Social Democrats themselves, and this made it easier for their ideas on housing and city planning to became official policy. During the 1930s, population forecasts had been essential to discussion of housing questions. The Population Commission for instance, forecast Sweden's population growth in two official reports on demography in 1938. As newly appointed head of the City Planning Office in Gothenburg in 1932, Åhrén produced a population forecast for the city with the help of geographers. The forecast was followed up and revised in 1940. Åhrén later argued that the development of a city could be quite precisely predicted—given that the time span considered was reasonable—if one was prepared to work, as in rational business life, with "scientific methods, with forecasts, with market analyses, with general plans."[35] Åhrén's colleague, the architect Sune Lindström, similarly pointed out that a city plan should be based on forecasts of economic and demographic development.[36]

According to Åhrén, forecasts were of "fundamental importance for city planning." He spoke of forecasts of industry's development and population trends.[37] They were part of a self-reinforcing process. Forecasts were necessary for the planning of society, and the planning would increase society's regularity, said Åhrén in 1942; he stated that "the greater the degree of regularity, the more accurate the forecasts." Åhrén, who was a spokesman for a *planned economy* (planhushållning), had a technocratic vision of how "a hundred per cent planned economy" would make forecasts superfluous.[38] The practice of planners established and reproduced the notion of the intelligible city, and thus they were able to *produce* intelligible cities.

IMPOSING SPATIAL ORDER ON THE CITY

The process of scientification highlights the relationship between knowledge and planning, and we can examine its connotations of power. What were the spatial implications of the attempts at regulating the city—imposing order on it?

In 1943, Uno Åhrén posed the rhetorical question: "Is there a need for planning?" He continued affirmatively: "One should not

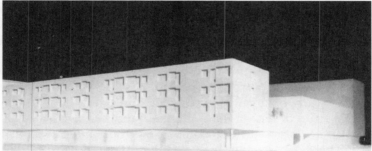

Figure 2. The modernist, scientifically planned city was opposed to the traditional city with its dark and chaotic backyards. The pictures show a district in the city of Uppsala. Above, the older district, and below, a model of a new, regulated district. Source: *Saneringsfrågan: Betänkande om förnyelsen av stadssamhällenas bebyggelse*, Swedish Government Official Reports 1954:31 (Stockholm, 1954).

need to take more than a glance at the older districts of our cities to be convinced that development by itself does not lead to good results. In spite of the existence of certain regulations for the settling of districts in olden times, the result has been something that can only be characterized as chaos."[39] The experts in the City Planning Committee agreed with Åhrén when in 1945 they pointed out that traditional societies had emerged "without regulation or supervision," with chaotic and uncontrolled cities as a result.[40]

The development towards well-arranged and "nicely" built cities should be achieved by planning, and the planning should be based on knowledge. The ideal, stated Åhrén, was a city that "could be planned and operated like a well-managed industrial enterprise. The construction of the factory, the organization of the operation and the sales, everything is prepared by thorough, practical, and scientific study, research, experiment."[41] His statement shows the influence that taylorist ideas on efficiency had on planning. And, said Åhrén, the more the need for planning, the more knowledge is needed.[42] In Åhrén's visions of the planning process, knowledge and planning seemed inseparable and interdependent.

Åhrén argued that the planner had to coordinate different interests, and evaluate priorities between them: "He should be not so much a *dictator* as an organizer, one who knows how to coordinate the many interests that assert themselves in social planning. The planner should serve as a clearing house." This was "the spirit [. . .] that should prevail in the work of planning."[43] The quotations illustrate a relational power rather than traditionally hierarchical power. Michel Foucault is maybe the thinker who has most systematically investigated the janus-face of power in modern society: on the one hand the productive side of power, on the other, the oppressive and restraining side.[44] The planner, wanting to reform society but to do so by exercising supervision and control, manifested those two sides.

On a basis of statistical knowledge and data, the planner surveyed, structured, and organized space, and hence exerted power over it. But for rational city planning it was not enough to "plan the space." The experts in the City Planning Committee of 1942 demanded a "chronology in the development" as well.[45] Scientific planning was a tool for controlling both space and time. As Le Corbusier said in *The Radiant City*: "The plan must rule."[46] The muddle of traditional cities and societies should be *restrained* with the help of science. In Foucault's terminology, power and knowledge reinforced each other.[47]

AN INSTITUTIONAL FRAMEWORK AND
MASS MOTORIZATION

The scope for city planning was not developed in early legislation on planning (the Building Act of 1928), and therefore, according to Åhrén, this document was nothing more than a "chimera."[48] The systematic planning proposed by the functionalists needed an overarching tool that could coordinate the more detailed city plans and the different interests in the city such as planning of housing areas, industry, public services, traffic systems, and so on. Åhrén emphasized that "planning cannot be a jigsaw puzzle of detail plans that are put together just as they come; the detail planning must be based on a systematic planning on a large scale, a *master plan*." Otherwise, it would not be possible to coordinate the different parts of the society in an "organic whole."[49] The *master plan* should regulate the community at a municipal level. Correspondingly, a *regional plan* should regulate the society at a regional level. The development of modern motor transport had made the traditional division into small municipalities superfluous, argued Lindström, and stressed that traffic could be rationally planned with a regional or an inter-municipal control.[50]

Influenced by official British reports on land use from the beginning of the 1940s by Barlow, Scott, and Uthwatt, a number of leading planners launched a campaign for planning legislation in Sweden. The Danish architect Otto Danneskiold-Samsøe had come to Sweden in 1938 and worked with Lindström. He was an important advocate of British planning and had good contacts with the British Council in Sweden, the most important link with Great Britain during World War II.[51] In 1945 he published the book *Nutida engelsk samhällsplanering* [Contemporary British Social Planning] in which he discussed the British planning legislation.[52] Danneskiold-Samsøe passed on his experience to Lindström, who served as an advisory expert to the City Planning Committee from 1941 to 1945. The Committee discussed a proposal for a new and much stronger Building Act. Arne S. Lundberg, undersecretary at the Ministry of Transport, had been influenced by Åhrén's thoughts and played a key role in the establishment of a new Building Act. Drawing upon the British land use reports, Lundberg wrote a new Building Act and during that time he also visited Great Britain, where he met Lewis Silkin, the member of the cabinet responsible for the UK's Planning Act.[53]

Lindström and Lundberg succeeded in having a new Building Act passed in 1947, and Lindström wrote enthusiastically: "The King and

Parliament have created the tools, the municipalities must do the work."[54] The Building Act of 1947 stated that master plans had to be established for every Swedish city or town. The master plans allowed municipalities to control land use in a community; they could decide *where*, *when* and *how* building should take place. Planning was institutionalized, creating a sudden demand for planners.

Two kinds of professional planners appeared: those who elaborated the guidelines for master and regional plans and hence interpreted the Building Act, and those who actually prepared plans based on those guidelines. The former worked in a state agency, the National Board of Building and Planning (Kungl. Byggnadsstyrelsen). One of its allotted tasks was to provide instructions on how the Building Act of 1947 should be interpreted. The latter were usually hired by consulting bureaus or worked for city planning offices. By 1953, 284 cities and towns had drawn up master plans.[55] Most municipalities were not familiar with planning and formal training for planners did not exist in Sweden. Architects working as planners, including such pioneers as Lindström and Åhrén, were in demand as experts. The Swedish Hydraulic Engineering Company (Vattenbyggnadsbyrån; VBB) had founded a Department of City Planning in 1945 with Lindström as its head. They prepared almost one quarter of all master and regional plans, and were the leading company in Sweden. The largest private consulting agency was led by Åhrén.[56] Through the institutional framework they had shaped, they offered a service as consultants.

A well-known comment on the Building Act, made in 1948, outlined the main features of the new legislation: "The increasing traffic density has given rise to a need for greater safety on the roads and a demand for better and considerably more expensive transport facilities of different kinds, hence necessitating a regulation of development that takes greater account of the needs of the traffic."[57] The Building Act of 1947 was implemented by functionalist planners who took British legislation on planning and adapted it to Swedish conditions. In doing so, they paved the way for a city planning that anticipated the growing motorization of Swedish society.

The advent of mass motorization during the first years of the Cold War era had a pervasive cultural, economic, infrastructural, political, and social impact on Swedish society. One might say that Sweden was transformed into a *car society*. The number of cars almost quintupled, from 252,500 in 1950 to 1,193,900 in 1960, and Sweden soon boasted the highest car-to-people density in Europe.[58] The rise of the Swedish car society was a complex and dynamic process, but among the key components were two interacting developments during the post-war period: the planning and construction of a nation-wide road system, and the adaptation of cities and towns to the car by the planning of new suburbs and towns and the replanning of old city districts.

One should not forget that cars were desired by the rank and file of people in the country,[59] and the governing Social Democrats acknowledged this desire during the 1950s, making the motorization of Sweden part of the larger modernization project mentioned, the *folkhem*. The idea of equality was manifested in the political goal that every worker should be able to afford his or her own car. That the Social Democrats, who had political power, adopted the car at an early stage meant that the mass motorization of Sweden never aroused any serious political controversy.[60]

Nevertheless, it is quite clear that neither the politicians nor the people had any clear vision of what the coming car society might look like. But then again, who did?

The institutional framework of the Building Act of 1947 reflected the planning discourse established by the functionalists during the 1930s and the 1940s, a discourse that favored non-political "scientific" methods. Taken together with increasing mass motorization, the institutional framework and the scientification of city planning prepared the way for the key technical actor of the 1950s: the traffic engineer.

THE TRAFFIC ENGINEER AND THE CAR-ORIENTED SOCIETY

It comes as no surprise that engineers could appear on the scene in the 1950s with the technocratic ambition of pointing the direction in which society was to develop. The functionalist architects of the 1930s had urged that architects should be technicians. The traffic engineer Nils Rosén wrote in 1959: "The more complex society becomes, the more responsibility must be transferred to the *right* technicians."[61] Bo Björkman, professor of Traffic and Transport Engineering at the Royal Institute of Technology, argued in 1961 for extending the role of the traffic engineer, and expressed this role metaphorically: "The traffic engineer wants to serve and should serve as the physician of the body social in those sectors that concern disturbance of the metabolism and in the circulatory system, but he should not only be consulted when the malady becomes acute; he should also participate in planning for the preventive health care that is necessary for shaping a sound social life."[62]

The argument for the central position of the technician or engineer was that he could make neutral judgements based on scientific knowledge. Rosén wrote: "Earlier one considered and thought that the traffic should be arranged this way or that way. This subjective 'traffic planning' has now begun to be replaced by objective methods. Far-sighted cities, municipalities, companies, etc. nowadays engage traffic engineers to plan traffic and traffic systems. [...] A traffic engineer should, without preconceived ideas, provide the most [...] effective traffic solutions."[63]

The traffic engineer's expert knowledge guaranteed political neutrality, and therefore, argued Rosén, posed no threat to the political system: "Since technicians may be dismissed if they prove incompetent, such a system constitutes no threat. On the contrary, delayed and incorrect decisions on technical matters expose the democratic system to unnecessary risks."[64]

Traffic engineering had developed as a profession in the United States during the 1930s. Its conceptual roots grew from a combination of emerging scientific management and traffic engineers who borrowed ideas from Taylor. It was basically a scientific approach to the management of traffic, and it was argued that traffic problems should be tackled with the same rationality as problems in other engineering fields. The principle of the free flow of traffic was fundamental, and traffic engineers sought to formulate it mathematically. The discipline gained academic credibility in the United States with the foundation of the Bureau of Highway Traffic at Yale University in 1943. Traffic engineering there distinguished between short-term techniques such as signals, road signs, markings, and geometrical design, and long-term techniques such as planning.[65]

There was no academic knowledge base in Sweden for the discipline of traffic engineering at Swedish engineering schools during the 1950s, a period that was a formative one for Swedish traffic policy. Instead, traffic engineering grew and developed in other arenas.[66] Among important bodies were consulting bureaus, state authorities such as the National Board of Building and Planning and the National Road Board (Kungl. Väg- och vattenbyggnadsstyrelsen), and the commercial interest group the Swedish Road Association (Svenska vägföreningen). The largest consulting bureau VBB was called "the university at Humlegårdsgatan" after the street in Stockholm where it was located.[67] There were also important training courses, often taking the form of large conferences, for architects, city planners, and traffic engineers. Åhrén, who in 1947 had been appointed head of the Department of City Planning at the Royal Institute of Technology, organized several sessions, including *Vad har USA att lära oss om trafikplaneringen?* [What can the USA teach us about traffic planning?] in 1954, *Bilstaden* [The Car City] in 1956, and *Hur kan våra städers cityområden göras livsdugliga i bilismens tidsålder?* [How can the central districts of our cities be made viable in the age of the car?] in 1958.

Åhrén's courses show once again the close collaboration between architects, city planners, and traffic engineers. Swedish planning favored scientific methods, and the discipline also had an institutional framework Swedish traffic engineers needed in order to apply their methods. Traffic engineering, on the other hand, dealt scientifically with the central aspect of city life according to the functionalist city planning paradigm—traffic. In a sense it was the perfect marriage.

But above all, engineers went abroad to acquire knowledge about the growing motorization of the society, and they went to the United States.[68] The traffic engineer Stig Nordqvist for instance followed a study program in traffic engineering during the academic year 1953–1954 at the Bureau of Highway Traffic at Yale University, which was considered the most prestigious in the world at that time.[69] Nordqvist travelled by car around the States and his experiences formed the core of Åhrén's 1954 training course *What can the USA teach us about traffic planning?* Convinced that the car would reshape society thoroughly, Nordqvist spoke enthusiastically of "the car society" and how it would affect "almost all phases of life,"[70] In 1955, he pointed out the way to the fully motorized society by asking the rhetorical question: "Should we adapt cars to the old society or build a car society?"[71] The architect and city planner Carl-Fredrik Ahlberg, who headed the Regional Planning Office in the region of Stockholm, agreed with Nordqvist, and after visiting the United States in 1956 he reported that a journey to the USA "is said to some extent to be *a journey into the future.*"[72] The ideological model for how the future Swedish car society should be arranged was found in America.

Although there were relatively few traffic engineers in Sweden, they played a crucial role, because traffic forecasts and traffic route plans became normative for the broader framework of master plans and regional plans during the 1950s and the 1960s. We shall see that the new city ideals imported from America merged with the concepts already employed by Swedish planners.

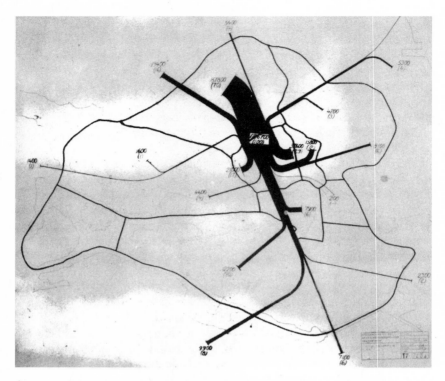

Figure 3. The principle of free flow was fundamental in traffic engineering, and traffic engineers depicted the flow with flow diagrams, known as "traffic spiders." These reduced the city from three dimensions to a two-dimensional flow. Source: *Trafikprognos för Stockholm* (Stockholm, 1955).

A delegation of architects, city planners, traffic engineers and politicians from the City of Stockholm visited the United States in the spring of 1956 to study the impact of mass motorization on American society. They asked what Sweden might learn from traffic and city planning in the United States. Uno Åhrén, by then Sweden's grand old man of city planning, offered an answer to the question when he organized the training course and conference *The Car City* in September 1956. The conference attracted much attention and echoed the assumptions that Åhrén and other functionalists had accepted since the early 1930s: technological change was autonomous and the car was a symbol of the future. Åhrén now wrote: "The enormous expansion in motoring has become the most acute problem of social planning. The forecasts of the future number of cars have had to be revised again and again. The master plans that have been worked out for our cities only a few years ago are already obsolete. They need to be revised to correspond better to the future volume of car traffic. [. . .] We therefore need to investigate whether motorization has to lead to a new city planning paradigm."[73]

The 1956 conference consisted of workshops in which the participating architects, city planners, and traffic engineers elaborated visions of future car cities. Everyone agreed that in the near future, Sweden would become a car society. A car society was defined by Åhrén as one where there was "one car for each person who can and is allowed to drive one." His statement translated into roughly 1 car per 1.5 inhabitants. Whether the number was reached a decade sooner or a decade later was of little importance.[74] What mattered was establishing the notion that a car society was to become a reality. The traffic engineer Erik Hasselquist spoke for the conference in claiming that a "new epoch in our history—the car age" had begun.[75]

An implication of the argument that progress towards a car society appeared inevitable was that no alternative directions were seriously considered. When alternative paths of development are dismissed, the issue becomes in some sense non-political and hence a question for apolitical experts.[76] I would like to point out the importance of the machine metaphor discussed earlier in contributing to the notion of the inevitable direction of technological change. Viewing the society as a machine justifies at least in part an understanding of societal change as a known trajectory in time and space just like a particle in an electromagnetic field or the performance of a machine. While gaining momentum, these visions acted as self-fulfilling prophecies. As the architect and city planner Carl-Fredrik Ahlberg explained at the 1956 conference: "we will reach 100% car ownership much sooner, if we build them [our societies] to meet such a development from the start."[77] And in a long-term economic forecast made in 1965, society's general automobilization was taken for granted with references to discussions including the 1956 conference *The Car City*.[78] The planners had pointed out the path leading to the car society, a path from which it became increasingly difficult to deviate.

The depiction of a car city came to alter greatly the spatial structure of cities. The traffic engineer Nordqvist argued as early as 1954 that "the human scale" would be replaced by a new scale defined by "driving distance" rather than "walking distance."[79] The impact of these visions must be seen in the context of the construction of

Figure 4. The architect and city planner Sune Lindström's sketch, made in 1961, of the satellite town of Täby north of Stockholm. Source: *VBB: Consulting engineers and architects* (Stockholm, 1965).

modern Swedish society during the 1950s, 1960s, and 1970s. Hospitals, schools, universities, libraries, community centers, sports centers, etc. were built. Historians have characterized this period as the age of the large scale, and the 1960s were later epitomized as *Rekordåren* (the Boom Years).[80] During these years the Swedish urban landscape was thoroughly reshaped and transformed into a modernistic utopia with the car as standard; Sweden became a veritable Motopia.[81] Lindström's plan for the new town of Täby north of Stockholm in 1961 epitomized these visions of the car city and the altered conception of city space (see Figure 4). The picture was not utterly utopian; Täby was realized between 1964 and 1971 according to Lindström's master plan. In 1966, Lindström's creation was commented on with the appraisal: "No other housing area seems so impressive, when observed from a car travelling at 100 kilometres an hour."[82]

CONTROLLING NUMBERS—CONTROLLING SPACE

The machine metaphor introduced by functionalist planners implied an intelligible city, and hence a city that could be planned scientifically. The planner gained knowledge by surveying, structuring and organizing space, while at the same time controlling space. Planners established a modernist city planning ideal. Their claims were successfully enshrined in legislation throughout the post-war period and formed a scientific and institutional base for the traffic engineers, who took these claims a step further. They were able to introduce their ideas and visions as objective statements resting upon a scientific foundation. By claiming the neutrality and universality of scientific knowledge, they gained and maintained a position as experts. They quantified, for instance, city space by describing the city in terms of traffic flow diagrams. In their visions, the notion of the city as a machine and the traffic as its primus motor merged in the city as a *traffic machine.*

This heterogeneous group of architects, city planners, and traffic engineers argued successfully with diagrams, formulas, numbers, or statistics. For them, these were more than mere *facts*, they were also *arguments*. This outcome forces a closer examination of the power of numbers. Theodore Porter notes in his study of mechanical objectivity, *Trust in Numbers* (1995), a "strong incentive to prefer precise and standardizable measures to highly accurate ones," since accuracy is meaningless if the identical procedure cannot reliably be performed elsewhere.[83] And precision was exactly the impression they wanted to convey with their numbers.[84] But behind the precision there was an arbitrariness, an arbitrariness not seldom permeated with cultural and political values. With numbers certain features of the city were emphasized, while others were suppressed. By controlling numbers, planners controlled space, thus changing our spatial understanding of cities.

NOTES

1. Uno Åhrén, "Planläggning och utveckling," in *Bygg bättre samhällen*, eds. Carl-Fredrik Ahlberg et al. (Stockholm, 1943), 7.
2. Michel Foucault, "Space, knowledge, and power," in *The Foucault Reader*, ed. Paul Rabinow (New York, 1984), 239–256.
3. Evelyn Fox Keller, *Refiguring Life: Metaphors of Twentieth-Century Biology* (New York, 1995), 92.
4. Michel Foucault, *The Archaeology of Knowledge* (1969), English transl. (London, 1972), 50.
5. Peter Collins, *Changing Ideals in Modern Architecture 1750–1950* (London, 1965), 149–166. Mikael Hård & Thomas J. Misa, eds., *The Urban Machine: Recent Literature on European Cities in the 20th Century*, a "Tensions of Europe" electronic publication, (July 2003), <www.iit.edu/~misa/toe20/urban-machine/>.
6. Hans De Geer, *Rationaliseringsrörelsen i Sverige: Effektivitetsidéer och socialt ansvar under mellankrigstiden* (Stockholm, 1978). Yvonne Hirdman, *Att*

lägga livet till rätta: Studier i svensk folkhemspolitik (1989), 2nd ed. (Stockholm, 2000).

7. Gunnar Asplund et al., *Acceptera* (Stockholm, 1931), 198.
8. Stuart Chase, *Men and Machines* (New York, 1929).
9. Gunnar Asplund et al., *Acceptera* (Stockholm, 1931), 141.
10. Mark Johnson & George Lakoff, *Metaphors We Live By* (Chicago, 1980), 145. Evelyn Fox Keller, *Making Sense of Life: Explaining Biological Development with Models, Metaphors, and Machines* (Cambridge, Mass., 2002), 117ff.
11. Andrew Abbott, *The Systems of Professions: An Essay on the Division of Expert Labor* (Chicago, 1988), 99f.
12. Quoted from Per G. Råberg, *Funktionalistiskt genombrott: Radikal miljö och miljödebatt i Sverige 1925–1931* (1970), 2nd rev. ed. (Stockholm, 1972), 304.
13. Ibid., 103.
14. Rabinbach discusses the metaphor of the human motor and finds an equality between technology and the working body. Anson Rabinbach, *The Human Motor: Energy, Fatigue, and the Origins of Modernity* (Los Angeles, 1990), 289f.
15. Richard Sennett, *Flesh and Stone: The Body and the City in Western Civilization* (New York, 1994), 255–281. See also Jes Fabricius Møller for a discussion of the biological analogy for the society. Jes Fabricius Møller, *Biologismer: Naturvidenskab og politik ca. 1850–1930* (København, 2002), passim.
16. Hugo Nicolaus Pallin, *Trafikteknik* (Stockholm, 1936), 71.
17. Peter Collins, *Changing Ideals in Modern Architecture 1750–1950* (London, 1965), 163.
18. Per G. Råberg, *Funktionalistiskt genombrott: Radikal miljö och miljödebatt i Sverige 1925–1931* (1970), 2nd rev. ed. (Stockholm, 1972), 103.
19. Quoted from Per G. Råberg, *Funktionalistiskt genombrott: Radikal miljö och miljödebatt i Sverige 1925–1931* (1970), 2nd rev. ed. (Stockholm, 1972), 58.
20. Ibid., 104.
21. Sven Wallander, "Stadsbygge," in *Arkitektur och samhälle*, ed. Sven Markelius (Stockholm, 1932), 21.
22. The organism metaphor, on the other hand, put the physician in the center, but here it was argued that the engineer should serve as the physician of the social body.
23. Uno Åhrén, *Arkitektur och demokrati* (Stockholm, 1942), 35f.
24. Ulf Larsson, "Socialingenjören: Hjalmar Cederström och kampen mot sjukdom och fattigdom," in *Vetenskapsbärarna: Naturvetenskapen i det svenska samhället, 1880–1950*, ed. Sven Widmalm (Hedemora, 1999), 274.
25. See for instance Yvonne Hirdman, *Att lägga livet till rätta: Studier i svensk folkhemspolitik* (1989), 2nd ed. (Stockholm, 2000).
26. Henrik Björck has for instance shown that the ideology the radical architects represented was shared by philosophers, engineers and industrialists. Henrik Björck, *Teknisk idéhistoria* (Göteborg, 1995), 177–239. See also David

Östlund, *Det sociala kriget och kapitalets ansvar: Social ingenjörskonst mellan affärsintresse och samhällsreform i USA och Sverige 1899–1914* (Stockholm, 2003).

27. Uno Åhrén, "Samhällsplaneringens uppgifter och metoder," in *Social årsbok 1947*, ed. John Olofsson (Stockholm, 1948), 5.
28. Uno Åhrén quoted from Eva Rudberg, *Uno Åhrén: En föregångsman inom 1900-talets arkitektur och samhällsplanering* (Stockholm, 1981), 56.
29. Quoted from Per G. Råberg, *Funktionalistiskt genombrott: Radikal miljö och miljödebatt i Sverige 1925–1931* (1970), 2nd rev. ed. (Stockholm, 1972), 99.
30. Sven Wallander, "Stadsbygge," in *Arkitektur och samhälle*, ed. Sven Markelius (Stockholm, 1932), 21.
31. Hence the social sciences followed the pattern of organization found in the scientific disciplines. Gunnar Eriksson, *Kartläggarna: Naturvetenskapens tillväxt och tillämpningar i det industriella genombrottets Sverige 1870–1914* (Umeå, 1978), passim.
32. Le Corbusier, *The City of Tomorrow* (1929), reprinted and enlarged from the 1929 ed. (London, 1987), 105.
33. See also Andrew Abbott, who discusses reduction as a rhetorical strategy. Andrew Abbott, *The Systems of Professions: An Essay on the Division of Expert Labor* (Chicago, 1988), 98ff.
34. One might wonder what role the aircraft played in the depiction of the city as two-dimensional. Le Corbusier exposed for instance a weakness for planes in his publication *Aircraft: The New Vision* (1935), reprint (New York, 1988), and a similar indulgence for high altitudes was echoed in the final picture of six aircraft underneath a cloudy sky in the Swedish functionalist manifesto *Acceptera* (1931).
35. Uno Åhrén, "Reformera den kommunala organisationen!", *Tiden* 1941:4, 210.
36. Sune Lindström, "Stadsplaneringens första förutsättning," *Tiden* 1943:2, 78f.
37. Uno Åhrén, "Prognoser: Några principiella synpunkter," *Byggmästaren* 1942:15, 195.
38. Ibid., 197.
39. Uno Åhrén, "Planläggning och utveckling," in *Bygg bättre samhällen*, eds. Carl-Fredrik Ahlberg et al. (Stockholm, 1943), 7.
40. *Stadsplaneutredningen 1942 III: Förslag till byggnadslag m.m.*, Statens offentliga utredningar (SOU) 1945:15 (Stockholm, 1945), 153.
41. Uno Åhrén, "Planläggning och utveckling," in *Bygg bättre samhällen*, eds. Carl-Fredrik Ahlberg et al. (Stockholm, 1943), 8ff.
42. Ibid., 12f.
43. Ibid., 15.
44. Roddy Nilsson, "Den närvarande frånvaron eller i väntan på Foucault: En diskussion om Foucault och den svenska historiedisciplinen," *Historisk tidskrift* 2000:2, 190.
45. *Stadsplaneutredningen 1942 III: Förslag till byggnadslag m.m.*, Statens offentliga utredningar (SOU) 1945:15 (Stockholm, 1945), 152.

46. Le Corbusier, *The Radiant City* (1933), 8.
47. Michel Foucault, *Discipline and Punish: The Birth of the Prison* (1975), English transl. (Harmondsworth, 1979), 224.
48. Uno Åhrén, "Samhällsplaneringens uppgifter och metoder," in *Social årsbok 1947*, ed. John Olofsson (Stockholm, 1948), 7.
49. Uno Åhrén, "Planläggning och utveckling," in *Bygg bättre samhällen*, eds. Carl-Fredrik Ahlberg et al. (Stockholm, 1943), 12.
50. Sune Lindström, "Regionplanering," in *Bygg bättre samhällen*, eds. Carl-Fredrik Ahlberg et al. (Stockholm, 1943), 48–54. Sune Lindström, "Regionplanering" (1944), in *Sagt av Sune Lindström*, eds. Stig Nordqvist et al. (Göteborg, 1966), 29.
51. Carl-Fredrik Ahlberg, "Till minne av Otto Danneskiold-Samsøe," *Plan* 1982:3, 170. Arne S. Lundberg, "Är det gammalmodigt med 'community centers'?", *Plan* 1977:4, 193.
52. Otto Danneskiold-Samsøe, *Nutida engelsk samhällsplanering* (Stockholm, 1945). See also Danneskiold-Samsøe's summary in the journal *Byggmästaren*, Otto Danneskiold-Samsøe, "Nutida engelsk samhällsplanering," *Byggmästaren* 1945:15, 271–290.
53. Eva Rudberg, *Uno Åhrén: En föregångsman inom 1900-talets arkitektur och samhällsplanering* (Stockholm, 1981), 193. Göran Sidenbladh, "Idédebatt och praxis i efterkrigstidens samhällsplanering," *Plan* 1977:4, 199.
54. Sune Lindström, "Markfrågans innebörd och betydelse," in *Social årsbok 1947*, ed. John Olofsson (Stockholm, 1948), 56.
55. "284 kommuner upprättar generalplaner," *Plan*, 1953:3, 72f.
56. Carl-Fredrik Ahlberg, "Sune Lindström in memoriam," *Plan* 1990:2, 116–117. Eva Rudberg, *Uno Åhrén: En föregångsman inom 1900-talets arkitektur och samhällsplanering* (Stockholm, 1981), 209.
57. Alfred Bexelius, Nils Aurén & Allan Nordenstam, *Byggnadslagstiftningen (byggnadslagen, byggnadsstadgan)* (Stockholm, 1948), 23.
58. See for instance Anders Gullberg, "Bilen som första stadsmakt," in *Miljö, media, makt*, ed. Svante Beckman (Stockholm, 1990); Emin Tengström, *Bilismen—i kris? En bok om bilen, människan, samhället och miljön* (Stockholm, 1991); Pär Blomkvist, *Den goda vägens vänner: Väg- och billobbyn och framväxten av det svenska bilsamhället 1914–1959* (Eslöv, 2001).
59. The geographer Torsten Hägerstrand has noted that the car, being "a cave on four wheels," appeals to atavistic human instincts while giving both protection (from six sides) and the chance of "release from the tyranny of space." These are indeed irresistible qualities. Interview with Torsten Hägerstrand, 5/9 2003. See also Torsten Hägerstrand, "The impact of transport on the quality of life," in *International Symposium on Theory and Practice in Transport Economics: Transport in the 1980–1990 decade*, 2 vol. (Paris, 1974), I, 2.
60. Pär Blomkvist, *Den goda vägens vänner: Väg- och billobbyn och framväxten av det svenska bilsamhället 1914–1959* (Eslöv, 2001), 144–150.

61. Nils Rosén, "Trafikingenjörer och trafikplanering," *Väg- och vattenbyggaren* 1959:1, 11.

62. Bo Björkman in *Vem skall planera?*, ed. Uno Åhrén, Fortbildningskurs i stadsbyggnad vid KTH 5–6 juni 1961, 37.

63. Nils Rosén, "Samordnad trafikplanering," *MOTOR* 1959:42, 26. See also Nils Rosén, "Trafikingenjörer och trafikplanering," *Väg- och vattenbyggaren* 1959:1, 9–11.

64. Ibid., 11.

65. *Annual Report 1953–54*, Bureau of Highway Traffic, Yale University (New Haven, Connecticut, 1954). Clay McShane, "The origins and globalization of traffic control signals," *Journal of Urban History* 25 (1999), 379–403. Pär Blomkvist, "Transferring Technology—Shaping Ideology: American Traffic Engineering and Commercial Interests in the Establishment of a Swedish Car Society, 1945–1965," *Comparative Technology Transfer and Society* 2 (2004), 273–302.

66. Interview with Olle Ahlström, 22/3 2004.

67. Intervew with Christer Sanne, 13/8 2003. VBB also went under the name "the Swedish planning monopoly." Interview with Olof Gunnarsson, 3/8 2003.

68. For a thorough investigation of the transfer of ideas on traffic engineering from the United States to Sweden and their adaptation, see Per Lundin, "American numbers copied! Shaping the Swedish post-war car society," *Comparative Technology Transfer and Society* 2 (2004), 303–334.

69. *Annual Report 1953–54*, Bureau of Highway Traffic, Yale University (New Haven, Connecticut, 1954), 26.

70. Stig Nordqvist, "Bilen i USA och dess betydelse för transportverksamheten," in *Vad har USA att lära oss om trafikplaneringen?*, ed. Uno Åhrén, Fortbildningskurs i stadsbyggnad vid KTH 13–15 september 1954.

71. Stig Nordqvist, "Bör vi anpassa bilismen till det gamla samhället eller bygga ett bilsamhälle?," *Industria* 51 (1955), 31–35.

72. Carl-Fredrik Ahlberg, "Intryck från USA: Urbanisering, allmänna tendenser: Stadsagglomerationerna ur regional synpunkt," in *Bilstaden*, ed. Uno Åhrén (Stockholm, 1960), 17.

73. Uno Åhrén, "Förord," in *Bilstaden*, ed. Uno Åhrén (Stockholm, 1960), 3.

74. Ibid., 5.

75. Erik Hasselquist, "Från bilprognos till trafikprognos," in *Bilstaden*, ed. Uno Åhrén (Stockholm, 1960), 130.

76. Donald MacKenzie, *Inventing Accuracy: A Historical Sociology of Nuclear Missile Guidance* (Cambridge, Mass., 1990), 168.

77. Carl-Fredrik Ahlberg, "Estradsamtal," in *Bilstaden*, ed. Uno Åhrén (Stockholm, 1960), 211.

78. Sven Godlund, *Trafikutveckling och trafikinvesteringar: Data, synpunkter och bedömningar för tiden från omkring 1930 till omkring 2000 med särskild hänsyn till åren 1950–1970*, Statens offentliga utredningar (SOU) 1966:69, 1965 års långtidsutredning, Bilaga 5 (Stockholm, 1966), 29f.

79. Stig Nordqvist, "Bilen i USA och dess betydelse för transportverk-samheten," in *Vad har USA att lära oss om trafikplaneringen?*, ed. Uno Åhrén, Fortbildningskurs i stadsbyggnad vid KTH 13–15 september 1954.

80. Peter Hall, *Cities in civilization* (New York, 1998), 842–887. Thomas Hall, ed., *Rekordåren: En epok i svenskt bostadsbyggande* (Karlskrona, 1999), passim.

81. The British architect Geoffrey Jellicoe coined the term "Motopia" in 1961. Geoffrey Alan Jellicoe, *Motopia: A Study in the Evolution of Urban Landscape* (London, 1961).

82. Björn Linn, "Tankar i Colosseum," *Arkitektur*, 1966:8, 102.

83. Theodore Porter, *Trust in Numbers: The Pursuit of Objectivity in Science and Public Life* (Princeton, New Jersey, 1995), 29.

84. In a sense, accuracy is quite meaningless when forecasting the future; it is the persuasive power of precision that matters.

NATURE'S PERIPHERY

*Rural Transformation by the
Advent of Infrasystems*

ARNE KAIJSER

INTRODUCTION

Technology is crucial in transforming places and creating spaces. This is particularly true of a certain category of technology, which I call infrastructural systems, or, more briefly, infrasystems, including transportation systems, communication systems, energy systems and the like. Infrasystems are enabling technologies, facilitating flows of commodities, information, and people. When new systems of this kind are established, this often considerably widens the "possibility space" available to people and organizations. Hitherto inaccessible natural resources may become possible to exploit, and new forms of coordination and cooperation among people dispersed in space may arise. This in turn transforms the character of places and the relations between them.

In his book *Nature's Metropolis. Chicago and the Great West* (1990), William Cronon tells a fascinating story of the transformation of places by the advent of infrasystems. He analyzes how Chicago and its hinterland—"the Great West"—developed in a symbiotic fashion in the second half of the 19th century. The leading merchants in the town were quick to grasp the potential of new infrasystems. In 1848 they established the Chicago Board of Trade, which was instrumental in influencing the construction of railways, canals and telegraph lines in such a way as to make Chicago the major "hub" in the mid-West. The new transportation networks enabled farmers to settle on the seemingly endless prairies and woodsmen to start exploiting the vast northern forests, and as a result ever-growing flows of grain, livestock and lumber entered Chicago, which became the gateway to distant

markets on the East Coast and across the seas. While Chicago grew
and expanded, its surrounding landscapes were profoundly transformed; the tall grass prairies became cornstalk and wheat fields and
the white pine forests of the Great Lakes turned to stumps. "Chicago
was remote from all of these events. And yet no place is more central
to understanding why they occurred."[1]

As its title suggests, this article is inspired by Cronon's work,[2] but
the focus is not on a city in the center of such transformation
processes, but on a small rural place on the periphery. I believe that
choosing the periphery as the point of entry gives a very different perspective from that gained by studying the center. At the center one
can find powerful actors who are actively exploiting the new possibilities provided by new infrasystems for their own ends. On the periphery most people have to adapt to changes initiated by others in
remote places.

I happened to read Cronon's book during a summer vacation in
Malexander, a little village located about 70 kilometres south of the
City of Linköping on the brink of the large Lake Sommen. Nowadays
it is primarily a summer resort, made very attractive by the lake with
clean water and hundreds of islands. Cronon's book made me think
about a number of questions: What happened to a remote place like
Malexander when it came within the reach of new infrasystems and
was gradually embedded in a wider economy of regional, national or
even global scope? How and by whom were new infrasystems built
and the flows through them controlled? What happened to the people, and the relations among them, and to their cultural identities?
How did the systems influence the landscape and the local resources?
I also started to wonder about the differences across the Atlantic. In
contrast to the American Mid-West, the region where Malexander is
located was not a "frontier" in the 19th century; on the contrary it was
a densely populated and intensively populated and cultivated area
when the new infrasystems were introduced. What did this difference
mean to the outcome? The purpose of this article is to try to answer
these questions, and I will come back to them in the final section.

The mid-1870s is a natural starting point for my story, as three
new systems were established in the Malexander region within only
one year: steam boat traffic on a lake, a railway line on the other side
of this lake, and the opening of a postal station. I will try to describe
the effect of these systems and of subsequent systems that have been
introduced into the region up till the present by focusing on three key
issues: How were possibility spaces widened by different kinds of systems? What kind of flows did they permit? And which actors could

control these flows? I will divide the period from the early 1870s to the present into four phases. I should point out that it is not the village but the parish of Malexander that is the object of my study. In fact there was no village in the 1870s. The parish has a total area of 200 square kilometres, of which 25% is covered with water; see the map in Figure 1.[3]

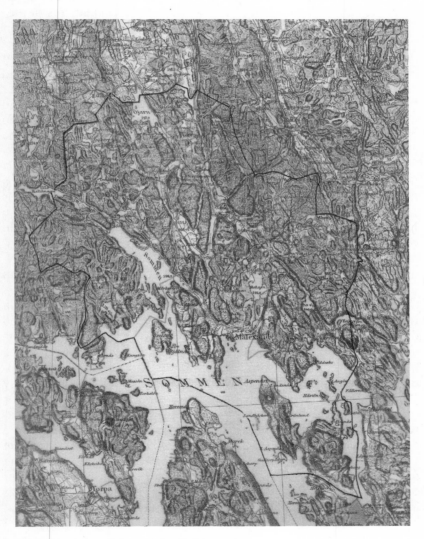

Figure 1.   Map of the parish of Malexander.

PHASE 1: MALEXANDER INCORPORATED, 1875–1920

Located in an area inhabited since pre-historic times, Malexander experienced a rapid population growth during most of the 19th century, from about 1000 inhabitants in 1800 to almost 1700 in 1875. They lived on forty farms, which were fairly evenly spread over the parish, and most of these farms had four or five crofts linked to them. The average farm had about 25 hectares of arable land, 50 hectares of pasture and 300 hectares of forest. There was only one road of rather poor quality to the surrounding world and the local economy was predominantly of self-subsistence character. Money to buy products that could not be locally produced was earned by selling meat, butter and cheese at markets in regional towns. Most inhabitants lived under fairly poor conditions. Furthermore, they were rather isolated and most of them left their farms only on Sundays, when they went to church to attend the service and listen to gossip and news on the church green.

The isolation of Malexander was dramatically altered in the last decades of the 19th century. It started in November 1874, when a new major railway from Stockholm to Malmö was inaugurated. This railway, the Eastern Main Line owned and operated by the State Railway Board, ran fairly close to Malexander along the other side of Lake Sommen. It was to have a major impact on the development of Malexander in the subsequent decades—not directly, however, but with the ironworks in the municipality of Boxholm as an intermediary.

"Boxholms bruk" was the name of an ironworks established in the 1780s by a local entrepreneur, Carl Daniel Burén. It was situated on Svartån, a river which received its water from Sommen. At Boxholm there were three waterfalls with a total drop of 30 metres, and a number of tilt hammers and forges were built along the river to produce nails, scythes, saw blades and other iron products. In the early 1870s Boxholm Ironworks had a little more than 100 workers. Poor transportation facilities were an important obstacle to the further expansion of the Ironworks. Iron ore and finished products had to be brought on bad roads by oxcarts from and to the town of Vadstena on Lake Vättern, 30 kilometres away. Therefore, the plans to build the new railway line west of Sommen were very good news to the owner of the works, Carl Pontus af Burén, grandson of the founder. He was able to have the line pass right through Boxholm with a station just beside the Ironworks.[4]

When the formal decisions to build the railway had been taken by Parliament, af Burén developed very ambitious plans for expanding the Ironworks. In order to finance these investments, he decided to transform the family business into a limited company. On 3 February 1872, an invitation to subscribe for shares was published, emphasizing that Boxholm was an ideal place for a large ironworks, with a major railway enabling cheap transport of ore to the plant and finished products to distant markets, with plenty of hydro power and Lake Sommen as a reliable reservoir, and with access to charcoal from the vast forests surrounding Sommen.

The floating of the company was successful. After not much more than a month, the share capital of 1.5 million kronor was fully subscribed and Burén could start to put his plans into effect. A large new blast furnace was built in 1873 and within a year or so was producing some 5 000 tonnes of pig iron annually. Three years later a new Lancashire forge was built and from the early 1880s onwards it was able to consume the whole output from the blast furnace. In 1875 the young and energetic Wilhelm Wettergren became general manager, a position that he held until 1910. Boxholm became a hive of activity as the works grew rapidly. However, the company's operations were not confined to the plant at Boxholm. Large quantities of charcoal were needed by both the blast furnace and the forges, and to secure its supplies the company bought many properties with forest land in the surrounding parishes. The land purchases also had a second purpose. They formed part of a strategy of broadening the company's business to include the production of sawn timber. And the actual property holdings themselves were also seen as a financial backbone that could be a valuable buffer at times of economic downturn.

A good many of these purchases of land involved Malexander. During the first five years of the new company's existence, eight Malexander farms with a total area of 5 000 hectares were bought. This meant that the company became the owner of one-third of all the land in the parish. The company was naturally the stronger party in these transactions, possessing more information than the sellers, particularly on the value of the forest. The official history of the company records that the management had virtually a free hand with regard to purchasing whenever the opportunity arose, "since it always proved that the purchases were to the advantage of the company."[5] After a first wave of purchasing, expansion continued at a more modest rate. Over the next four decades the company bought an additional fourteen farms in Malexander and by 1918 the company owned two-thirds of the land in the parish.

Charcoal

The principal aim of the Ironworks' land acquisitions was to secure the supply of charcoal for ironmaking. Previously the Malexander forests had been used only for the fuel and timber needs of the local farms, and there was no local knowledge of charcoal-burning. Wettergren therefore set about organizing a transfer of knowledge. He had previously been an inspector at a works at Kolmården, 100 kilometres north of Boxholm, where there were many skilled charcoal burners. He induced some of these to come to Boxholm's estates and teach their skills, after which knowhow then spread rapidly in the area.[6]

Charcoal-burning was labor intensive. Trees were felled and brought to the charcoal platform in the summer. In autumn the pile was built and after that came the critical stage when the pile was lit and the actual burning began. Charcoal-burning took between two and three weeks and during this period the burner lived in a hut beside the pile in order to be able to watch it round the clock and make sure that it did not catch fire. When winter came and snow arrived, the charcoal was hauled away by draught animals on sledges. Between fifteen and twenty-five sledge loads were needed for each pile, and often it was miles to one of the charcoal houses that the company had built on the shores of Sommen. In summer the charcoal could then be carried across the lake to Boxholm in barges drawn by one of the company's two steamers, which were built in 1866 and 1874.[7]

In other words, a huge amount of labor was spent on supplying the works with charcoal. Much of this work was done by the crofters on the farms that the company had bought. They often lived deep in the forest, and could build piles close to their croft. The crofter's had previously had to work a specified number of days each year for the freehold farmer, or peasant, who owned the land. This liability in kind came to an end. Instead, the crofter had to produce a certain amount of charcoal each year as rent. If he produced more than the amount of the rent, he would be paid at market rates (however, the company had a monopoly). The leaseholders on the company's farms who had draught animals usually paid part of their rent by hauling charcoal. As well as the occupants of the company's own farms, who were obliged to produce and transport charcoal, many crofters and freeholders on

Figure 2. Charcoal burner at his pile. (Photography from the collection at the museum of the Folklore Society in Malexander.)

other Malexander farms opted to supply charcoal to the company to augment their income.[8]

Timber

In order to make full use of the newly acquired forest areas, the company built a modern sawmill in Boxholm in 1873 with a capacity for sawing around 100 000 logs per year.[9] The timber could be cut in the company's forests around Sommen and floated across the lake with the aid of the two steamers. But first the timber had to be felled and cross-cut with saws and axes and then brought to the shore of Sommen. Knowledge of tree-felling was widespread among the men of the area. On the other hand, there was no log-hauling tradition, because formerly it had been possible to fell trees near the place where the timber was needed.

Just as with the charcoal-burning, the company organized a knowledge transfer with regard to this skill. In the early years the company contracted experienced loggers from Värmland, something over 300 kilometres north-west of Boxholm. They came in the winter with their small, but hardy horses, and with special sledges. Oxen were often used as draught animals in the forests of Östergötland at this time, and the horses were at first viewed with suspicion. But it soon became clear that the Värmlanders earned a good income from their piece rates and several residents of Malexander tried to learn their methods, which involved not only the haulage itself, but also the preparation of suitable winter roads through the forest. A few also managed to buy the Värmlanders' horses when their owners returned home in the spring.[10] To facilitate the timber haulage, the company also took the step of excavating a number of log channels, one of them very close to Malexander Church. During the spring thaw, large quantities of timber could be floated to Sommen in this way.[11]

The division of labor in log-handling resembled that in charcoal-burning. It was mainly crofters and farm laborers who did the heavy work of felling the trees. They were also the ones who floated the timber, whereas leaseholders and freeholders who had draught animals hauled the timber to the shores of Sommen or to a drivable watercourse.[12] Where charcoal was concerned, Boxholms AB was the only buyer in the district and this gave the company a monopolistic position. In the case of logs, on the other hand, there were sometimes also other purchasers. But Boxholm Ironworks had a dominating position and for a time operated a purchasing cartel together with the main competitor. Sawn timber was the most profitable of the company's activities in the late nineteenth century.[13]

Milk

The farms purchased by Boxholm Ironworks covered not only forest land, but also arable and meadow land. To the general manager Wettergren it was obvious that these parts of the company's assets also had to yield as high a return as possible and he called in agricultural experts to develop the farming. The company increased the area of arable land on the farms purchased by as much as 10 per cent or slightly more by extensive ditching of wetland or lowering of lakes. In addition, large arable fields were improved by carrying away the larger stones and cairns and pulling down many stone walls. The leaseholders were offered loans in order to invest in tools, new stock, and so on. The company also paid for the refurbishing of many houses and cattle sheds. Around the turn of the century, all the houses and sheds on the company's lands were painted uniformly in red with yellow door frames and window linings.

The company also encouraged a development of stockkeeping in the area by establishing three dairies in the early 1890s, one in Boxholm and two in Malexander, on leasehold farms bought by the company. The dairies specialized in the production of high-quality cheese. The investment in dairies was connected with the fact that the ironmakers' need for charcoal declined during the 1880s and 1890s as a result of improved efficiency in both blast furnaces and forges. Some of the Ironworks' tenants of crofts and farms were now given the opportunity to pay for their rent with deliveries of milk instead of or as a supplement to charcoal. One of the company's steamers fetched milk every morning from farms around Lake Sommen. Freehold farmers and crofters not belonging to the company also delivered milk to the dairies, thus stimulating more intense stockkeeping on this land.[14]

Steamers, Roads and Postal Services

The opening of the new main line between Stockholm and Malmö in the autumn of 1874 led to the establishment of other new infrasystems. A number of small steamers had appeared on Sommen in the 1850s, primarily for the transport of farm produce. However, a new era of steamer traffic opened in 1874 when the *Carl-Johan* was launched. This was considerably larger than previous craft and could carry 200 passengers. The vessel was owned by a private company that anticipated an increased need for transport across Sommen when the railway main line was opened. At first it was used as both tugboat and passenger vessel, but gradually the latter use came to predominate and a regular timetable was introduced. On Fridays there were market trips to Tranås, which was a rapidly growing station community beside the lake. Then the boat was filled not only with people but with livestock and crates of butter, cheese, fish, berries and mushrooms.[15]

On 1 January 1875, a post office opened in Malexander, just after the opening of the main line. There seems to have been a latent demand for literature in the parish. Before the post office opened there had been two newspaper subscribers (the priest and one of the landowners), who had the paper brought out from a village 20 kilometres away by a crofter's wife. By 1900 the post office was handling no fewer than 189 newspaper subscriptions. The subscribers were at

92 different farms and crofts in the parish and each copy was no doubt read by many individuals. So in only a few decades the people of Malexander became mass media consumers, receiving regular news of events taking place far beyond the parish boundaries. Formerly they had received news only by hearsay, often outside the church. It is hard to imagine a more comprehensive information revolution.[16]

The steamers and the railway represented a radical improvement in long-distance transport facilities in the region. But at the same time the need grew for connecting transport to steamer jetties and railway stations. As long as it was possible, timber, firewood, charcoal, hay and straw were carried on sledges drawn by animals during the winter. However, there were sometimes mild winters with little snow, and then roads and paths had to be used. There was only one major road out of the parish, from Malexander Church to Strålsnäs, where there was a railway station. On the other hand, there was no road from Malexander to Boxholm, which was particularly inconvenient for Boxholm Ironworks, where the need to bring in charcoal was no less urgent during winters with little snow. The works was to play an important part in instigating improvements to the roads. The general manager Wettergren succeeded in obtaining a government grant for 65% of the estimated cost of a road from Boxholm to Malexander and on to the village of Kisa, 20 kilometres east of Malexander. The road was opened in 1893, and made the works' transport situation a great deal easier. But the road was naturally also of great benefit to the people of Malexander, who now had a reliable all-year-round link with both Boxholm and Kisa.[17]

A Connected Place

As we have seen, the last quarter of the nineteenth century saw radical changes in Malexander, initiated largely by the opening of the Eastern Main Line. The management of Boxholm Ironworks were the first to see the "possibility-spaces" opened up by the new railway in combination with the natural resources around Lake Sommen. The company succeeded in buying up large areas of land bearing forest that had hitherto been regarded as almost valueless. It realized that an enormous amount of work would be involved in exploiting these resources and managed to bring in a large number of the local population into the works' production system.

Boxholm Ironworks thus came to play a key role in the transformation of the Malexander area, a role reminiscent of that played by

Chicago for many places in the Midwest. Boxholm became a gateway for the growing flows of charcoal, timber and milk. The company organized and controlled a large part of these flows all the way from charcoal pile, felling site and barn to the shores of Sommen, and by steamer on to Boxholm for processing and forwarding to distant markets. Moreover, the company controlled a flow of money in the opposite direction as compensation for the work done by the local people. In this way money began to circulate on a far greater scale than before, and four shops were opened in the parish in the 1880s and 1890s. Malexander thus became firmly connected to the outside world and the high level of self-subsistence began to decline, although the people of Malexander still produced a good deal of their daily necessities locally.

There was also a dramatic change in the development of population during this time (see the diagram in Figure 3). After more than a hundred years of steady growth during which the population doubled, there was a striking change in the trend in 1875, when the population of the parish was at its largest ever. In the period up to the turn of the century, the population declined by roughly 25 per cent, from just under 1700 to just over 1200 inhabitants.[18] It may appear a paradox that the decline in population took place just when forestry became an important new industry and when railways, steamer traffic and postal services came to the area. These changes might reasonably be expected to have made it easier for people to support themselves in the area. The process is the direct opposite of the one observable at the same time in the Midwest and in the northern parts of Sweden.

The explanation lies in the fact that Malexander was in no way a "frontier." It was an area that was very densely populated relative to its capacity to produce food. It is true that the new systems brought improved economic prospects to many, but at the same time it became easier to move out. The post brought newspapers and letters that increased the awareness of alternative possibilities of securing a livelihood either in more industrial parts of Sweden or far away in America. These were opportunities that many must have found more promising than the prospect of staying in their croft with little plots of land or of breaking new ground in the parish. The monetary income from work in the forest or from sale of the home could also create the capital needed for moving, and the move itself became easier with the advent of steamers and railways. In this way the new infrasystems became not only a way of sending Malexander's natural resources to

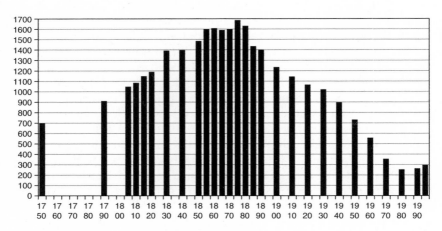

Figure 3. The population of Malexander, 1750–2000.[19]

distant parts: a substantial proportion of the population chose to go the same way.[20]

For those who stayed in the area, life changed in many ways. The forest became an important workplace for men during the winter half of the year. Their autumns, winters and springs were filled with work on charcoal piles and on felling, and along the winter roads and watercourses. The women remained on the farms and crofts and had a greater sphere of responsibility in the absence of the men in the forests. The company's purchases of farms led to a new social stratification in Malexander. The number of peasant proprietors was halved and a new group of tenant farmers arose, whereas landowners almost disappeared (three of the four estates were bought out by the Ironworks). This new stratification was strengthened by the geographical pattern of the purchases; see the map in Figure 1, where the darker parts mark areas belonging to the Boxholms company. All the farms in the vicinity of the church remained owned by the peasants, whereas those on the edges of the parish became part of the Ironworks.

Incorporation in the Ironworks was emphasized by the fact that the farms and crofts were consistently weatherboarded and painted red with yellow corner boards and frames. "This resulted in a standard appearance, a kind of uniform, which was very pleasing and made it easy for a stranger to identify that he had arrived at a 'company farm,' " states the official history of the company, written by

Elias Wettergren, son of Wilhelm Wettergren and his successor as general manager from 1910 until 1933. The fact that the company management found "pleasing" this clear indication of "company farms" is hardly surprising. However, it is not certain that the tenants and the crofters shared their opinion.[21]

PHASE 2: A CENTER ON THE PERIPHERY, 1920–1945

Boxholm Ironworks enjoyed a boom before, during and just after the First World War. Sales of iron and iron products grew particularly rapidly. But in the autumn of 1920 this boom was superseded by a deep and long-lasting depression, which continued until the middle of the 1930s. Once again it was iron products that were most sensitive to the fluctuations in the economy. The company's earlier diversification was what saved it. Forestry and wood products were able to cover the loss on ironmaking. The buying of properties came to a complete halt after 1920 and instead the Ironworks sold roughly a tenth of its landholdings during the depression, although none of the Malexander farms.[22] The crisis at the Ironworks naturally affected Malexander, and gave the period 1920–1945 a somewhat different character from the preceding one. Dependence on the works decreased slightly and the church village of Malexander itself, which lay in the middle of the non-company-owned parish, experienced a thriving development. It became "a center on the periphery," to borrow an expression.[23]

Increased Mobility—But not for All

When the new road between Boxholm, Malexander and Kisa had been built in the 1890s, it had been laid mainly with horses (or oxen) and carts in mind. Between the wars, however, new vehicles came along: cycles, buses, motorcycles and cars. The cycle became the most important. It was well adapted to the countryside, being possible to use on poor roads and even footpaths and simple to maintain, requiring no fuel and being relatively cheap. Those who could afford to buy a cycle gained a totally new mobility. It became possible to reach quite distant places of work and simpler to go to the village to shop or take part in other community life and social activities. Young people particularly appreciated being able to cycle to dances in neighboring parishes and form new friendships. There were, however, many Malexander households that could not afford a cycle, especially crofters who lived a long way from the village. And in those households that

Figure 4.   Bicycle tour in Malexander in the 1930s (Photography courtesy of Kristina Garpevik, Malexander).

did acquire one, it was usually adult men who used them. One category derived no benefit from bicycles at all, the schoolchildren.[24]

School attendance in the Malexander area was largely a transport problem, because of the distances between the homes. Until the mid-1800s the children had had to learn to read at home on farms and crofts, with the priest checking their reading ability at regular home examinations. In the 1850s a peripatetic schooling was introduced, with a teacher giving instruction at different farms at different times of the year. But the requirement for school attendance became more stringent, and late in the nineteenth century five schools opened in the parish. Even with five schools, many children still had a long way to go on narrow paths through dense woods, and many of them had more than an hour's walk to and from school every day.[25]

Buses became another important form of transport. A private operator began a service between Boxholm–Malexander–Kisa in 1926. The bus made it possible to travel to Kisa or Boxholm quickly and relatively cheaply at any time of the year to shop or for other reasons. Bus traffic competed fiercely with the steamer, and the *Carl Johan* was withdrawn early in the 1930s. The inter-war years also saw the arrival of other motor vehicles. Lorries began to be used for transport of goods, for example churns to the dairies. Some men whose trades involved travelling bought motorcycles to reach remote places of work. And the first cars began to appear on the roads, being used by the post office and as taxis. But the total number of motor vehicles in the parish at the end of the 1930s was no more than ten.[26]

Thriving Church Village

Improved transportation led to a development of the church village. Previously it had been a busy place mainly on Sundays when people came to morning service from farms and crofts far and near and the church stables were full of horses and oxen. During the inter-war period, the church village gradually acquired an increasingly central position in the parish. The new road running west and east to Boxholm and Kisa crossed the old road to the north just beside the church. The bus service that started in 1926 set off from the church village to Kisa and Boxholm. There was also a landing stage for steamers near the village, which contributed to its importance as the center of the parish. But in particular it was cycle traffic that stimulated the growth of the village and led to an increasing range of services and entertainment. In the 1930s there were no less than three shops, a cafe, a cooperative dairy and two blacksmiths. Many club activities began: a sports club, a local folklore society, a housewives' league and also political associations. A community center was built in the early 1930s, and used frequently for films, revues and dramatic productions, lectures, auctions, parties, and so on. An outdoor dance floor was also laid, to which young people cycled from all over the parish.[27]

The church village was first and foremost a place where people met. Not many people lived there. During the first half of the twentieth century, the population of Malexander was fairly evenly distributed across the parish, with only about 5 per cent living in the church village itself.[28] In the late 1920s an "own-home movement" was formed in the village and about a dozen new houses were built. Those who settled there were for the most part shopkeepers, craftsmen and retired farmers. A preliminary small-scale extension of two new infrasystems also began in the church village. In the early 1920s one of the village blacksmiths installed a diesel-electric generator in his forge and began to supply 110-volt direct current to a number of households in the evenings. A few years later the activity was formalized as an electricity distribution association. In 1922 the national telegraph office set up a telephone exchange in the village, with six subscribers.

The arrival of telephones in the parish gave an opportunity for more rapid communication with the outside world even for those who did not have a telephone at home, for example if they needed to summon a doctor. Radio also came in the 1920s. Here Malexander had the advantage of being situated quite close to the first large Swedish radio transmitter in Motala, which began broadcasting in 1927. Even those households that did not have access to electricity could listen to the broadcasts of Sveriges Radio with a battery-operated crystal receiver and keep abreast of what was happening in the wider world.[29]

The Modernization of Agriculture

There was no fundamental change in the economy of Malexander in the inter-war years. Timber and charcoal remained the most important products for sale, and work in the forest proceeded largely in the same manner in the 1940s as in the 1870s. This whole period may be described as the craftsman phase in the forest, when men and horses felled trees, burned charcoal, and hauled logs or drove them along the rivers. This was an intensive forestry, which occupied most adult men in Malexander during the winter half of the year. One of the preconditions of this skilled forestry was the presence of crofters, tenant farmers and peasant proprietors who lived scattered across all parts of the parish, and could fell trees and carry them in the neighborhood of their crofts and farms, together with the fact that all these men could supplement winter work in the forest with farm work during the summer. All the charcoal and most of the timber was still sold to Boxholm Ironworks, but many attempts were made to reduce dependence on the works. During the inter-war period, two steam sawmills were started close to the church village and in 1945 an electrically powered sawmill was built, all by private individuals.[30]

In other words, forestry continued in an unchanged form throughout the period between the wars. Agriculture, on the other hand, was modernized in important respects. Urbanization and new dietary habits led to a sharp increase in demand for those products that were the Malexander area's particular speciality—dairy produce and meat. And lorries and railways permitted quick transport of fresh goods to the consumers in the cities.[31] Between the wars, many Malexander farms went over to a more intensive system of production: crop rotation. The yield from the fields was greatly increased by refraining from letting them lie fallow every third year and instead alternating systematically between crops that required more or less nutrition—especially

Figure 5. Forest work in Malexander in the 1930s (Photography courtesy of Kristina Garpevik, Malexander).

cereals and leguminous plants. The use of commercial fertilizer was a necessary ingredient of the production system, otherwise the land would become impoverished. The changeover to crop rotation meant that it was possible to produce more and more nourishing winter fodder for the animals. This led in turn to a substantial increase in both the number of animals and the yield per animal.[32]

Another factor that contributed to a change in agriculture was a gradual decrease in the size of the population. In the 1920s a number of new machines were introduced to the farms in the parish: seeders, mowers, horsedrawn rakes, binders and reapers. All these machines were horsedrawn; what was involved was *horse mechanization*.[33] The large farms were the first to go over to this new capital-intensive agriculture, and their example was eventually followed by many of the medium-sized farms. But on the small farms and crofts, the old three-crop rotation was retained, with the scythe and the rake the most important harvesting implements. Here agriculture remained largely of a subsistence nature and was only a supplement to forestry work.[34]

During the inter-war years, the peasant proprietors tried to reduce their dependence on Boxholm Ironworks. The improved transport

facilities simplified the selling of meat in Kisa or Tranås, but for milk
they were totally dependent on the Ironworks dairies. There was a
general opinion that the works did not pay enough for the milk, and
so in 1931 six farms formed a cooperative dairy in the church village.
This dairy operated for ten years, but there were financial problems,
partly because the Boxholm dairy raised the price for its milk once a
competitor had become established. After ten years the dairy was
closed and thereafter all the milk went back to Boxholm.

A Social Place

One important change during this period was connected with the
greater mobility offered by the new means of transport, and it was
largely the people of Malexander themselves—not Boxholm Ironworks—that managed to utilize the opportunities. Cycle traffic in particular expanded the local labor market and stimulated the
development of the church village. Commercial service was established and developed. Several shops were opened, buses started from
the village, there was a telephone exchange and a little electricity
network. The village also became the center of a growing number of
recreational activities with its new community center and dance floor.
But not everybody was able to take part in the social activities.
Crofters and leaseholders on Boxholm farms lived quite a long way
from the village, and many of them had no cycle.

The population of Malexander continued to decline during the
inter-war years, although at a slower rate than previously. Some thirty
crofts were abandoned, but the area under cultivation remained almost unchanged. The social dichotomy that had arisen in the parish
around the turn of the century, between a company-dominated part
and the rest, persisted between the wars. This can be seen in, for example, the local politics. Of the fourteen people who were nominated
to be chairman of the two most important municipal bodies in
Malexander between 1873 and 1950, not one lived on a leasehold
farm. The same pattern is discernible in the village's social activities,
and schooling, too, contributed to the persistence of the dichotomy.
Almost all the children of peasant proprietors went to the school in
the church village, whereas the children of tenant farmers went almost exclusively to the four schools on the edges.

Those who were tenants of the company farms and crofts remained
strongly dependent on the Boxholm company during the inter-war
period, whereas the peasant proprietors in the central parts of the vil-

Figure 6. Milking maids in Åsbo in the early 20th century (Photography courtesy of Wera Lövgren, Åsbo).

lage became somewhat less so. Buses and lorries gave them an alternative to selling their goods to the works, even if the attempt to run a cooperative dairy failed. But forestry continued to be the most important economic activity and the works remained the most important market outlet. This meant that Boxholm remained Malexander's most important gateway to the wider world.

PHASE 3. MECHANIZATION AND EMIGRATION, 1945–1970

The decades after the Second World War saw comprehensive changes in Malexander, to a considerable extent connected with the spread of a number of new infrasystems throughout the parish. Some of these had been introduced on a small scale before the war, but their more general breakthrough came from the mid-1940s onwards. They were electricity, the telephone and motor vehicles.

New Infrasystems

The advent of electricity had the greatest effect on daily life on farms and crofts. We have noted that a dozen households in the church village formed a distribution association in the late 1920s. But it was not until the mid-1940s that electricity became more widely installed in Malexander. It was expensive to run cables to remote farms and crofts, and electrification was made possible only by the introduction of a government grant in 1944. One condition was that every home in the parish had to be connected. By this time all urban areas in Sweden had long since had electricity, as had large areas of the countryside. Electricity began to be seen as something of a right and for this reason the Government made grants for the installation of electricity in country areas that did not yet have it.

AEG Norrköping began to install electric lines in the parish in November 1944. Within a few weeks all farms and crofts were connected to the mains. Mains electricity provided the homes a substantially wider possibility-space and the extent to which the family could make use of that was a matter of money. Every household installed electric lighting in both the house and the outbuildings, and most of them gradually went on to acquire electrical domestic appliances. Refrigerators, vacuum cleaners and food mixers made work easier for women in the kitchen, and electric motors for cutting wood, trimming hedges and running other machinery saved a lot of labor for the men. Those households that could afford it installed running water with the aid of electric pumps, which meant an enormous saving of labor, especially when supplemented by a washing machine in the house and milking machines in the cowshed. The availability of electricity also made it possible to listen to radio sets plugged into the mains without needing headphones. To put it simply, electricity brought about a revolution in everyday life.

The telephone also became much more widespread after the Second World War, and here, too, the state played an important part. The Swedish Telegraph Office had been granted a de facto monopoly of telephony in Sweden in 1918, and in the decades that followed there was a gradual levelling out of the difference between phone charges in towns and in the country, thanks to a substantial subsidization of telephones in country households. When it became cheaper both to acquire and to use a phone, more and more Malexander homes obtained one. In 1940 a second exchange was opened in the parish and by 1948 the total number of subscribers had risen to 73.

By the end of the 1950s, nearly every home had a phone. The phone became particularly important to women working at home on farms and crofts. They were able to keep in regular touch with friends and family in other places in a way quite impossible before.[35]

Cars also spread rapidly throughout the parish in the 1950s and 1960s, adding greatly to mobility. This meant not only that it became easier to travel to the village for shopping or social activities, but also that the labor market expanded. It became possible to commute by car to work in Boxholm and other places in the area. Many of the large farms also obtained tractors for work in the fields and the forest.

All in all, the spread of new infrasystems meant that households in Malexander acquired a much wider possiblitity-space. Electrical appliances and tractors made many jobs easier in the home, the cow-shed and the fields and meadows, and the phone and the car gave people a previously unimagined range and mobility.

The Mechanization of Forestry

The end of the Second World War marked the start of a period of radical change in forestry. Three changes were particularly important. The first was that charcoal-burning came to an end. The need for charcoal at the works had begun to decrease in the 1930s, and it ended completely in the 1950s when the blast furnace at Boxholm was closed down. The second change was the introduction of power saws at the end of the 1940s. The first models were heavy, expensive and difficult to use, but within a few years it was possible to buy much lighter, cheaper and handier ones. The new power saws and the introduction of piece rates forced up the pace of work and productivity levels. The third change concerned the movement of logs and pulp wood. In the 1950s and 60s lorries and tractors replaced work that had been done with a horse and sledge and log-driving in the streams and across Sommen.[36]

An important precondition for the mechanization of forestry was the building of special forest motor roads, enabling forest workers to be transported to cutting areas with their saws and other implements, and allowing lorries to fetch the logs after felling and take them straight to the sawmill and the pulp mill. During the 50s and 60s roads were built throughout the Malexander countryside as never before or since, and the Boxholm company was particularly active. This road-building was greatly facilitated by the advent of new machines, Cater-pillars, and by the fact that the state gave financial assistance. It is estimated that some 150 kilometres of new forest road was laid during these years, in other words an average of 1 kilometre of forest road per square kilometre! In addition, the road from Malexander to Boxholm was improved and surfaced in the 60s and 70s, not least for the sake of log haulage.[37]

These three changes meant a dramatic reduction in the need for labor in forestry, and that the work became increasingly specialized. Boxholm Ironworks employed a few of the crofters who were most skillful in the use of power saws to work in the forests full-time. The company built a number of modern houses in the church village and encouraged its forestry employees to leave their crofts. There was no longer any point in having them living in the forest when more and more felling was taking place at a few large sites to which the workers could travel by bus or car. From the point of view of the company, the vast majority of tenant farmers and crofters became superfluous. Tenancies were terminated and many farms and crofts were pulled down and fields and meadows were planted with forest. The previous inhabitants were obliged to move, often to towns and urban areas in the region.[38]

The whole character of Boxholm Ironworks changed. Formerly the works had had a diversified and integrated production of iron, forest and agricultural products, with the many freeholders and crofters occupying a central role as suppliers of charcoal, timber and milk to the company's blast furnace, sawmill and dairy in Boxholm. But the local character of the company came to an end in 1965, when Iggesunds bruk, a larger company supplying similar ranges of iron and forest products, bought all the shares in Boxholms AB. With this, the company's landholdings became more specifically geared towards forestry, and a growing proportion of the timber felled was used as pulpwood and hauled by rail to the Iggesund pulp mill, some 600 km to the north.[39]

The Transformation of Agriculture

The changes in forestry had their greatest impact on the parts of Malexander that were owned by Boxholm Ironworks. In these areas all the crofts and most of the farms were abandoned during the 1950s and 60s. In the other parts of the parish, agriculture played a more important part and many peasant proprietors invested in technological modernization during the years after the war. As we have already seen, the availability of electricity meant that many new devices could be installed in stables and cowsheds. Milking machines and refrigeration systems were particularly important. Tractors were also bought by many farms. The light, versatile and flexible Ferguson tractor was ideal for Malexander's stony fields. It could use the same implements as had previously been harnessed to the horse.[40]

The rapid technical transformation of agriculture was given impetus by competition from outside. A new agricultural policy was adopted in 1950s Sweden, designed to improve efficiency and increase yields. Gradually the farms of Malexander parish found it increasingly difficult to compete with the agriculture of the great plains, and in the late 50s and early 60s many farmers gave up. This was a time when there were many jobs to be had in the towns and cities, and regulated working hours in factories and service industries became for many an attractive alternative to arduous and time-consuming labor in farming or forestry in Malexander. Some families were able to continue running their farms because somebody in the family had employment outside the work on the farm.

A Thinning Place

There is an interesting parallel between the periods 1875–1900 and 1945–1970. Both were marked by a speedy introduction of new infrasystems and an unusually rapid decrease in population. The post-war period is the period when the decline in population was more rapid than in any other, dropping from about 800 residents in 1945 to about 350 in 1970.

Initially, the decrease concerned only farms and crofts, mainly on the outskirts of the parish, whereas the church village was not affected. Some forest workers even moved in, occupying new homes in the village. And municipal services in the village improved. An old people's home had been built in 1940, and seven years later a retirement home was built with flats not only for pensioners but also for a district nurse and a home help. In the late 1940s the school board decided to close the four schools on the fringes of the municipality and concentrate all teaching in the village school. A new, modern school building was erected and opened in 1955. For this to work, the local authority had to provide school transport. A school bus brought children in from the outlying countryside every morning and took them home again after school. It must have been a great relief to many children no longer to have to walk long distances every morning and afternoon.

Towards the end of the 1960s the population of the church village also began to fall. As fewer and fewer people lived in farms and crofts in the rest of the parish, the position of the village was undermined. A number of shops shut in the 1960s; the post office was closed in 1967 and the old people's home two years later. Schooling also changed with the introduction of the nine-year compulsory school in 1963. Pupils went to school in Malexander for the first six years and then for the final three to Boxholm, which meant a lot of bus-riding for the children. As amenities in Malexander became more sparse, the reasons for remaining weakened, especially for those who commuted to Boxholm or elsewhere to work.

There may appear to be a paradox in the fact that the decline in population was once again particularly rapid just when a number of new infrasystems became available. These systems brought considerably increased spatial scope to families in Malexander, and meant that at last they had access to the same conveniences as had long been taken for granted in households in urban areas. But the improvements in transport, in particular, also facilitated a mechanization of forestry that greatly reduced the need for labor. From the point of view of the Boxholm company, the tenants on farms and crofts became redundant. The company could maintain a flow of forest products from the parish using far fewer people.

This period also brought a change in Malexander's political status. After the Second World War many municipal amalgamations took place in Sweden at the instigation of the Government and the Riksdag, with the intention of creating larger units that could offer a higher standard of service to their residents. Malexander had been an independent municipality since 1863, but in 1951 it was amalgamated with two adjoining municipalities of similar character to form a single new municipality called Göstringe. This meant a fairly even division of political influence between the three previously independent municipalities. A resident of Malexander became the chairman of Göstringe Municipal Council.

PHASE 4: TRANSFORMATION INTO A LEISURE VILLAGE, 1970–2000

In 1971 there was a new amalgamation of municipalities. The Municipality of Göstringe and another rural municipality were merged with the Municipality of Boxholm. Boxholm was clearly the largest of these three municipalities (in population) and Malexander and its inhabitants had little influence in the new enlarged authority.

The decline in agriculture continued during the last decades of the 20th century. At the turn of the century there were only about a dozen working farms left. Most farmer households had to complement the incomes from agriculture with salaried work and had given up the very work-intensive production of milk. The last dairy cows in Malexander disappeared in 2003. This meant the end of the flow of milk from Malexander, which had been so important to the parish for over a century. But meat was still an export product, and most farms concentrated on raising young cattle.[41]

The large forest landholdings that had belonged to Boxholm Ironworks changed ownership twice in the late 20th century, but were kept together in one company, Boxholms skogar AB. The mechanization of forest work continued in the Malexander forests, both on lands belonging to the company and to individual farmers. In the 1970s the first processor appeared, a machine which could limb trees and cross-cut them, after they had been felled with a power saw. In the 1980s the harvester was introduced, which as well as limbing and cutting could also fell the tree. The gigantic machines were mostly owned and operated by contractors, often working alone and sometimes even at night.

This meant that forestry in Malexander became fully industrialized. The export of pulpwood and timber continued on approximately the same scale as over the past century, but with much less manpower than before. It was largely people from outside the parish who were in charge of this work. The epoch, lasting almost a century, when forestry was the main source of livelihood for most households in Malexander, was definitely at an end.[42]

The population of Malexander continued to decrease in the 1970s, although at a slower rate. By the early 1980s the number of inhabitants was down to just over 250, and the number of children at the school was so low—only 13 pupils in 1982—that its survival was under threat. Because of the distance to Boxholm, the school was allowed to remain open provisionally for a few years, and the trend turned. During the 1980s and 90s the resident population of Malexander had started to rise again. This rise is connected with the gradual transformation of the parish into a leisure village.

Back in the inter-war period, the first summer guests were attracted to Malexander by the beautiful landscape of lakes and dense forests. Dozens of leisure houses were built in the village during this period. But the increased mobility made possible by the car led to a rapid growth in tourism. During the 60s and 70s a total of about sixty second homes were built in the church village and at the same time many farms and crofts became second homes. Camping places opened, together with other amenities for tourists.

At the end of the 1990s weekend cottages accounted for almost two-thirds of the total stock of housing. During the summer half of the year, the population increased manifold, bringing the village to life. Caravans stood closely packed on the camp site. Many of the holiday guests had their roots in Malexander, but there were also a number of visitors from farther afield who had found their way to the village and were coming back summer after summer. Service to summer guests and maintenance of second homes gave employment opportunities to some of the permanent residents. The café, the holiday village, the camp site, the petrol station, the boarding house and the riding school were entirely dependent on the income they could obtain during a few intensive months of summer. But this irregular demand posed a problem for a number of services. For example, the only remaining shop in the village closed down in 2001.

A Commuting Place

The growing number of summer guests brought a fundamental change in the character of Malexander. The previous division of the parish into a central part and an outer part no longer had any relevance, as there were hardly any permanent dwellings in the outlying areas. Instead, the division between permanent residents and leisure visitors and their mutual dependence characterized the place. The flow of tourists into Malexander became a more important source of income than the flows of forest and farm products in the opposite direction.

Life in Malexander was increasingly characterized by two kinds of commuting. Most permanent residents commuted to jobs in nearby towns, and many owners of second houses commuted to Malexander during vacations and weekends. The improvement of roads in the previous decades had stimulated this development and made it is possible to reach Boxholm and Kisa in 20 minutes, and Linköping in an hour. Also, modern communication systems finally reached the village. But as usual, Malexander was among the last regions in Sweden to be hooked up. And several cell phone operators could not provide access. In 2004 a fibre optic network was established in the village. A

Figure 7. Malexander was called the Riviera of Sommen. Postcard from ca 1960. (Photography by Bengt Åkerblom).

home page was set up for the village (www.malexander.se) at the same time containing all the information about activities of various kinds that had previously only been accessible at the notice-board in the center of the village. These new facilities made it easier both for permanent and part-time dwellers not only to work in Malexander but also to participate in local activities, and in the future the dividing line between these two categories is likely to become more diffuse.

INFRASYSTEMS AND RURAL TRANSFORMATION

In this final section I shall summarize my analysis of how infrasystems have helped to change life in Malexander by explicitly discussing the questions that I formulated in the introduction. In my description I have concentrated on the way in which, largely due to the advent of infrasystems, Malexander was gradually embedded into a wider economy, with Boxholm as the major gateway to the outer world. I have discussed how possibility-spaces were widened by different systems, what kind of flows they enabled, and which actors controlled those flows. But so far I have hardly touched on some of the other questions posed in the introduction.

How and by whom were new infrasystems built?

The state, in particular government authorities in charge of railways, postal services, the telegraph and the telephone, electric power and road-building, has played an important but, from the point of view of the people of Malexander, often relatively invisible part in the building of infrasystems. The railway that was built through Boxholm and Tranås was one of the many main lines that the Swedish state and its specialist body, the National Railways Board, not only financed but also built and operated during the second half of the nineteenth century. With the exception of Belgium, Sweden was the first country in the world where the Government took such an active part in railway-building. The purpose from the state's standpoint was to stimulate an economic development of the regions through which the railway was laid, to arouse "the great power and rich assets that lie dormant in the bosom of the land," to quote the words of one of the leading advocates of this policy. The state's very active role in railway-building became a model for its involvement in the construction of later infrasystems.[43]

The post office that opened in Malexander in 1875 was a part of the national postal system that was built up by the government post office administration, and the sub-postmaster at Malexander was paid by this body. When the first telephone exchange was opened in Malexander in 1922, it was also the state telegraph service that extended the lines and engaged the telephonist who connected the calls. And when from the late 1920s onwards the people of Malexander were able to start listening to radio broadcasts, it was transmissions from the government transmitter in Motala, built and driven by the state telegraph service, that they were able to pick up on their sets.

The active part played by the state was made particularly clear to the people of Malexander when electricity came in 1944. The Government financed the building of a distribution network in Malexander, and demanded that every farm and croft should be connected up. This meant that this system and its many uses suddenly became available to every household, as manna from heaven, even if of course they had to pay for the current they used.

Where road-building is concerned, the role of the state has varied over time. Starting in the mid-nineteenth century, the state gave contributions to urgent road construction projects through the National Road Board. This was the form of support that Boxholm Ironworks managed to obtain for the building of the road between Boxholm–Malexander–Kisa in the early 1890s. In 1944 the National Roads Administration was set up and assumed responsibility for the building and maintenance of public roads in Sweden. The great majority of all roads in Malexander are however what are generally called private roads, built and maintained by private property owners or cooperative roadowners' associations.

The state has thus played a very important role in the extension of infrasystems in Malexander, and especially in the building of the most capital-intensive networks. From the end of the nineteenth century onwards there gradually developed a view that infrasystems were a fundamental right. In accordance with this view, the state had a duty to ensure that households in rural areas also had access to these systems on the same basis as people in urban areas. But it is also apparent that Malexander was among those districts that were the last to gain access to many systems. When the development of such systems was of direct benefit to the Boxholm company, the company has applied positive pressure. Road-building in the 1890s is an example. But in other cases, a little local authority like Malexander has not carried much clout with the politicians in Stockholm.

There have also been other players who have contributed to the establishment and operation of infrasystems. The steamer traffic on Lake Sommen was particularly important to Malexander. The *Carl Johan* was owned and operated by a shipping company in which local landowners were shareholders. Boxholm Ironworks bought steamships that it used for its own goods transport across the lake. Bus traffic on the road from Boxholm to Malexander and Kisa, which took over the role of steamboat traffic during the inter-war period, was also owned and operated by local private entrepreneurs. Taxi traffic has been run by individuals who have owned cars.

The municipality has long played a subordinate role in the building of infrasystems in Malexander. There is a big difference here by comparison with towns and urban areas where municipal bodies have had a central role. It is only during the post-war period that the municipality has actively built, for example, water and sewerage systems in the church village in Malexander, and organized school transport for schoolchildren and also other public transport. But even today the municipality has a relatively small role in infrasystems compared with that in urban areas.

Who used the infrasystems and controlled the flows through them?

As should have been clear from what has already been said, Boxholm Works has since its inception as a limited company in 1872 played an important part in the utilization of the new infrasystems. It was the management of the company that realized the new opportunities offered by the main line for the expansion of the Ironworks' activities and that organized a large-scale exploitation of forest resources in the surrounding region with the aid of steamers and of an enormous amount of labor on the part of the local population. They made an active contribution to the development of local competence in the haulage of timber and charcoal by horse and sledge along winter roads. And they organized transport of milk and dairy products to and from the three dairies that they set up in the area. In the years after the Second World War, they also played an important part in the building of forest roads.

The Boxholm company bought up most of the farms in Malexander and thus acquired very direct control of large parts of the flows of goods out of Malexander. But they also influenced to a high degree the freeholders and crofters who were not bought out. These, too, often chose voluntarily to supply charcoal, timber and milk to the company. The Malexander area became an integrated part of the Boxholm company's production system, and Boxholm became the major gateway for flows of goods out of Malexander. It is tempting to call the authoritative general manager Wilhelm Wettergren a system builder, and he certainly organized an impressive production system in the region. But he was not a system builder in the sense that Thomas P. Hughes uses the concept. The Boxholm company did not build and operate the infrasystems that it used. These were for the most part built and financed by the state.

What happened to the people and relations between them?

The introduction of new infrasystems has greatly influenced people's everyday lives. The first wave of infrasystems that rolled over the area in the mid-1870s led to a situation in which the men of the district devoted much of the winter to work in the forest, while the women were more autonomous in caring for farms and crofts in the men's absence. But it also gave many Malexander families the option of leaving the district and moving elsewhere. The new forms of transport during the inter-war years—particularly the cycle and the bus—gave the men of the area, in particular, a greatly increased mobility within the village and also to two urban areas nearby, Boxholm and Kisa. The second great wave of infrasystems after the Second World War did a lot to ease many of the tasks carried out by both women and men, and the car, the phone, the radio and, later, TV gave considerably greater mobility and range.

The systems have also influenced relations between people. At the start of the period there was a social division in Malexander between crofters, freehold farmers and a handful of privileged families on the estates. When Boxholm Ironworks began to buy up many Malexander farms around the turn of the century, this led to an additional social division, between tenant farmers under the Ironworks, who nearly all lived at some distance from the church, on the one hand, and the remaining population on the other. This social division came to be reinforced and maintained in several ways. For example, Boxholm Ironworks painted all the tenant farms and crofts in a characteristic style with red walls and yellow windows, so that it would be clear which farms belonged to the works. School attendance also contributed to the division. As schoolchildren usually attended the nearest school, the children of leaseholders went to the four schools around the edges of the district, while the children of peasant proprietors were for the most part enrolled at the school in the church village. The increase in mobility during the inter-war years contributed to the growth of a much more vigorous social life in the village. That social activity slowly declined in the post-war period, partly as a result of the sharp decrease in the population, partly because radio and TV induced more people to stay at home in the evening.

The spread of car ownership in the 1960s led to increased use of weekend cottages and a new social division between permanent residents and visitors. These are two groups which are strongly dependent on each other for their income and their comfort, respectively. The new groups have also made their mark on clubs and associations. The church choir, to give one example, consists during the winter half of the year of a small but loyal group of singers who practice often and sing at church services. In the summer the choir is augmented by many holidaying visitors and is able to put on summer concerts, during which the choir fills the whole church with their singing and with their listening families.

What happened to the cultural identity of the inhabitants?

Before 1875, Malexander was a rather isolated place. Most people only left their farms for the Sunday sermon, and they identified themselves firstly with their farm and secondly with their parish. The opening of a postal office and later on the introduction of telephones and broadcasting increased the news flows to Malexander and the contacts with the outside world, not least with those former inhabitants who had chosen to emigrate from the parish. Furthermore, the schools played an important role in bringing a national consciousness to the children. Gradually the inhabitants of Malexander obtained additional identities linked to their province and country. They became increasingly aware of Malexander´s strong linkages to the outer world, and that these connections were largely controlled by the Boxholm Ironworks. This dependency on the Ironworks fostered a certain resentment vis-à-vis Boxholm, which was amplified when Malexander became a part of the municipality of Boxholm in 1971.

Not only the permanent residents identify themselves with Malexander; many of the owners of second houses also have strong and long-time relations to the place, and have a certain cultural identity with it. For many of these part-time residents, Malexander has become a firm base in their lives, a place to which they and their relatives return summer after summer. Quite a few even choose Malexander as the place where they want to be buried.

What happened to the landscape and to the local resources?

The first wave of infrasystems made it possible to exploit and export forest resources that had previously been inaccessible. The Boxholm company started felling in the woods of Malexander on a large scale, transforming the former virgin forests into well tended and managed woodland, in which a succession of different silvicultural philosophies have repeatedly altered the appearance of the forests. The agricultural land changed gradually. The dairies established by the Boxholm company around the turn of the century encouraged the local farmers to go in for dairy cows and to try and enlarge their grazing areas. Many ditches were dug to drain wetlands and bogs, and at the start of the century farmland reached its maximum extent, making up 18% of the total land area. At this time there was roughly twice as much meadow as arable land. Between the wars the larger farms went over from three-crop to two-crop rotation, making the arable land relatively much more significant. The area of arable land remained roughly constant despite the fact that a number of small farms and crofts were abandoned. But the area of meadowland declined sharply.

Since the war there have been extensive new changes to the landscape. During the 1950s and 60s agriculture saw rapid changes and decline. Despite the introduction of tractors, milking machines and many other electric appliances, it became harder for the farms in the district to compete with large farms on the plains. More and more farms were abandoned and trees were often planted on fields and meadows. The proportion of grassland and arable land has gradually diminished and by the mid-1990s it made up only 3% of the land area. In the course of a century, in other words, the area of open landscape has been reduced by more than 80%.

An intensive building of forest roads permitted an increasing mechanization of forestry. Felling sites became greater in extent and more often resulted in large clear-felled areas. The reduced need for labor in the forest led to the closure of many forest crofts. The forests were filled with roads but emptied of people. Or, in the telling words of an old resident of Malexander: "There used to be narrow paths between the homes and people on the farms. Now there are wide forest roads but no people."[44]

What are the differences between Malexander and other rural areas, e.g. the mid-West, studied by Cronon?

There is a clear similarity between Malexander and, for example, the forest districts in Michigan described by Cronon, namely that in both cases it was players with capital and knowledge at a distance from the area who realized the value of the natural resources and showed initiative in exploiting them. Boxholm Ironworks therefore came to play an important role in the transformation of the Malexander district, which is reminiscent of that played by the timber purchasers of Chicago regarding many places in the forests of Michigan. And which sawmill owners and wholesalers in cities along the coast of northern Sweden played for many inland areas of northern Sweden, to make a different comparison.

But there is also a fundamental difference. Malexander was not a sparsely populated "frontier" like that in Michigan and the inland areas of northern Sweden. On the contrary, it was a district that was very densely populated relative to its ability to produce food. The size of the population constituted an important resource for Boxholm Ironworks when it wished to exploit the forest lands in Malexander. The crofters on farms that the company purchased were urged to remain in place and supply charcoal to the works. And as tenants of the farms that were purchased, the company often recruited enterprising and industrious people from the district. This means that the works obtained relatively cheap labor in the winter, whereas in summer these people worked on their own account. The forest workers could live at home and eat their own food, even in the winter season, unlike those in Michigan and northern Sweden who as a rule lived in log huts for long periods. This was a great advantage to the workmen themselves, and it also meant that the works did not have to pay large advances to forest workers to support them while they were working.

It is this character of a densely populated rural area that is also the explanation of the apparent paradox that when infrasystems permitted an exploitation of hitherto unutilized natural resources in Malexander, and at the same time improved the possibility of support, a significant emigration began. In the forest districts of Michigan and the inland areas of northern Sweden, on the other hand, exploitation of the forests contributed to significant immigration to what were formerly almost uninhabited lands.

However, in the second half of the 20th century, these areas too have experienced a sharp decrease of their population mainly due to the mechanization of forestry made possible by the advent of infrasystems. Most farms have been abandoned and replaced by planted forests. The general patterns of development have thus been rather similar in many forest areas in different parts of Sweden and in the northern parts of the U.S., and are heavily influenced by their roles as producers of raw materials in global commodity flows. But within these general patterns, each place, just like Malexander, has experienced a unique history of its own.

NOTES

1. William Cronon, *Nature's Metropolis. Chicago and the Great West.* (New York, 1991), 93.
2. There are of course also other books that have provided inspiration. Primarily I would like to mention Fernand Braudel's book *Civilization and Capitalism, 15th–18th Century, Volume III. The Perspective of the World* and Manuel Castells's *The Information Age. Economy, Society and Culture, Volume I: The Rise of the Network Society.* Braudel analyzes the role of leading merchants in cities like Venice, Antwerp and Amsterdam in the creation of a world economy based on flows of commodities and information provided by sailing ships across the oceans. Castells focuses on developments triggered by the ICT-revolution in the 1970s, which he argues has given rise to a new spatial logic, which he denotes "flow-space." Like Cronon, Braudel and Castells analyze the relations between places interconnected through infrasystems, and they all primarily focus on actors in the centers of such networks.

3. This article is largely based on the work of a local folklore society (Hembygdsförening), which has done a lot of research on many aspects of Malexanders history. Much of this research is presented in an edited book: Malexander Hembygdsförening, *Malexander—sockenbor berättar*, [Malexander—The People of the Parish Tell Their Story] (Mjölby, 1999). Another important source is the official history of Boxholms bruk written by a former managing director: Elis Wettergren, *Boxholms aktiebolag, 1872–1947* (Uppsala, 1947). Furthermore, together with my wife I have done interviews and field studies for another article on Malexander that we wrote together, Arne Kaijser and Ulrika Sax, "När systemen kom till byn" in Dag Avango and Brita Lundström (eds.), *Industrins avtryck. Perspektiv på ett forskningsfält* (Eslöv, 2003). The present article is partly based on this article and for more detailed references, the reader can consult this article.

4. This section is largely based on: Elis Wettergren, *Boxholms aktiebolag, 1872–1947* (Uppsala, 1947).

5. Ibid., 133.

6. Ibid., 137.

7. Elis Kågén, "Sjöfart på Sommen," in Elis Kågén (ed.), *Mellan Sommen och Vättern, Andra samlingen* (Linköping, 1970), 211.

8. Wettergren, 96; *Malexander—sockenbor berättar*, 165f.

9. Wettergren, 91f.

10. Ibid., 136.

11. Ibid., 137.

12. Ibid., 139ff; *Malexander—sockenbor berättar*, 165f.

13. Wettergren, 127–130.

14. Wettergren, 136–143.

15. Kågen, 207–221.

16. *Malexander—sockenbor berättar*, 211–21.

17. Ibid., 168–72; Wettergren, 136f.

18. *Malexander—sockenbor berättar*, 31–33, 38.

19. Diagram from ibid., 38.

20. The course of events in Malexander followed a pattern widely seen in the Swedish countryside; see for example Mats Morell, *Jordbruket i industrisamhället 1870–1945. Det svenska jordbrukets historia, del 4* (Stockholm, 2001), 76–79.

21. Wettergren, 138.

22. Ibid., 164ff.

23. Svante Lindqvist (ed.), *Center on the Periphery: Historical Aspects on 20th Century Swedish Physics* (Canton, MA, 1993).

24. *Malexander—sockenbor berättar*, 172f.

25. Ibid., 250ff.

26. Ibid., 172f.

27. Ibid., 176ff.

28. There is a table showing the number of occupants of the various farms in Malexander in 1891 and 1994 in ibid., 39.

29. Ibid., 176ff.
30. Ibid., 60
31. Cf. Morell, especially pp. 84–108, 142–156.
32. *Malexander—sockenbor berättar*, 43–57.
33. The concept "horse mechanization" is from Morell, 288.
34. *Malexander—sockenbor berättar*, 23–57.
35. Ibid., 222ff and interviews with Margareta Malgeryd and Gurli Eriksson. Cf also Lena Andersson-Skog, "De osynliga användarna. Telefonen och vardagslivet 1880–1995" in Pär Blomkvist and Arne Kaijser (eds.), *Den konstruerade världen. Tekniska system i ett historiskt* (Stockholm, 1998), 277–98.
36. Sten Nordquist, *Strövtåg i Boxholms skogar. Bruksskog i utveckling* (Boxholm, 2001), 125ff.
37. Ibid.; *Malexander—sockenbor berättar*,171.
38. Ibid., 34ff.
39. Nordqvist, 172ff, 219ff, 234.
40. *Malexander—sockenbor berättar*, 49ff.
41. Ibid., 49, 79f.
42. Ibid., 61ff.
43. This section is based on Arne Kaijser, *I fädrens spår. Den svenska infrastrukturens historiska utveckling och framtida utmaningar* (Stockholm, 1994), chapter 5. Quote from p. 11.
44. Quotation from *Malexander—sockenbor berättar*, 167f.

PART III

Moving to Macro-Places

Caution sign placed in the dried out river-bed of the Lule river in northern Sweden. Photography by May-Britt Öhman, July 2004.

ON VISIBLE PLACES AND INVISIBILIZED PEOPLES

Swedish State-supported Hydropower Exploitation of Indigenous Peoples' Territories

MAY-BRITT ÖHMAN

"When the water came closer to the village, some of the villagers tried to write to the government to protest. But it was already too late. The water was already there. We had to move."[1]

Mr. Magomba Meshack, a married man and father of seven children, is one of the displaced inhabitants of the "Great Ruaha Power Project." He and his family lived in the (Old) Mtera village, submerged since the early 1980s by the Mtera Dam. The Mtera Dam became the largest artificial lake in Tanzania when it was finalized and reached its full supply level for the first time in 1984.[2] The dam was constructed with the objective of giving the downstream Kidatu hydropower plant a capacity to produce 200 MW.

Before the era of the Mtera Dam, Mr. Meshack was a farmer cultivating the fertile land surrounding the old village. Once the water threatened his village, Mr. Meshack was one of the fortunate few. Because he could show proof of his land tenure, the family was paid one of the highest amounts of compensation that any of the displaced villagers could receive. Even so, the 5000 Tanzanian shillings they received was not enough to pay the cost of constructing a new house for the family. Since then his wife and the children have lived in the

I wish to thank Camilla Sandström for comments, suggestions and valuable information as well as great hospitality during my field trip in Dikanäs and Daningen, Sapmi. I also wish to thank Sunna Kuoljok (Ajtte Museum) and Linda Ekmark (Västerbottens Museum) for valuable information regarding photos and Sapmi.

"Italian camp," a housing area within the Mtera Dam construction site. After construction was finalized, the consulting firm Sweco handed over control of the regulation reservoir to the Tanzanian electricity company, Tanesco. Mr. Meshack then was one of five lucky villagers who managed to obtain employment at the dam.[3]

The fates of Mr. Meshack and his co-villagers of the (Old) Mtera village are similar to those of many people living close to large-scale hydropower projects around the world. Nevertheless, there are differences in the power relations between the different affected riparians, depending on the historical and societal context. The Mtera Dam, and the whole Great Ruaha Power Project, was a state project, with massive financial support from development assistance donors, the Swedish Development Assistance Agency, Sida, and the World Bank. The local inhabitants seem to have been unable to exert any influence whatever, and attempts at resistance were futile. When the water came, they had to move.

The Swedish development assistance participation in the financing of the Great Ruaha Power project is not too surprising. Sweden is a major hydropower nation. Early in the 20th century the Swedish State Power Board became the main actor within the sector, which it has remained ever since. Unlike the initiators of the Great Ruaha Power Project, the power companies, whether private or state enterprises, have in many cases been forced to enter into extensive negotiations and have had to pay compensation to landowners.[4] Yet, the state-supported hydropower exploitation in Sapmi, in the northern parts of the Swedish territory, shows many similarities to the project on the Great Ruaha River. Sapmi stretches across the borders of Sweden, Norway, Finland and Russia, and has been inhabited by the Sami ethnic group for many thousands of years. When Sweden and the neighboring states colonized the territory, and the borders were demarcated, the Sami became citizens of different nation states. Then, as hydropower construction began in the area, any land and water not judicially proved to belong to a private person was considered to belong to the Swedish state, which was free to initiate industrial activity.[5] The inhabitants, many of them belonging to the Sami ethnic group, descendants of Sami or mixed with Sami, suffered severe losses. A particularly severe blow was inflicted on a traditional Sami economic activity, reindeer-herding, an activity already under heavy pressure from industrial mining and forestry.[6]

Drawing on the experiences of the Sami minority in Sweden, and specifically along the Lule River, this essay is an attempt to argue that the Swedish state has established a "technoscientific paradigm" in re-

Figure 1. The large Suorva regulation dam on the Lule River, turning five small lakes into one inland sea. The tour boat takes tourists from the village Vaisa to the Ritsem tourist station. When water is low in the dam, people can cross over by foot. Photo: May-Britt Öhman, July 2004.

lation to large-scale hydropower. The term is related to the notion of the "big dam era" described by, amongst others, Sanjeev Khagram.[7] The term "technoscientific paradigm" is used in an attempt to describe the basis for the big dam era, being an elaboration of Thomas Kuhn's "scientific paradigm." According to Kuhn, scientific thinking and performance are predestined by a historical social context. The scientific paradigm gives the framework for the interpretation of an examined object, as well as the methods and theories to be used in the interpretation and the definition of "good science."[8] Kuhn describes how a crisis may appear within a paradigm, when discoveries show an anomaly between the existing theory and nature. The crisis may be resolved in three different ways—"normal science" may prove capable of handling the problem—and then everything reverts to "normal." The problem may persist, and be labelled, but then be perceived as a result of a failure within the scientific field and set aside for future generations to deal with. In a few cases, the anomaly may lead to an overthrow of the paradigm, after a period of paradigm war.[9]

Dealing with large-scale hydropower, which raises a complex mixture of social, economic, technological and scientific issues, I have opted to use the term "technoscience" because it signals the nonexistent boundaries between science and technology, and furthermore allows a closer look at the design of the artifacts produced. The term also indicates the multitude of actors involved in the making and is inspired by the work of Donna Haraway.[10]

The main pillar in the technoscientific paradigm, in relation to hydropower, I define as the view that equates large-scale hydropower plants with progress. This view sets the basis for related science and technology—technoscience performed—and helps to exclude opposing views and knowledge. One precondition of the persistence of this specific technoscientific paradigm is access to land areas for reservoirs and rivers. In order to achieve this, the state makes use of territory inhabited by peoples (often indigenous and/or ethnic minorities) without a strong voice. In the process of planning the large-scale hydropower project, these peoples are "invisibilized," which can be seen as a kind of problem-solving within the paradigm. There are, as the term "technoscience" indicates, other important components of the paradigm, in terms of technoscience as well as of social and economic factors. However, my main focus in this essay is on the land question and related issues. This technoscientific paradigm, with its inherent view of the land, I argue, has been exported to Swedish-funded development assistance projects in Tanzania.[11] This essay, however, will concentrate on the Sapmi case.

TAKING AND INUNDATING THE LAND OF INDIGENOUS PEOPLES

In the 20th century, large-scale hydropower construction and electricity became a model for energy supply, a symbol of progress and of modernization.[12] Hydropower is, as the name indicates, energy taken from water. Electricity is provided by using the potential energy of falling water, from a higher level to a lower one. A problem within hydropower production is that electricity has to be consumed immediately; it cannot be stored. The consumption of electricity varies over 24 hours, over the year and over long periods, depending on a number of climatic, economic and political factors. The demand does not correspond to the natural flow of a river. All rivers have their own unique flow of water, depending on climatic and environmental context. The solution to the problem is to save the water in reservoirs, and to release it according to the need for electricity.[13] The larger the hydropower plant, i.e. the greater its capacity measured in megawatts, the larger the water storage facility—the regulating reservoir—has to be. In consequence, hydropower plants with a high capacity demand large reservoirs. Or at least this is the technical solution that has come to prevail throughout the 20th century.[14]

The creation of the reservoirs has a number of serious negative impacts on the local inhabitants. Land is inundated, to various degrees. The inundation results not only in a loss of land for agricultural and pastoral activities, but also in chemical pollution, and, depending on the environmental context, often in fatal waterborne diseases.[15] The regulation of the water is in itself troublesome to local inhabitants. In Sweden, with its cold climate, water regulation in winter affects snow and ice tracks on frozen lakes and rivers. Furthermore, the change of the exploited landscape may also lead to gender-related changes in economic activities.[16]

Large-scale hydropower generation thus causes numerous kinds of environmental, social and health hazards to those in the area where it takes place. Yet, when it comes to large-scale hydropower exploitation in "remote areas," i.e. areas far from the central decision-making institutions and inhabited by people who have few opportunities to make themselves heard in political arenas, the hazards are easily disregarded, invisibilized, as are the affected people themselves.

With the big dam era that started in the 20th century, power companies, construction companies, governments and financiers within the development assistance area tended to share a common view of the land where the projects were to take place: the land belongs to the state. In most cases, indigenous people/ethnic minorities living in an area for centuries or even thousands of years have been treated as though they do not have a right to stop or influence major hydropower projects. Nor have they been acknowledged the right to generous financial compensation. In her thesis on the negotiations preceding displacement of indigenous people for the construction of a hydropower dam in Mexico, Inga Lill Aronsson has described the land inhabited by indigenous people as being considered "empty" by the dam developers.[17]

The main issue discussed in this paper is thus the relations between the state and the people living in the land to be inundated. The state in this case is represented mainly by the State Power Board, but other state authorities are also mentioned.[18] As a model for understanding how opposition from the affected people in Sapmi was met by the Swedish state, I use the term "invisibilization." States may make use of violent measures to stop any opposition to a state project—such as torture and imprisonment of opponents, but "softer" measures may also be used. One "soft" strategy is to deny affected people access to a national political agenda, moving the cases to different courts and thus depoliticizing the issue.[19] A further step is to belittle and play down the damage inflicted upon a certain group of people within a framework of official rhetoric and historiography. The term "invisibilization" has mainly been developed within theories on gender, to refer to the phenomenon of social and economic activities performed by women being neglected, declared unimportant or even ridiculed.[20] However, the concept can also be used to define peoples of (internally) colonized territories, as well as people without strong voices or influence.[21] Using the term "invisibilization" reflects how the affected people are turned into "non-actors" by the decision-makers. One important connotation of the term "invisibilization" is that the peoples affected by hydropower development are not actually invisible—they are "invisibilized." That is, the failure to see the affected people is a matter of choice, not a miscalculation. There is, furthermore, an attempt to avoid meeting the affected peoples on their own terms, designed to reduce and/or make it possible to ignore their demands.

The NIMBY (Not In My Back Yard) syndrome is a term used to describe the often fierce local opposition to environmentally hazardous industrial activities, considered necessary for the public good or for the benefit of a whole nation.[22] Opposition to hydropower exploitation conducted by a state company in the name of progress and for the alleged benefit of a whole nation could be cited as a perfect illustration of the NIMBY syndrome. However, the NIMBY syndrome assumes a state in which there is space for opposition. It also assumes that affected people are informed of the project plans and their consequences, have enough skills to deal with judicial processes, and have the time and organization to make their voices heard. Finally, and maybe most important, for the resistance to be successful, the people affected have to be considered the rightful owners of the land to be inundated and damaged. When it comes to large-scale hydropower exploitation, or other industrial exploitation, in "remote areas," it seems appropriate to describe these areas as a sort of "nobody's back yard." The ones objecting and protesting are unimportant, they are "nobodies."[23]

A SWEDISH TECHNOSCIENTIFIC PARADIGM FOR
HYDROPOWER CONSTRUCTIONS IN SAPMI

"We have not been able to avoid damages for the inhabitants along the river, for the Sami, for the conservation of nature nor for the interest of recreation. The issues raised have, however, to a large extent, been resolved through negotiation and one might even say on the best of terms."[24]

The above quotation is from the speech made by the then Swedish prime minister Mr. Tage Erlander, at the inauguration of the Messaure Dam on the Lule River in 1963.

The Lule River is today the most hydroelectrically developed river in Sweden. The first hydroelectric plant was inaugurated at Porjus in 1915.[25] Construction of the first stage of the great reservoir at Suorva, upstream from Porjus, took place between 1919 and 1923. Since then the Suorva Dam has been enlarged three times, to its present level and size.[26] Over the years, the Lule River has been made into an energy-producing factory, with fifteen hydropower plants and a total installed capacity of 4350 MW, or an annual output of 13.6 TWh. The Lule River alone now produces about a fifth of all the electricity from hydropower in Sweden.[27] Yet, more than eighty years after the first hydropower constructions in Sapmi, there has still been very limited academic research into the effects of the displacement of the people, many of them Sami whose major economic activity and livelihood was reindeer-herding.[28]

The basis for the introduction of the big dam era, and thus the technoscientific paradigm, in Sweden has been described by the historian Eva Jakobsson.[29] In her thesis, Jakobsson has identified a specific group of actors, whom she calls "hydropower developers." They were engineers who owned hydropower companies, leaders in the Swedish state hydropower production, consultant engineers in the water development area, and water rights lawyers who campaigned and won the battle that paved the way for large-scale hydropower construction in Sweden at the beginning of the 20th century. Prior to 1918, the complete harnessing of a river was prohibited by law, and thus no large-scale hydropower plant could make use of the water according to the demand for electricity. With the new Water Act, the principle of "reasonable use" was established. If the "benefit" of the regulation could be proved three times greater than the damage, engineering projects and water regulation would be allowed. One important tactic

Figure 2. The Lule River is no longer a river but a series of reservoirs, forming a staircase: Dry river bed downstream of the Ligga hydropower plant. Photo: May-Britt Öhman, July 2004.

of the hydropower developers in achieving their objective was to de-politicize the controversial issue of water regulation. The hydropower developers managed to shift the decision-making process from the political agenda to special water courts. These water courts were staffed not only by lawyers, but also by technicians, and thus a highly political issue was handed over to technicians and bureaucrats. Against this background, large-scale hydropower construction could take off; the "industrialization" of the Swedish rivers, as Jakobsson describes it, could start.[30]

The industrialization of the rivers was dependent on another important factor, the financing of the hydropower projects. At the start of the 20th century, hydropower plants in Sweden were built mainly by private companies. As the potential of the rivers of the northern part of Sweden was discovered, the State Power Board, established in 1909, became the prominent player, and paved the way for far bigger investments, technological development of transmission lines and consequently large-scale projects.[31] The hydropower exploitation of the northern parts, in Sapmi, took off with furious haste. It was part of a national strategy to make use of the dormant resources of northern Sweden.[32] Initially, exploitation did not meet with any serious protests, although the national conservationist organization, the SNF, and the national tourist organization, the STF, made their voices heard from time to time. Sami people protested, the first organized protest of any size starting in the 1950s, in the Sami national organization, SSR.[33]

By the early 1960s, the opponents of large-scale hydropower construction managed to get themselves onto the national political agenda and to assemble political support to slow down the harnessing of certain rivers.[34] Still, they did not manage to completely stop further hydropower exploitation until the 1990s. Only in 1993 did the Swedish parliament pass a law that stopped further hydropower exploitation of a number of Swedish rivers.[35] All the major rivers rising within and flowing through the land of Sapmi, except three, are now regulated.[36]

SAPMI—A NON-EXISTENT LAND?

As mentioned above, protest and resistance against hydropower exploitation has come from the Sami people and the SSR, in particular. Yet, until today, there has been very little research into the impact of hydropower on Sami culture and livelihood. To understand why, it is important to recognize the depiction of Sapmi as a "remote area," an "empty land," a "terra nullius" or "nobody's back yard."

Sapmi is the Sami name for the area populated by the Sami people.[37] The area stretches over four states, Norway, Sweden, Finland and Russia. As ethnic categorization is not allowed in Sweden, Norway and Finland, and as it is difficult to establish who actually is a Sami, an exact number is impossible to give. The majority of Sami live in Norway, while in Sweden there are an estimated 20,000 to 40,000 Sami.[38] The term "Sapmi" has not gained official recognition. In the Swedish language, the north-western part of Sapmi within the Swedish territory has been known as "Lapland." The name dates back to the 16th century, while the demarcation on the western side, towards Norway, was settled in the 18th century. However, "Lapland" does not have any administrative function, merely a symbolic one. Nor does "Lapland" correspond to "Sapmi." Neither does the area denoted by the other name that has become a Swedish designation for the vast Swedish territory north of the River Dal, "Norrland" (corresponding

to about 2/3 of the whole of Sweden today). Directly translated into
English, this means "north land."[39] The name given to the area is in itself of interest, as it represents a view of the land as being far removed
from the centers of power in the Swedish capital, Stockholm, and the
southern parts. "Norrland" is a remote area, unfamiliar to the majority of the Swedish people living outside it.[40] When I use the term
"Sapmi," it is to emphasize the perspective of a person familiar with
the area and with a personal historical relation to it, as well as to
protest against the connotations of the terms used in Swedish.[41]

The inhabitants of Sapmi, the Sami, have lived here since long before the Swedish state was founded. Archeological research bears witness to a territory, not of wilderness, but full of economic activity
going back thousands of years.[42] The Sami people were never an exotic group, foreign to others. Researchers have pointed out that
the area consisted of a mixture of ethnicities, generally categorized
into Sami, Swedish and Finnish. Intermarriage and economic exchange were common. Until the early 20th century, peasants of ethnic
backgrounds other than Sami had reindeer that were tended by Sami
reindeer-herders, who earned extra income through this arrangement.[43] With the establishment of the Swedish state under Gustav
Vasa in the 16th century, a state-conducted colonization of Sapmi
began. Along with the wish to establish Swedish control over the territory at this early stage, there was a view of the area as a prosperous
land to develop for the benefit of the Swedish nation. A number of
scientific explorations of the area and of its inhabitants have been
made by outsiders since the 18th century. In many cases, the Sami
have been depicted as closer to nature than to civilization, and different ideas on how they should be developed—or on the contrary kept
in their "natural state"—have even been discussed on a national level
by the Swedish Riksdag.[44] One important issue has always been the
land rights of the Sami peoples versus the Swedish state, an issue that
still remains unresolved in the 21st century.[45] One concrete example
of the problems occurred when the union between Sweden and Norway was dissolved in 1905 and the frontier between the two countries
was closed for the traditional grazing of reindeer. The reindeer used
to migrate freely between the two countries for pasture. When the
pasture in Norway was restricted, the area within the Swedish territory became too small to feed all the reindeer. Certain Sami families
were then forced by the Swedish state to move southwards, and to integrate with other Sami villages. This was problematic for many reasons; not only did the incoming Sami feel that they were intruding on

Figure 3. Reindeer and Samis resting on the frozen lake Malgomaj during spring migration, the sledge *raid* going from the coast zone towards the mountains, some time between 1913 and 1925. The people in the photo are probably south Samis. Photo: Lage Dahlberg/Västerbottens Museum.

other Sami, but there were also differences in language, as well as in ways of managing the reindeer.[46]

CONSTRUCTING THE SUORVA DAM AND NEGLECTING THE SAMI

The Suorva Dam was first constructed as the reservoir regulating the Porjus hydropower plant. The area in which the dam was planned to be constructed had actually already been protected from exploitation, as it had been declared a national park in 1909. Furthermore, the area had earlier been assigned to the Sami, by the Swedish law on reindeer pasture of 1898, primarily for reindeer-herding and related activities.[47] However, the strong economic interest of the State Power Board in obtaining permission for hydropower exploitation led to its receiving approval for the project. Among the Swedish authorities that were asked to express their views on the proposed venture was the Royal Swedish Academy of Sciences (Academy of Sciences). The

Academy replied in 1917 that regulation would damage the area, and reduce its value as a natural environment. However, the Academy of Sciences also stated that the benefit to the national economy would be such that it could not oppose the plans.[48] Other bodies that were consulted were the Norrbotten County Administrative Board, and the National Board of Agriculture. Both stated that there might be a negative impact on the Sami people in the area, but that this should not be allowed to put a stop to the project, in view of its great national importance. On the strength of these opinions, the State Power Board appealed two years later to the water court for the right to construct a dam at Lake Suorva. In the appeal, the State Power Board claimed that the landed properties that would be affected belonged to the Swedish state and were located above the geographical limit for cultivation. Thus, as this land was located in "uninhabited territory, unused for agricultural or industrial purposes," there was no other holder of legal rights than the state.[49]

In the 1950s, the recently established national association of Sami villages and Sami organizations, SSR, started to protest against the regulation of the water. In 1953, the SSR wrote to the Swedish Government, demanding that profit from the hydropower plants in Sapmi should be distributed among Sami peoples, in the form of funds for education and research. The SSR also encouraged Sami people to be active in the judicial process, and to be skeptical and cautious regarding the short-term compensation promised by the State Power Board. Yet, the demands and proposals from the SSR were left unheard by the Swedish state representatives. For instance, in the instructions for the establishment of the state hydropower enquiry in Norrland, the Sami and their reindeer-herding activities were not mentioned.

In the report presented two years later by the commission, the issues were still not mentioned.

Moreover, the state inquiry commission on electric power of 1943, which published its main report in 1954, although touching upon the hydropower exploitation and its impact in Norrland, did not mention the Sami and their reindeer-herding.[50]

"INVISIBILIZATION" BY THE STATE POWER BOARD

Thirty-seven years after the first regulation of the river at Suorva, Mr. Åke Rusck, the then General Manager of the State Power Board, expressed his views on hydropower exploitation in Sapmi at a conference on the future of the administrative district of Norrbotten.[51] In his paper, Mr. Rusck told a story of how the State Power Board first entered "pure wilderness," to build the Porjus hydropower station.[52] Mr. Rusck continued by stating that Sweden had a great advantage in its access to harnessable waterfalls "of which most are located in Norrland" at a low cost.[53] The Lule River would become the most productive river in Sweden, providing "12.5 billion kWh per year."[54]

Besides the high figures for the Lule River's energy potential, Mr. Rusck's address is full of verbal images of the future, of how the State Power Board would bring wealth and progress, by means of large-scale hydropower exploitation in "Norrland," to both the region and the whole country. In the reprint of the speech, the Messaure Dam on the Lule River, at that time under construction, is pictured together with a sevenfold image of the Cheops pyramid in Egypt. The subtitle reads: "The dam at Messaure will have a volume corresponding to seven Cheops pyramids."[55] At the end of his speech, Mr. Rusck referred to the cost of the exploitation for protection of the environment and tourism. He stated that the development would improve the prospects for tourism, through the construction of "better communications."[56] There was no mention whatever of the Sami as an ethnic group or of their dependence on traditional economic activities that were damaged by large-scale exploitation.[57] The "local inhabitants," though, are mentioned, as Mr. Rusck stated that a "few" of them would have to move, but that their losses were to be fully covered:

> I will not deny that damage often occurs—people have to move, homes are abandoned. It is of course not enough to claim that the water law ensures more than full compensation for this. The problem is not only economic, it has also a human aspect. The State Power Board also tries in various ways to alleviate this dislocation—whenever the person concerned so wishes, we try to help him to a new estate. [. . .] On the other hand there will be quite a few people that will have to leave their homes on account of these new hydropower constructions in the Lule River.[58]

By the 1980s, the harnessing of Sweden's rivers had run into fierce opposition and there were at the time a number of campaigns against further hydroelectric power in Sweden.[59] Probably in response to the criticism, the State Power Board produced five folders dealing with different aspects of the impact of hydropower on different economic activities and the environment. In the folder dedicated to the problems of the Sami people entitled "Hydropower and Reindeer Management," it is stated that there are a number of negative impacts of hydropower exploitation—but that there are also positive effects, such as the construction of roads that facilitate transport to the benefit of the local inhabitants and their economic activities.[60] Furthermore it is also declared that the State Power Board and the Swedish state have paid for the construction of fences, specific enclosed work areas, reindeer-herder cottages, slaughterhouses, roads, migration routes and bridges for the animals, as well as paying compensation for the damage:

> The power companies have aimed to give full indemnity for damage and intrusion through a combination of measures and financial compensation. [. . .] The power companies have now settled the issues of damages and intrusion with most of the Sami villages affected by hydropower exploitation.[61]

One example is mentioned: the Sirkas (Sirges) Sami village which, according to the folder, received SEK 11.7 million in 1983 for damage to its fishery, and SEK 10 million in 1984 for damage to reindeer-herding.[62] Together with the amount of money that is mentioned, a statistical perspective is used to show that reindeer-herding has not suffered any great losses. In six diagrams and a table, it is stated that the actual number of reindeer has not gone down as a consequence of hydropower exploitation.[63]

Finally, by the end of the 1990s, the State Power Board had developed an environmentally friendly profile. In the age of the Internet, the strategies and achievements in "life cycle analysis," environmental protection, and risk analysis of the company are presented on the State Power Board home page in downloadable documents.[64] In this setting, the issue of reindeer-herding had almost completely vanished. On the company website, the term "reindeer-herding" is mentioned once, when referring to the effect of hydropower exploitation on the activities:

> Hydropower exploitation affects agriculture, forestry and reindeer-herding in different ways. The most concrete is the loss of land and damage to land due to inundation for water regulation. On the other hand the water flow becomes more uniform with less risk of flooding.[65]

The same sentence is found in the document on life cycle analysis of electricity production by the State Power Board.[66] In the environmental declaration on the Lule River,[67] a number of risks—environmental and health hazards—related to hydropower dams and power plants during and after construction are discussed. Yet this document says nothing about risks or health hazards faced by reindeer herders.[68] On the main Internet site, describing how hydropower is adapted to the environment, hydroelectricity is referred to as an "economic, renewable resource which is in principle free from environmentally damaging depletion."[69]

It is important to stress that during the 20th century the State Power Board has never been unaware of the Sami people's situation. On a number of occasions, the State Power Board has actually financed scientific investigations of the Sami villages and Sami traditional activities, the first as early as 1922.[70] The State Power Board has thus had several indications of the severe negative impact on reindeer-herding and related activities.

In this section I have mentioned a few examples stretching from 1917 to 2004 of how Sapmi has been considered deserted, sparsely populated, and roadless and how the damage inflicted upon the "few inhabitants concerned" has been considered fully compensated. Another phenomenon I have identified is the invisibilization of the ethnic group of the Sami, their traditional activities, their attempts to protest and their culture. Hydropower exploitation has, by the state representatives, been considered a way of developing the area. The examples are collected mainly from the small amount of existing research literature dealing with the impact of the hydropower industry on Sami activities and traditions, together with a brief analysis of the views argued by the State Power Board. It is obvious that more research is needed in this area, but I consider it possible to argue that the examples mentioned are indicators of a technoscientific paradigm promoted by the Swedish state, with the "invisibilization of the Sami people" and their land rights being used as a way to overcome a severe anomaly in the paradigm.

VIEWPOINTS OF THE "INVISIBILIZED"

As a contrast to the view adopted by the Swedish state and presented in the preceding part, I will now deal with the issues from the viewpoint of the "invisibilized": roadlessness, compensation and cultural values and how these things have a great impact on their "back yard."

First of all, the issue of roadlessness is of great interest, as it is a good example of the way in which perspective changes with the beholder. Sapmi has never been a roadless land or a "pure wilderness."

I have already described the inhabitants of Sapmi and their long history. Furthermore, the Lule River, desired by the State Power Board for the production of electricity, is assumed to have received its name from the Sami language, Lulij-jokko, meaning the river of the Forest Sami or the river of the Easterners.[71] The Lule River was for many centuries a central highway between two seas, the Atlantic Ocean and the Gulf of Bothnia, and as such an important cultural and economic link between eastern and western societies.[72] As a consequence of the hydropower exploitation, transport has been made much more difficult, both in summer and in winter. The former water link between the two seas has been replaced by a bitumen road built to give access to the different construction sites. The river is nowadays no longer a river but instead a series of reservoirs, like a staircase. At the hydropower sites, the water disappears underground for some kilometers, leaving the old watercourse bare, like an open wound in the landscape. In wintertime, the ice that used to provide safe and easily accessible roads is damaged by constant variation of the water level, in response to the peak demands of electricity in the Swedish cities.

In a book based on her academic investigation of the impact of the Suorva regulations on the people of the Sirges Sami village, Gertrude Hanes describes the issue of the ice tracks:

> One of the problems that came after the second and third regulation of the river at the Suorva Dam was the deteriorated ice conditions. There was so much water on the frozen lake and the cracks in the ice and the hanging ice by the shores made it difficult to reach land. The sledges broke and reindeer were hurt. Sometimes reindeer fell into the cracks and they had to worry all the time in case the children fell too. There was no longer pasture to be found for the reindeer during their yearly migrations, as the islets were flooded. They had to start bringing reindeer moss to feed them during the migration. As there was no pasture in the valley they had to move faster and so the reindeer herd was moved separately from the family. The reindeer herd was moved partly over the mountains instead of through the valley all the way as before. The protected areas where the reindeer cows used to calve were gone and they had to use sites for calving in the border mountains and on the Norwegian side. After the third regulation boats were more often used when moving up to Vaisa. They continued to move with the *raid* to Vaisa early in spring, but then took the sledges back to Suorva and went by boat back to Vaisa. In the autumn boats were used to go to Suorva, and then they

Figure 4. Amma and Sunna Spik, Lule Samis of the Sirges Sami village, Aktse-Njunjes group, during spring migration, heading for their summer residence by the lake Sitojaure of the Lule River system, 1946. Photo: Lars Hermodsson/Ajtte.

waited for the ice to be able to continue with sledge *raid* to the winter pasture. Downstream from Suorva the delayed freeze and water on the ice were the biggest problem. Finally they gave up, one by one, and started moving by boat on open water even below Suorva. The younger men who did not have a family stayed behind and watched the reindeer. Then the men, the family fathers, went back and took the reindeer herd down. Eventually some families chose to stay in Porjus in spring and wait for open water, while only the reindeer herders followed the reindeer westwards. Thus, the reindeer herd and the family were separated during both spring and autumn migrations and the activity became something that men dealt with. The time when the whole family and the reindeer lived close together had gone.[73]

The ice road problem discussed above is one very important consequence of the hydropower exploitation in Sapmi. The State Power Board is obliged by agreements to strengthen the ice tracks. There also exists an agreement that when required by reindeer herders, the

State Power Board has to make measurements to establish whether the passage at a certain location is safe or not. However, in real life, the request to the State Power Board has to come in one or two days before passage, while reindeer-herding is not predictable work. The herders cannot know if the reindeer will be at that specific location or not, two days later, which means that this option is never used and thus is irrelevant.[74]

Not only have the traditional paths for the annual migration been damaged by the hydropower exploitation, the working environment of the reindeer herders has also been affected. The animals have to be collected at certain times and the herders sometimes have to cross the reservoirs in order to succeed. These reservoirs are dangerous at any time of the year. When the water is open, the size of the reservoirs makes them windy and thus difficult to navigate. In winter the ice is fragile and treacherous due to the changing water levels, caused by peak demands. This has helped to make reindeer-herding one of the most dangerous economic activities in Sweden.[75]

The damaged snow roads have led some Sami villages to start moving their reindeer by truck, which has had a great economic impact.[76] The activity has become a lot more expensive, and even led some to give it up.[77] Amft has presented a calculation of costs from one informant:

"If the transport, at a low estimate, costs around sixty crowns [SEK] per reindeer, and a family needs about 700 animals to manage their economy, and if you then consider that all reindeers have to be transported back to the summer pasture, the final cost will be around 84 000 crowns for the reindeer transport alone every year."[78]

For reindeer owners with small herds, these costs are likely to make the whole enterprise much too expensive. Amft refers to how this, in combination with the fact that the Swedish legislation assumes as a norm that the reindeer herder is a man, has led to a masculinization of the activity, as few women have been able to continue it.[79] Yet another complication of the damming of the Suorva was that the trees were not removed before the flooding. As a consequence, the fishery, which is an important ancillary occupation for the reindeer herders, has been disturbed as, for instance, nets are damaged by the wood debris.[80]

Financial compensation was, as mentioned, promised by the State Power Board and representatives of the Swedish Government as good enough to make up for the losses.[81] Before, during and after the exploitation of the great rivers in Sapmi, judicial proceedings actually took place on a number of occasions, but in several cases the Sami minority did not manage to make their voices heard. Amft refers to an informant who has described how he was treated during the judicial proceedings in his village in the 1940s. The villagers had to go to court to get any compensation at all. According to the informant, it was more difficult for the reindeer-herders to be compensated for their losses. The informant stated that the Swedish farmers received a lot more compensation, that every word they said was believed, while the Sami reindeer-herders were not believed.[82]

The issue of categorization of ethnicities also forms a part of the hydropower exploitation. The category "farmers" had already earlier been restricted to non-Sami. By the early 20th century, the Swedish state had introduced the "Lapp should be Lapp" policy, with clear racist overtones. Sami were considered to have specific characteristics, which made them suitable only for nomadic reindeer-herding. If they were to turn to anything else, they would in this view sink into wretchedness. Thus, it was considered important to keep them as far from the Swedish culture as possible. Sami who were not reindeer-herding were to be considered Swedish. Through the Swedish state policy of "Swedification," they had been transformed into Swedes.[83] As Amft describes, the ones that already had been "Swedified," the peasants and landowners, were again separated from the reindeer-herders, and received better compensation than those without any formal land ownership.[84]

When it comes to the cases in which financial compensation has been paid, the Sami reindeer-herders have had to pay a great part of it back to the Swedish state, in the form of taxes. One example is presented by Mr. Lennart Pittja, who tells the story of how he was compensated in 1984, but then ten years later was asked to pay taxes on the compensation. This meant that he had to pay back half of the compensation to the state.[85]

One issue rarely touched upon by the representatives of the Swedish state is the emotions and cultural values of the displaced Sami peoples. Lennart Pittja has expressed some of the emotions, speaking of sadness over the intrusion into the landscape of the power lines. He stated that one consequence is that the children no longer have to learn to find their way in the terrain via traditional knowledge, because instead they just follow the power lines.[86] Other examples of these emotional and cultural values, and the sense of being expelled from one's own land, are expressed in the poetry of Paulus and Inger Utsi, of Vaisa (and the Sirges Sami village). Paulus and Inger Utsi started writing poetry in response to the regulation of the Suorva Dam in the 1940s. I will deal further with this in the following section.

REVISIBILIZATIONS OF THE SAMI IN CONSEQUENCE OF HYDROPOWER EXPLOITATION

Although the hydropower exploitation of the rivers in Sapmi was based on the invisibilization of the Sami people, the very same phenomena has led in certain respects to revisibilizations of the Sami.

First of all, according to Patrik Lantto, Sami reindeer-herders who were not capable of resisting the constructions and expropriations focused instead on organizing themselves to receive as much financial compensation as possible. This has led to an ethnic mobilization amongst the Sami, which has had a concrete outcome in the establishment of the Sami parliament in the 1990s.[87] Secondly, as a result of the early investigations of Sami culture at the time of the hydropower development of 1922, and specifically since 1942 and the passing of the law on ancient monuments that forced the exploiter to finance archeological investigations before any larger industrial project, thousands of ancient Sami habitations have been discovered along the harnessed rivers of Sapmi.[88] There are, however, two peculiar aspects to these investigations. Research on Sami settlements has shown that the early investigations were quite faulty.[89] Sami settlements, graves and holy sites are now inundated, and lost forever to any future research. The results of the investigations have also led to a debate on historical ownership. The question has arisen of who the peoples were that used the settlements that were discovered and who made the rock-carvings near, for example, the power stations in Nämforsen and Stornorrfors.[90] The State Power Board, which is responsible for the maintenance of the rock-carvings in Stornorrfors, presents them not as a Sami heritage, but as a national heritage without any specific ethnic background.[91]

Thirdly, Vaisa, by the Suorva Dam, is one of the villages within the Sirges Sami Village, which has been used by the State Power Board in support of the assertion that compensation has been adequate. The view of the affected people, though, seems quite different when interpreted through the poetry of the poets Paulus and Inger Utsi.[92] Their poetry writing, starting in the 1940s, and published from the 1960s, became an emotional response to the exploitation of the area. The poetry of Paulus and Inger came to serve as a sort of wake-up call to Sami people, expressing the sense of loss of ancient traditions and cherished landscapes.[93] Newspapers have written about the poetry, and Paulus appeared on radio and television and at concerts. Some of the texts were also set to music and as such they have reached Sami youth as well as an international audience.[94]

Molested village

In anguish breathes the village
Fleeing in terror from new waters
   The water rises to the dwellings
Toiling to move the tents
smooth slopes, green pastures
   they must leave with heavy hearts
Hard the roads they wander
bearing the weight of their burdens
to a new place to live
Without mercy the Sami
are driven to move
   Landscape, streams, lakes
   become deeps, sounds, open seas
   their bounds unseen
The lake's high water draws nigh
the molesting winds do blow

Ráfehisvuođa siste

Ráfehisvuođa siste vuoigná siida
   ođđačàzi baluin báhtaraddet
Dulvi bàisa oruhagaide
Váigatvuođain gođiid sirdit
jalges dievaird, ruonas gittiid
   losses mielain fertejit guođđit
Golgangeainnut váivin šaddet
lossa noađđebáttiid vuolde
ođđa báikai saji dahkat
Árpmukeahtta sápmelaččat
rissejuvvun johtimii
   Luonddueanan,jogat, jávrrit
   fávlin, nuorrin, áhpin šaddet
   oaidnemeahttun ravddat
Jávrri dulvi lahkanadda
ráfehisvuođa biekkat bossut

Old Vaisa

In the heat of the summer you shone
like a star on the mountainside
High mountains rising to heaven
You were the loveliest of villages

Warmly you embraced
every soul in your bosom

Little blue lakes
have become a sea
Light breezes are now strong winds
the waves dash hard

Boares Váisa

Geassebáhkkan don báitet
degu násti várregilggas
Alla várit áimmu ravddas
Čábbasmus leat siidan leamaš

Liekkusvouođainat vuosta váldet
juohke sielu iežat fátmai

Jávrražat mat alihahtte
leat mearran muktašuvvan
Biekkažat leat ožžun vuoimmi
bárut doidet garrasit

Paulus and Inger Utsi

These two poems are by Paulus and Inger Utsi, from the second collection, Giela Gielain, 1980. The poems are originally written in the North Sami language and via Swedish translated into English.[95] The first poem is called "Molested Village," and describes how the people of a village flee the rising waters in fear, carrying their old homes, how former creeks and lakes turn into an open sea—the Suorva dam. It says that there is no mercy for the Sami, they are forced to move. The second poem is a tribute to their village "Old Vaisa," which was inundated by the Suorva dam.

Recently, the State Power Board has on two specific occasions contributed to the revisibilization of the Sami culture. In 1998, the inauguration of a new technical innovation, the "Powerformer," at its first location at Porsi Power Station on the Lule River had a Sami cultural contribution. A woman dressed in Sami costume performed a yoik, standing on top of the Powerformer unit.[96] The State Power Board has also invited artists to make a painting inspired by Sami symbols called *Uvssat davás*, in the Sami language meaning "the Doors to the West," at the Akkats Power Station on the Lule River. Both these events can be and have been questioned: do they represent further exploitation of Sami culture by the Swedish state, treating the Sami as a kind of cultural curio, or are they actually a step towards the revisibilization of Sami identity.[97]

CONCLUSION

In the 20th century, electricity produced in large-scale hydropower plants has become a symbol of progress and modernization. This period has been referred to as the "big dam era." This essay discusses the issue of states taking land from indigenous people/ethnic minorities for the construction of large hydropower projects. I have discussed this using the term "technoscientific paradigm," setting the limits to the kind of technoscience—science and technology realized—that is considered good technology/science. The paradigm also gives guidelines on the kinds of objects that are investigated, and the kind of questions that are asked in the investigations, excluding other views. I have identified as the main pillar in this technoscientific paradigm, as it is related to hydropower, the view of large-scale hydropower plants as synonymous with progress. An important condition for the survival of the technoscientific paradigm is the access to territory on which the large dams may expand and within which the waters may be regulated. In Sweden, these areas are inhabited by the

Figure 5. Uvssat Davás—"the Doors to the West," work of art on the Akkats hydropower station on the Lule River. Photo: May-Britt Öhman, July 2004.

indigenous Sami people, many of whom have been performing a nomadic pastoral activity (with yearly migrations) highly dependent on the water/ice/snow routes. Their land Sapmi, or Lappland/Norrland, as it is called in Swedish, was considered by the Swedish state representatives "empty" or "sparsely populated." The inhabitants were considered to have few or no formal rights to the land on which they depended for thousands of years, because the territory was claimed by the Swedish state.

Earlier studies have shown how a part of the success in establishing the basis for the technoscientific paradigm (and thus the big dam era) within Sweden, access to land, was due to the strategy of refusing affected people access to the political agenda by transferring the conflicts to water courts. A further step was for the water courts to deny the Sami people their right to extensive compensation, which could have placed a heavy cost burden on the projects. In order to achieve its objective, the Swedish State Power Board, the main actor in the hydropower exploitation in the area, has used a strategy of "invisibilization" of the people living in Sapmi, and of the Sami with traditional economic activities in particular. Throughout the whole big dam era of the 20th century, the Swedish state has had to deal with the Sami through different authorities as well as through scientific investigations. There has also been organized opposition from Sami groups, particularly since the 1950s. Yet, the choice of the state representatives has been to invisibilize the Sami instead of fully recognizing their specific rights as traditional landholders. To avoid a NIMBY syndrome, which could have proved costly to the state and even contributed to a severe contestation of the technoscientific paradigm, the affected peoples have been invisibilized, turned into "nobodies," and seen their land treated as "nobody's back-yard." As a result, the hydropower exploitation has led to far-reaching consequences for the Sami way of living, economically as well as socially and culturally.

However, although hydropower exploitation has had a severe impact on traditional Sami activities, as well as on Sami cultural values, there is also another perspective that has emerged in this essay. The response of Sami peoples to the extensive hydropower exploitation and the inadequate compensation has led to a certain revisibilization of Sami culture in Sweden.

Yet, the main issue, an anomaly that could undermine the prevailing technoscientific paradigm in Swedish large-scale hydropower exploitation, the question of land ownership, has remained unsolved and is left for future generations to deal with.

NOTES

1. Personal interview with Mr. Magomba Meshack, Mtera hydropower station, November 17, 2000.
2. Dick Johansson, *Mtera Reservoir: Ecology of a new man-made lake in Tanzania* (Stockholm/Sweco, 1985), 2.
3. Magomba Meshack.
4. See Eva Jakobsson, *Industrialisering av älvar: studier kring svensk vattenkraftutbyggnad 1900–1918* (Göteborg, 1996); Evert Vedung and Magnus Brandel, *Vattenkraften, staten och de politiska partierna* (Nora, 2001); Jonas Anshelm, *Vattenkraft och naturskydd: en analys av opinionen mot vattenkraftutbyggnaden i Sverige 1950–1990* (Linköping, 1992).
5. Sverker Sörlin, *Framtidslandet: debatten om Norrland och naturresurserna under det industriella genombrottet* (Stockholm, 1988); Gertrude Hanes-Nutti, *Samernas rättsliga ställning vid de tre första Suorva regleringarna*, un-

published (Dept of History, Umeå University, 1988); Lars Elenius, "Selma Lagerlöf och Norrland: Nationella idealbilder i Nils Holgerssons underbara resa" in Ann-Katrin Hatje (ed.), *Sekelskiftets utmaningar: Essäer om välfärd, utbildning och nationell identitet vid sekelskiftet 1900* (Bjärnum, 2002), 15–41, 30ff.; Kjell-Arne Brändström, "Bilder av det samiska i den svenska 1800-tal-slitteraturen" in K-A Brändström (ed.), *Bilden av det samiska: Samerna och det samiska i skönlitteratur, forskning och debatt* (Umeå, 2000), 51–87, 75.

6. Agriculture had earlier been a complementary activity, with exchanges between reindeer-owning peasants and Sami reindeer herders. This relation changed in the early 20th century, due to Swedish state policy, and instead agriculture also became a competing interest. See for instance Åsa Nordin, "Samerna och jordbruksbefolkningens renar—om skötesrensystemet i början av 1900-talet" in Peter Sköld and Patrik Lantto, *Den komplexa kontinenten: Staterna på Nordkalotten och samerna i ett historiskt perspektiv* (Umeå, 2000), 173–198. Recently activities within tourism and ecologism have also become competitors for the territory. Hugo Beach, "Negotiating nature in Swedish Lapland: Ecology and Economics of Sami Reindeer Management" in Eric Alden Smith & Joan McCarter (eds.), *Contested Arctic: Indigenous people, industrial states and the circumpolar environment* (Seattle, 1997).

7. According to Sanjeev Khagram, it was during the 1950s that large dams had become the leading technology for water resource development in the world, Sanjeev Khagram, *Dams, democracy and development—transnational struggles for power and water* (Ann Arbor, 1999), 6ff. A "large dam" is usually defined by ICOLD (International Commission on Large Dams), as "one measuring 15 metres or more from foundation to crest—taller than a four storey-building." Patrick McCully, *Silenced Rivers. The Ecology and Politics of Large Dams* (London, 1997), pp 2.

8. Thomas S. Kuhn, *The structure of scientific revolutions* (Chicago, 1962).

9. Ibid.

10. Donna J. Haraway, Modest_Witness@Second_Millenium.FemaleMan©_ Meets_OncoMouseTM (New York, 1997), 3.

11. May-Britt Öhman, "On Visible Places and Invisible Peoples in Sweden and in Tanzania," in J. Tempelhoff (ed.), *African water history: transdisciplinary discourses* (North-west University, Vanderbijlpark, in press, 2005).

12. See for instance Ann Danaiya Usher (ed.), *Dams as aid: a political anatomy of Nordic development thinking* (London, 1997); McCully; Sanjeev Khagram, *Dams, democracy and development—transnational struggles for power and water* (Ann Arbor, 1999); Thomas P. Hughes, *Networks of Power: Electrification of Western Society, 1880–1930* (Baltimore, 1983); Arne Kaijser, *I fädrens spår . . . 'Den svenska infrastrukturens historiska utveckling och framtida utmaningar'* (Stockholm, 1994); Jakobsson; Mats Fridlund, *Den Gemensamma Utvecklingen: staten, storföretagen och samarbetet kring den svenska elkrafttekniken* (Stockholm, 1999); Staffan Hansson, *Porjus: En vision för industriell utveckling i Övre Norrland* (Luleå, 1994); Lars Thue, "Electricity

Rules: The formation and development of the Nordic Electricity Regimes" in Arne Kaijser och Marika Hedin (eds.), *Nordic Energy Systems: Historical perspectives and current issues* (Canton, Massachusetts, 1995).

13. Jakobsson defines regulated rivers as technical systems. Jakobsson, 20ff.

14. The capacity of the hydropower plant depends not only on the water available, but also on each technical component of the construction, as well as the daily management, including maintenance of the technical components, of the plant. The "Powerformer" is an example of how a technical innovation can increase the capacity of an existing hydropower plant. Personal communication, Kjell Isaksson, Technical manager at the State Power Board, Porjus, June 21, 1999; Personal communication, Florence Gwang'ombe, Research engineer at TANESCO, Kidatu, November 16, 2000. See also for instance Peter Fröst, Hans Bergström, Camilla Freby and Pernilla Hanssen, "Water power—improvement of existing power stations and prospects for new plants: Powerformer TM" ALSTOM Power, Västerås, 2001, http://www .energikontor-so.com/Localaction/Powerformer_V%C3%A4xj%C3%B6_ 010119.PDF, (October 28, 2004).

15. See for instance E. Goldsmith and N. Hildyard (eds.), *The Social and Environmental Effects of Large Dams*, (Camelford, 1984); Philip M. Fearnside, "Environmental impacts of Brazil's Tucuruí Dam: Unlearned lessons for hydroelectric development in Amazonia," Environmental Management, 2001:3, http://springerlink.metapress.com/app/home/contribution.asp?wasp= f62clce4wn4vthdb3j3y&referrer=parent&backto=searcharticlesresults,4,6;jo urnal,1,1;linkingpublicationresults,1:100370,1 (January 31, 2005) 377–396.

16. Andrea Amft, *Sápmi i förändringens tid: en studie i svenska samers levnadsvillkor under 1900-talet ur ett genus- och etnicitetsperspektiv* (Umeå, 2002), 43–44, 69–99. Since the outbreak of the fatal virus HIV and the disease AIDS the relation between hydropower construction and prostitution has been recognized by a few researchers dealing with the epidemic. See Joseph Decosas, " 'HIV and Development,' Plenary presentation at the XI International Conference on AIDS, Vancouver, 1996," http://www.ccisd.org/ang/a_ documents/a_decosas.htm, (September 16, 2004).

17. Inga Lill Aronsson, *Negotiating involuntary resettlement* (Uppsala, 2002), 28. See also Gustavo Lins Ribeiro, *Transnational capitalism and hydro politics in Argentina: The Yacyretà High Dam* (University Press of Florida, Gainesville, 1994), 8ff, 86ff; Thomas R. Berger, *Village Journey: The report of the Alaska native review commission* (New York, 1985); Thomas R. Berger, *Northern Frontier Northern Homeland: The report of the Mackenzie Valley Pipeline inquiry* (Toronto, 1977). In an analysis of the relation between the modern western state and indigenous people within its borders in Canada, Norway and Australia, Noel Dyck argues that the state always has had a leading part in the exploitation of the land and resources. Noel Dyck, "Aboriginal Peoples and Nation-States: An introduction to the analytical issues" in Dyck (ed.), *Indigenous peoples and the Nation-State: 'Fourth World Poli-*

tics in Canada, Australia and Norway, Social and economic papers 14 (St. John's Memorial University of Newfoundland, 1985), 190–235, 1–26.

18. The state authorities or representatives of the state, besides the State power company mentioned in this essay, are county administrative boards, state commissions and inquiries, the Royal Academy of Sciences, water courts and the National Board of Agriculture.

19. Jakobsson. I will discuss the "depoliticization" further in the part that follows.

20. See for instance Valerie Frissen,"Gender is calling: Some Reflections on Past, Present and Future Uses of the Telephone," in R. Gill & G. Keith (eds.), *The Gender-Technology Relation* (London, 1995); Carolyn Hannan, *Promoting equality between women and men in bilateral development cooperation. Concepts, goals, rationales and institutional change. Part two: Empirical studies in two sectors in Tanzania: Household water supplies and health development* (Lund, 2000), 4 ff.; Anita Nyberg, "Feministiska ekonomer och feministisk ekonomi—exemplet nationalekonomi" i *Kvinnovetenskaplig tidskrift*, 2001:3/4, 5–24; Michèle Martin, "Struggling to take part: A feminist approach to Telecommunications" in Ewa Gunnarsson and Lena Trojer (eds.), *Feminist voices on gender, technology and ethics* (Luleå, 1994), 177–191.

21. See May-Britt Öhman, *Kidatu vattenkraftverk i Tanzania—vatten och elektricitet från kolonialtid till biståndsepok* (Stockholm 2003), 10.

22. See for instance Michael E. Kraft and Bruce B. Clary, "Citizen participation and the NIMBY syndrome: public response to radioactive waste disposal," *The Western Political Quarterly*, 1991:2, 299–328; Euston Quah and K.C. Tan, *Siting environmentally unwanted facilities: Risks, trade-offs and choices* (Cheltenham, UK, Northampton, MA, 2002).

23. Only in a few cases has opposition from indigenous people towards hydropower exploitation been fierce, although even then not very successful in the end. The alliance between Indian environmentalists and local inhabitants of the Narmada rivers is an exception, as is the opposition of Sami people in Norway when fighting against the Norwegian state over the River Alta. May-Britt Öhman, *Världsbankens miljöpolicy: specialstudie i fallet Narmada*, unpublished paper (Dept. of Pol. Sciences, Uppsala University, 1993); Nils Roar Saeltun, "The Alta hydropower development: Hydropower vs environmentalists and indigenous interest groups—the great showdown," *International Water History Association Conference Papers*, Bergen, Norway, 10–12 August 2001; Robert Paine, Ethnodrama and the 'Fourth World': The Sami Action Group in Norway, 1979–1981 in Dyck (ed.), 190–235.

24. The then Swedish prime minister at the opening of the Messaure Dam on the Lule River, August 31, 1963, quoted in Hans Andersson, *Längs stigarna: En vandring i tid och rum i Lule Älvdal* (Värnamo, 1992), 10.

25. Hansson, 272; Nils Forsgren, *Porjus: Pionjärverket i ödemarken* (Stockholm, 1982), 76.

26. The second and third regulations took place in 1937–1941 and 1942–1944. The last regulation took place in 1966–1972. Tore Nilsson, *Fyra gånger Suorva- en tillbakablick på regleringsarbetena i Suorva* (Stockholm, 1972), 10; Nils Forsgren, Suorva: *Dammbygget i vildmarken* (Stockholm, 1987), 123.

27. Vattenfall, "Vattenfall AB Elproduktion certifierade miljövarudeklaration för el från Lule Älv, 20020315," www.vattenfall.se/downloads/produktion/VF_epd_lule_alv.pdf, (February 2, 2005).

28. Two of the very few academic studies on the specific issue of the Sami people and hydropower exploitation are by Gertrude Hanes-Nutti, who has described the judicial proceedings in which the Sami protested at the first three regulations of Suorva, as well as the impacts on the Sami of Vaisaluokta and Änonjalme: Gertrude Hanes-Nutti, *Karesuandosamer i Vaisaluokta och Änonjalme: Dislokationens och vattenregleringarnas inverkan på deras näringar och hushållning*, unpublished (Dept. of History, Umeå University, 1987); Hanes-Nutti, *Samernas rättsliga ställning.* Two doctoral theses dealing with Sami questions discuss the issue: Patrik Lantto, *Att göra sin stämma hörd: Svenska samernas riksförbund, samerörelsen och svensk samepolitik 1950–1962* (Umeå, 2003), 91ff. Amft, 43–44, 69–99.

29. Jakobsson.

30. Ibid., 251ff.

31. Jakobsson describes it as the establishment of a "Swedish system," Jakobsson 65–109. Fridlund has described the close cooperation in the development of the electricity technology between the State Power Board and the company ASEA. See also Vedung and Brandel, 24f.

32. Sörlin, 94ff; Hansson; Vedung and Brandel, 35f; Lantto, *Att göra sin stämma hörd*, 90ff; Amft, 44.

33. Lantto, *Att göra sin stämma hörd*, 99f.

34. Vedung and Brandel, 32ff, 60–68; Anshelm.

35. Vedung and Brandel, 397, 416.

36. Four rivers in Sapmi are supposedly protected from hydropower exploitation. However, one of them, the Vindel, has a confluence with a regulated river, the Ume, and thus its status as an unexploited river has been questioned.

37. See for instance http://www.fjallen.nu/sapmi/index_en.htm or http://www.sametinget.se/sametinget/view.cfm?oid=1238, (September 30, 2004).

38. See Sami Parliament, "The Sami People—A People in Four Countries," http://www.sametinget.se/sametinget/view.cfm?oid=1238, (October 26, 2004); Sven Hassler, P. Sjölander, A.J. Ericsson, "Construction of a database on health and living conditions of the Swedish Sami population," in P. Lantto and P. Sköld, *Befolkning och bosättning i norr—Etnicitet, identitet och gränser i historiens sken* (Umeå, 2003), 107–124.

39. The 25 traditional provinces called *landskap*, in Sweden, of which Lappland is one, have long been without administrative functions. Instead, Sweden is divided into a number of regional administrations, "*län*," which have county

administrative boards. Of these, five are found within the borders of "Norrland": Västernorrland, Jämtland, Gävleborg, Västerbotten and Norrbotten. Västerbotten and Norrbotten together contain "Lapland." At the same time, all these five *län* lie wholly or partly within Sapmi. See Lennart Lundmark, "Nu prövas samernas rätt till land och vatten," *Hela Jorden*, 1999:2, 7–9; T. Hägerstrand and U. Sporrong, "Landskap," *Nationalencyklopedin, 12* (Höganäs, 1983), 95; K. Lundholm, "Lappland-historia," *Nationalencyklopedin, 12* (Höganäs, 1983), 132.

40. Sörlin, 12ff, 21ff.
41. My own family historical background displays quite a typical mixture of ethnicities of "Swedish" people in the north. It is a combination of Forest Sami, late and early immigrants from southern parts of Sweden as well as natives of Tornedalen. I grew up in Luleå, at the delta of the Lule River, and spent numerous summers in Skällarim, by the Little Lule River, with my maternal grandparents.
42. According to archeological researchers, Sapmi has been inhabited since the last ice age, i.e. for about 9000 years. However, there is an ongoing debate as to whether the inhabitants were Sami, "Scandinavian," or a mixture of the two. See Evert Baudou, *Norrlands forntid—ett historiskt perspektiv* (Höganäs, 1992), 151ff, 157; Tim Bayliss-Smith and Inga-Maria Mulk, "Rock engraving from the mountains in Laponia, Sweden," *Folklore* (Tartu, 1999) 11:70:70–112, http://haldjas.folklore.ee/folklore/vol11/sami.htm (October 1, 2004).
43. Elenius; Nordin, 174f.
44. See for instance Karin Granqvist, *Samerna, staten och rätten i Torne lappmark under 1600-talet. Makt, diskurs och representation* (Umeå, 2004); Roger Kvist, "Swedish Sami policy, 1550–1990," in Roger Kvist (ed.), *Readings in Sami history, culture and language. 3* (Umeå, 1992); Sörlin, 33f; Ulf Mörkenstam, *Om "Lapparnes privilegier": föreställningar om samiskhet i svensk samepolitik 1883–1997* (Stockholm, 1999); Göran Bäärnhielm, *I Norrland hava vi ett Indien: Gruvdrift och kolonisation i Lappmarken under 1600-talet* (Stockholm, 1976); Anne-Li Lindgren, "Att utbilda barn till ett nationellt medborgarskap. Folkhemmet och föreställningar om 'vi' och 'de andra,' " *Historisk Tidskrift*, 2002:1; Lennart Lundmark, *'Lappen är ombytlig, ostadig och obekväm': Svenska statens samepolitik i rasismens tidevarv* (Umeå, 2002); Gunnar Eriksson, Darwinism and the Sami Legislation in The Sami National Minority in Sweden (Uppsala, 1983), 89–101; Gunnar Broberg, "Lappkaravaner på villovägar: Antropologin och synen på samerna fram mot sekelskiftet," *Lychnos* 1981/1982, Stockholm, 27–86.
45. Concerning Sami and the Swedish state position regarding their land ownership, see Kaisa Korpijaakko, "Land ownership among the Sami of Sweden-Finland: theory and practice" in Roger Kvist (ed.), *Readings in Sami History*, 3, 79–89. Korpijaakko states that Sami do not retain rights to the land and water in their environment comparable to actual ownership. This is

based on an understanding of the nature of Sami livelihoods: hunting, fishing and reindeer husbandry are not considered to need possession of land.
Still today, the issue of who has the rights to the territory has not been settled. For instance, the ILO convention no. 169 of 1989, which states the right
of indigenous people to their traditional territory, has still in 2005, fifteen
years later, not been ratified by Sweden. ILO—the International Labour Organisation—is a United Nations organization. Concerning the Swedish discussion on ratification of the convention see, for instance, Sven Heurgren,
*Samerna—ett ursprungsfolk i Sverige: Frågan om Sveriges anslutning till
ILO:s konvention nr 169*, SOU 1999:25 (Stockholm, 1999); Robert Johansson and Maria Klang, *Konflikterna i lappmarken—är ILO 169 lösningen?*
(Luleå 2003).

46. Hanes-Nutti, *Karesuandosamer*, 18ff.
47. Hanes-Nutti, *Samernas rättsliga ställning*, 12, 23.
48. Ibid., 23.
49. Ibid., 24.
50. See Lantto, *Att göra sin stämma hörd*, 105f, referring to *Norrländska vat-
   tenkraftfrågor: Betänkande avgivet av norrländska vattenkraftutredningen*
   (Stockholm, 1957) + annexes and SOU 1954:12 Elkraftförsörjningen, (Stockholm 1954), 303–308, 463–473.
51. Mr. Rusck was also a member of the TANESCO board 1965–1968. Öhman,
   Kidatu vattenkraftverk, 34.
52. Åke Rusck, "Ett 20 års program för 2 miljarder" in Folke Thunborg (ed.),
   Jorden, skogen, malmen, vattenkraften i morgondagens Norrbotten (Stockholm, 1956), 208.
53. Ibid., 203, 206.
54. Ibid., 208.
55. Ibid., 214.
56. Ibid., 223.
57. See also Lantto, *Att göra sin stämma hörd*, 97.
58. Rusck, 203–224, 221.
59. See Vedung and Brandel.
60. Torvald Lif, *Vattenkraften och rennäringen* (Vällingby, 1986). The other
   folders deal with fishery, tourism, demography/employment/municipal economy, and natural environment. The author of the 19-page folder on "hydropower and reindeer herding" is, according to the introductory text, Mr.
   Torvald Lif, of the State Power Board unit for investigations and water court
   cases. The main information in the folder derives from two state reports
   from the 1960s concerning the reindeer-herding land areas, and another concerning the reindeer-herding economy of 1983 together with statistics on the
   number of reindeer within certain Sami villages. The official reports referred
   to are: *Renbetsmarkerna, SOU 1966:12, the Appendix 5 of "Betänkande
   avgivet av 1964 års svensk-norska renbeteskommission"* and *Rennäringens
   ekonomi, SOU 1983:67*. The statistics concerning the number of reindeer are
   from Norrbotten, so called "*Renlängder.*"

61. Lif, 18.
62. Ibid.
63. Ibid., 5, 12, 13, 33, 35.
64. Vattenfall, www.vattenfall.se. (September 24, 2004).
65. Ibid.
66. Vattenfall and Explicare AB, "Livscykelanalys av Vattenfalls el, 2004," http://www.vattenfall.se/downloads/produktion/lcasve_maj04.pdf. (September 24, 2004), 6.
67. On environmental product declarations see further for instance http://www.environdec.com/, (October 18, 2004); Karin Jönsson, *Communicating the environmental characteristics of products: the use of environmental product declarations in the building, energy and automotive industries* (Lund, 2000).
68. Vattenfall, "Vattenfall AB Elproduktions Certifierade Miljövarudeklaration för el från Lule älv," http://www.vattenfall.se/downloads/produktion/VF_epd_lule_alv.pdf, (January 31, 2005).
69. Vattenfall, "Vattenkraft," http://www.vattenfall.se/om_vattenfall/var_verksamhet/forskning_och_utveckling/vattenkraft, (January 31, 2005).
70. See Ernst Manker, *Lapsk kultur vid Stora Lule älvs källsjöar: en etnografisk inventering inom uppdämningsområdet vid Suorva* (Uppsala, 1944); Ernst Manker, *The nomadism of the Swedish mountain lapps: the siidas and their migratory routes in 1945* (Uppsala, 1953). Ernst Manker, *Lappmarks gravar: Dödsföreställningar och gravskick i lappmarkerna, anteckningar av Ernst Manker* (Uppsala, 1961).
71. Lars-Erik Edlund, "Luleå, Harads, Gerosriset—Ortnamnsstrukturer i norra Sverige" in Evert Baudou (ed.), *Att leva vid älven—Åtta forskare om människor och resurser i Lule älvdal* (Ceweförlaget, 1996), 111–131, 112.
72. Phebe Fjällström, "Humanekologiskt system i Lule älvdal—fjällbygd, skogsbygd, kustbygd," in Baudou (ed.), *Att leva vid älven*, 79–110, 83.
73. Getrude Hanes, *Vaisaluokta under 100 år* (Kiruna, 2000), 118 f.
74. May-Britt Öhman and Camilla Sandström, "Sapmi's vita kol: En exposé over tillämpbara perspektiv på kraft, konflikt och kulturella kurositeter längs Norrlands älvar," conference paper at *Teknikhistoriska dagar*, Luleå, Sweden, March 15–17, 2004.
75. S. Hassler, R. Johansson, P. Sjölander, H. Grönberg, and L. Damber, *Causes of death in the Sami population of Sweden, 1961–2000*. Southern Lapland Research Department, Vilhelmina. Centre for Musculoskeletal Research, University of Gävle. Department of Radiation Sciences/Oncology, Umeå University, no. 1, 2003. See also Inger Utsi, "Vattnet över bräddarna" in *Sveriges Natur* 1958:4, 49, 118–120.
76. A Sami village is an economic association for the administration of reindeer-herding, in a certain geographical area. Only persons belonging to a Sami village have the right to carry on reindeer-herding in Sweden. With the passing of the reindeer grazing acts of 1886 and 1898, the Sami definitely lost their ownership to land and individual pasture rights were made into an

exclusive right of the Sami villages. The latest regulation of Sami villages was established in the Reindeer Grazing Act of 1971. Today there are 51 Sami villages. By 2002 the number of reindeer-herding enterprises was 928, reindeer owners 4487 and the number of reindeer was just above 228,000. See H. Ritzén, *Vattenbyggnadsföretags inverkan på renskötseln i Väster-bottens län: Utredning verkställd genom länsstyrelsen i Västerbottens län* (Umeå, 1960); Roger Kvist, *Swedish Sami policy*, 1550–1990, 70. Samernas Riksförbund, "Samebyn," http://www.sapmi.se/ssr/samebyn.html (January 31, 2005); Jordbruksverket, "Antal renar," http://www.jordbruksverket.se/ startsida/amnesomraden/djurveterinar/rennaring/nyckeltalforrennaringen/ antalforetagochrenagare.4.7502f61001ea08a0c7fff54245.html (January 31, 2005).

77. Amft, 43f.
78. Ibid., 43.
79. Ibid., 44, 69–99.
80. See Inger Utsi, "Vattnet över bräddarna."
81. See for instance Vattenfall, *Vattenkraften och rennäringen* (Vällingby, 1986).
82. Amft, 44.
83. Lundmark, '*Lappen är ombytlig*,' 63. According to Lundmark, the "Laplan-der should be Laplander policy" was an attempt by the Swedish state to cat-egorize the "Laplanders." Although racism was an important part, the economic policy was also of interest. This led to a position in which state pol-icy regarding the Sami had to pay respect to three different criteria: First of all the race, i.e. the origin. Secondly the way of living, i.e. whether the person was nomadic or not. Thirdly, the economic activity, i.e. if the person was a reindeer herder or not. This led to three distinct categories: the real "Lap-landers" were the ones who were nomadic, living in special huts and herding reindeer. The second category was the "forest Laplander," living in normal houses but still reindeer-herding, who were considered something in be-tween Laplanders and the other population. Finally, the persons of Laplan-der origin but living in houses and not involved in reindeer-herding, who were considered to have lost their Laplander origin and thus were defined as part of the general non-Sami population.
84. Amft, 44.
85. Lennart Pittja, "The impact of dams on Sami land and culture," in *Nordic Dam-building in the south, Proceedings of an international conference in Stockholm, 3–4 August, 1994* (Stockholm, 1994).
86. Pittja, 1994.
87. Lantto, *Att göra sin stämma hörd*, 91ff. The Sami parliament was established in 1993. The sessions are held in Kiruna, in Sapmi, 1500 km north of the Swedish capital. The parliament is not a public authority and has little to no political impact in Sweden. There is no specific representation of the Sami in the Swedish national parliament. See further http://www.sametinget.se, (October 27, 2004).

88. Baudou, *Norrlands forntid*, 32f, 43, 151ff. Sverker Janson and Harald Hvarfner, *Från norrlandsälvar och fjällsjöar: Riksantikvarieämbetets kulturhistoriska undersökningar i samband med kraftverksbyggen och sjöregleringar* (Stockholm, 1960); Mulk.
89. See for instance Ernst Manker, *Lapsk kultur vid Stora Lule älvs källsjöar.*
90. Baudou, *Norrlands forntid*, 39.
91. Visit to the Stornorrfors power plant and rock carvings by the author in July, 2004.
92. Paulus Utsi lived from 1918–1974, and his wife Inger Utsi, from 1914–1984. Their life and poetry has been described by amongst others Nils-Aslak Valkeapää, "Med språket med språket" in Paulus Utsi, *Följ stigen: texter 1941–1974* (Kautokeino, 2000).
93. Paulus became internationally renowned, while his wife Inger only after the death of her husband officially claimed to be a part of the creative process when she presented herself as co-author of the second collection, Giela Gielain, in 1980. See for instance Harald Gaski, *Sami culture in a new era: the Norwegian experience*, (Kárásjohka, 1997); Israel Ruong, "Saame Poetry," in Martin Allwood (gen. ed.), *Modern Scandinavian Poetry* (Mullsjö and Walnut Creek, Calif., 1986), 147–156.
94. Erik-Oscar Oscarsson, "recension av Paulus Utsi, Följ stigen: texter 1941–1974," *Oknytt*, Holmsund, 2000:3/4, 95–96; Valkeapää, 35–55, 53.
95. Translation into Swedish by Elli Sivi Näkkäläjärvi and Per Mikael Utsi, translation from Swedish into English by Bernard Vowles/the author.
96. "Internationellt kraftcentrum invigt," *Vattenkraft-magasinet*, 1998:2, 4–5. The Sami yoik is one of the oldest musical expressions in Europe.
97. The paintings inaugurated in 2000 have been made by Sami artists Mr. Lars Pirak and Mr. Lars J:son Nutti together with a Swedish artist, Mr. Bengt Lindström. See for instance Katarina Hällgren, Uvssat davás—Dörrarna västerut" in *Fjärde världen*, 2000:4, 10–11.

PLACE AS A RESOURCE IN BUSINESS NETWORKS

HÅKAN HÅKANSSON,
ANNALISA TUNISINI,
ALEXANDRA WALUSZEWSKI

PLACE—A DRAWBACK OR AN ADVANTAGE?

In Castells (1996, Vol. 1) it is argued that the forces of globalization, the new information technology included, have replaced "*space of place*" with "*space of flows*" and made economic activity "deterritorialised." Castells's interpretation reflects an underlying assumption that colors approaches ranging from traditional economics to internationalization theory—*place is a drawback that the individual company has to overcome.* An almost opposite view of place is brought forward in Porter (1990, p. 119), where it is argued that "*Vigorous local competition not only sharpens advantages at home but pressures domestic firms to sell abroad in order to grow.*" With this statement, Porter expresses an interpretation that has influenced not only business strategists but also many economic geographers—*place as a creator of advantages for the individual company.*

Whether one is engaged in resource utilization in a company, or one is a researcher trying to understand how company resources develop and are utilized, it is rather confusing to be left with two such divergent views on the implications of geographical location. Before we discuss the geographical dimension from the perspective of resource development, let us consider what is behind the different interpretations of the meaning of place.

Despite the fact that the issue of place and its role in the prosperity of firms have been discussed since the days of Ricardo (1817, p. 156), who said "*each country naturally devotes its capital to such employment as are most beneficial to each,*" the question is still controversial. Modern researchers seem to agree that companies tend to co-localize within certain geographical areas, and that such ag-glomerations make sense. Or as Dicken (1998, p. 11) puts it, *"the geographical concentration of economic activities, at a local or sub-national level, is the norm not the exception."* However, there is much less agreement in the perception of the mechanism behind such co-lo-cations, and how these affect industrial activities—something that is perhaps not so surprising if we consider the perspectives from which the issue is investigated, and the tools used.

Perceived Advantages of Place

With Marshall (1890) as one of the earliest and most influential sources of inspiration, scholars in disciplines ranging from economics and economic geography to applied economics and economic history have accepted the idea that spatial agglomeration facilitates the de-velopment of localized knowledge, whether in the form of skilled labor, or specialization and know-how at the company level (see e.g. Hoover 1948, Myrdal 1957, Arthur 1986, Krugman 1991). With the observations of Marshall (1890) forming the setting, the research fo-cused on the issue of how agglomerations within geographically de-fined areas, such as villages, cities, regions, countries, affect economic activities. There are two main angles from which this issue has been investigated: the cost of production and the market area of the firm—approaches that, however, not have been easy to combine. As Dicken (1998, p. 75) points out, in general these theorists "have been more concerned with incorporating space into economic theory than with attempting to explain the actual location of economic activities."

The transfer of the issue of place from a macro to a meso and business level, and also to a higher place on the research agenda, has been actively urged by one of the most prominent authors in the field of business strategy, Michael Porter (1990 and 1994). Or, to use his own words (Porter 1994, p. 38): *"Economic geography must move from the periphery to the mainstream."* Studies of business strategy have concentrated largely on how the performance of a company is connected to place. In Porter's perspective, which has influenced many scholars in the field of both business strategy and economic geogra-phy, the agglomeration of several similar companies spurs each of them to develop unique competitive advantages: *"Competitive advantage is created and sustained through a highly localized process"* (1990, p. 19). Thus, while the scholars mentioned above can be regarded as focus-ing on the positive effects of "urbanisation economies," i.e. the agglomeration of firms irrespective of sector origin, Porter points to the effect of an agglomeration of firms active in the same industry (Malmberg, Malmberg & Lundequist 2000). The main mechanism behind prospering regions populated by similar companies, so called *clusters*, is, according to Porter, the intense rivalry such agglomerations create. Thus, questions of place are framed with the underlying assumption that this is an important part of the issue of competition.

Perceived Disadvantages of Place

Even if we can see a division between approaches according to whether place is seen as an issue of urbanization or of localization, there is a strong common denominator in the approach to place among economists, economic geographers and business strategists, which concentrates on its role as a *benefactor of economic activities*. However, an almost opposite view of place appears among students of the process of internationalization. According to Dicken (1998), the role of place in this process during the last decade has been overshadowed by the "emblematic" issue or the "mantra of our time," namely the phenomenon of globalization. Regardless of one's standpoint in this debate, i.e. of whether *"a scenario of unstoppable global forces leading to an ultimately homogenized world"* or *"the globalization story is little more than hype"* (Dicken, 1998, p. xiii), in an internationalization or globalization perspective the question of place boils down to the problem of how to overcome distance.[1] A current subject of research in this field is the development of "space-shrinking technologies," signed to overcome the *"friction of space and time"* (Dicken, 1998, p. 151). This focus can be regarded as a legacy of a time when there existed numerous limits to international and other long-distance communication and interconnection among companies—although these problems are perhaps exaggerated from the perspective of recent communication technologies. As Lindqvist (1984) shows, in the mid-1700s news of a new technological breakthrough could travel from London to Stockholm in less than a week, with the help of a well-developed system of mounted couriers. (This is about the time it takes to go through the e-mail inbox after being out of the office for some days.) However, we will not go more deeply into the issue of how much modern information technology has helped to reduce the problems of distance, but merely conclude that from an internationalization perspective, a company's location is a problem to overcome. That companies actually seem to be influenced by features related to the place where they are located is seldom seen as an advantage—rather a circumstance whose importance has to be reduced.

Place as a restriction is also a view characteristic of the theoretical tradition to which the authors of this paper belong, the industrial network approach, although Markgren (2001) and Törnroos (1991) are two inspiring exceptions. The understanding of place as a hindrance can be traced back to the early studies, where it was equated with distance (see e.g. Håkansson 1982, Johanson & Wiedersheim-Paul 1975). The spatial location of a company was considered to impact exchange episodes, and in particular social exchange. Thus, a company's geographical location was studied in terms of how it affects social interaction between people in different companies, and it was approached in terms of physical distance, whereas the issue of how place influences the resource that is the object of these interaction processes was neglected. With this underlying categorization, it is easy to understand why a company's location became interpreted as a problematic element in interaction processes, and not as something that can contribute to the creation of benefits—and thus not of interest as a specific unit of analysis. In consequence, more recent studies within the network sphere have given greater attention to issues considered important for the prosperity of a company, for example technological and product development, purchasing and marketing, rather than investigated as to how space is related to these questions. Place can in such analysis be given a much more dynamic role, to which we now will turn.

AN IMPORTANT SOURCE OF INSPIRATION: THE ITALIAN DISTRICT RESEARCH

However, if we want to approach place as a dynamic feature and investigate its role as an active part of company life and development, we can, at least if we take a look outside the mainstream of the literature on place, find some useful research tools. An important source of inspiration, which also deals directly with the issue of place, is the Italian "industrial district" field research. A main theme in this research tradition is how spatial proximity between companies affects their exchanges and their business behavior (see e.g. Piore & Sabel 1994, Becattini 1987, Brusco 1989). The role and function of industrial districts and local production systems have also been, and still are, the object of much debate among these scholars.

In general, at least two main perspectives can be distinguished (Boari & Lipparini 1999). One is very much "district-oriented," i.e. it identifies the district as a spatially concentrated community of small and medium-sized companies and tends to focus on the economic and social variables that explain the functioning of such contexts. These types of studies rest on a macro-perspective, whose underlying assumption is that the determinants and the advantages of industrial districts are the division of labor between companies, the role of the social dimension and, in particular, the "industrial atmosphere." Co-ordination of companies' activities is seen as solved by price mechanisms, information circulation and informal co-operation. This approach was first adopted by scholars with a background in industrial economics, which tends to neglect the analysis of the role of the individual actor—the single company—and of the impact of its own behavior in its market context. However, although these scholars have risen above the traditional, structural level of analysis in industrial economics, they still base their approach to the companies within an industrial district on the old foundations. The firms of the district are treated as homogeneous—interacting uniformly with one another in an area where institutions may matter more than the individual firms.

The second way of approaching industrial districts has developed very much as a reaction against the first, and focuses upon a *heterogeneous actor dimension* in the industrial districts (Varaldo & Ferrucci 1997). It has grown especially from the analysis of the role played by individual actors—small and medium-sized companies that have grown rapidly in the district—in promoting the growth of the whole local context where they are situated. Some aspects of the investigated heterogeneity among firms in a district are how certain companies are capable of playing a driving role for many other local companies and handling a large set of relationships significantly influencing and directing the development of the industrial district.

Attention is paid to the business behavior of the single actor: how it can develop its role in a certain context—and how individual business behavior may impact on the dynamics of the whole context. Some authors have developed an approach that is very useful in our studies of some Italian and Swedish industrial districts; it is the combined analysis of the actor level and the district level. With Lorenzoni & Baden-Fuller (1995) and Lipparini & Lorenzoni (1999) in the forefront, a network/constellation approach to the analysis of local production has been developed, focusing on some individual leading actors—the strategic center—and its set of relationships with other actors, especially local suppliers. In other words, these authors have taken a "meso-level" perspective and have attempted to investigate how both the individual and the collective dimension of entrepreneurship influence each other and how both promote the development of local contexts. They have particularly stressed the role of local emerging companies with superior co-ordination capabilities and their business relationships in promoting the development of a local context, i.e. district development. They have emphasized the view of relationships as a means of developing capabilities, and the importance of collective strategies and of interactive learning. Furthermore, they have stressed the relevance of these aspects also with respect to internationalization processes in which business relationships also represent a means by which new enriched competences are developed through the interaction with other contexts (Caroli & Lipparini 2001). In their perspectives, leading companies do not "cut off" from their own context, but they change their way of being part of the district. Thus, they make use of the location because of the advantages it can bring about—but they also go beyond their own location and handle the latter as a resource to be combined with others. In these terms, with a large set of both local and global relationships, such leading companies mobilize their own material and social resources and those of the context where they are embedded and combine these with those of other contexts.

Other scholars with a similar approach have investigated the dynamic aspects of industrial districts in terms of how new foreign companies "enter into" them, involving local companies and their partners in the international production and distribution circuits. Furthermore, attention has been directed to how regional firms start up production facilities abroad and increasingly relate to inter-regional and international suppliers (see e.g. Pilotti 1998, Grandinetti & Rullani 1996, Corò & Micelli 1999, Corò & Grandinetti 1999). What these authors have observed is the opening up of districts to globalization, thus questioning many elements that have always been considered an advantage of the division of labor among local clusters of companies, first of all their physical distance. In this respect, a question arising is how much district origins can put a brake on the development of companies and how much they can give impetus to development. Co-location may give small district companies a gain in knowledge diffusion and exchange of experience, and form shared infrastructure and innovation. At the same time, it may be an obstacle to companies that are firmly rooted in their own perspective. With this perspective, it is easy to understand the intense discussions of whether and how districts will survive.

However, if we focus on districts as networks of companies and on the interaction effects on utilization of resources, the question can be formulated somewhat differently. Instead of considering how the qualities of the district will enable it to develop and prosper in itself, we would then *ask how single companies within the district can use the place in order to develop and how this in its turn will affect the attractiveness of the place.* This is an issue that can be investigated with an industrial network approach.

INVESTIGATING PLACE WITH THE INDUSTRIAL NETWORK APPROACH

Although the industrial network approach[2] does not deal directly with the issue of place, it can be used as an important complement to the Italian district approach. While the latter focuses on the relation between spatial features and company life, the industrial network approach investigates the interaction between companies/organizations and the effect this has on how resources are created and activated in these processes. The interplay between companies/organizations is treated as a phenomenon that may have a wide variety of expressions—ranging from more distant relationships to close interactions— where the social and technological resources are confronted and adapted. One of the main assumptions is that a company's technological, social and economic features are the result of its interaction with other companies/organizations. Thus, resources are seen as heterogeneous—their value is dependent on how they are combined with other resources. This is done within organizations but also through the interaction processes between organizations. To put it briefly, this is an approach colored by the understanding that developments occur when companies and organizations encounter one another in terms of sets of resources (Håkansson & Waluszewski 2002, Waluszewski 2002).

As the word "network" indicates, companies are seen as "nodes" that are related to each other through different "strings." Both the nodes and the strings are assumed to consist of resources. One way of investigating these nodes and strings has been by analyzing the "position" of companies/organizations (see e.g. Johanson & Mattsson 1985 and 1988, Henders 1992). When, for example, Henders (1992) is discussing the position concept, she draws attention to both its *relative dimension* and the *resource dimension*. Every position in a network is based on some resources but it is also determined by the positions of the counterparts and their resources. Thus, in any network analysis there is an obvious relative dimension very similar to place. However, place has rarely been touched upon in the discussion of the position of companies/organizations. In discussions of the position concept by Henders (1992), the place issue is not even mentioned. But it seems both possible and fruitful to make *an analogy between position and place.*

If we use the position concept for investigating the place dimension, the latter appears not just as a location in a geographic grid but also as a *combination of a set of resources.* Thus, with such a research tool, place has to be investigated in terms of how the resources existing there are related to and combined with each other as well as with resources at other places. Furthermore, in the analysis of position it is stressed that every business/organizational unit has several counterparts with different characteristics; i.e. any position has a number of different dimensions—it is multidimensional. This means that the company/organization can act in different ways to develop its own position—or to change it in one way or another. The issue of place can be approached in the same way. The often very complex set of resources existing in a certain place can be related in a lot of different ways with a large number of varied resources at other places. Within this intricate web of resource interdependencies, a company will be taking advantage of the interdependencies to a greater or lesser degree. Thus, both the web and the company's ability to take advantage of the web can vary.

Place as the Result of Interaction

By using the industrial network approach, we can investigate *how features of place are created by companies/organizations and their long-term interaction.* Certainly such interaction takes place within focal geographical areas, but also through connecting resources activated at different places. Through these interaction processes, the resources activated at a certain place acquire new features—which may be the result of development work carried out a long way away. That the qualities of a certain region can be the result of development activities that are far from local is also something to which scholars within disciplines such as history of science (see e.g. Widmalm 2001) and history of technology (see e.g. Edgerton, 1996) draw attention. Another common interpretation made in these studies is that the use of the spatial dimension can include different aspects for different companies—even if these are located next door. Features of an industrial region that fit some companies' resource combinations may be of less value to those of others. Furthermore, while some companies seem to be very skilled in utilizing local resources, others may be ignorant of these possibilities.

What these experiences call for is an investigation of place as a heterogeneous phenomenon—as something both created and used differently by companies/organizations. To be able to catch these aspects, we need to approach place both as a *result but also a source of dynamics*—i.e. as a phenomenon that is not given but created and changing over time. This implies that we have to consider place as something that affects not only the individual company, but also the way the individual company interacts with other companies as well as how the companies' interaction creates the place. Thus, place has to be approached both from the perspective of the individual company and in the context of the company as in some of the Italian "district" studies.

When we investigate place from the perspective of resource development and utilization—if place is seen as a systematic combining of resources—then its effects, positive or negative, are dependent on how successful companies are in taking advantage of this dimension in their combination. This way of approaching companies is based on Penrose (1959) and has been more fully developed in relation to the industrial network approach in Håkansson & Waluszewski (2002). In principle, various elements, technical and organizational, tangible and intangible, material and symbolic, can be considered as resources when use can be made of them. Resources, in fact, have in this context a value only when they are used. They have a value in relation to others, not as elements in themselves. Resources have only an economic meaning in constellations—in combinations that imply use. Place may in such situations certainly be regarded as a resource in itself, since within a certain boundary it incorporates a number of other resources—technical as well as organizational. The value of a place is, in such a case, dependent on how sets of resources are combined with each other and used. In this case place is seen as an organization comparable to a company. Place as an organization is, like every company, a unique combination of resources that can be regarded as a meaningful entity in relation both to companies and to other places;

it becomes a resource with a certain value because it can be regarded as a part of a larger resource constellation.

This is clearly an interesting issue that is well addressed in the studies of Italian districts. However, the network approach also indicates another important issue. Place is not just a resource in itself—it is also one inevitable feature of most other resources. This can also explain why place has sometimes been looked upon as a restriction—as a hindrance or a problem. In other words, place is a feature that will be part of the combining of all resources, and by such combining processes resources characterized by different "places" will be mixed and embedded into each other. Thus, it is a dimension that will characterize more or less all resources in one way or another. This dimension can then be more or less consciously utilized in the combining and recombining of resources. Place appears here as an embedded dimension—that a company/organization can lift forward and relate to in its daily activities. Instead of approaching place as a one-dimensional entity, as an object of analysis in itself, the industrial network research tool allows us to investigate it as a multidimensional and embedded phenomenon interrelated with other variables defining the attributes and dynamics of the context of companies/organizations as well as their resource constellations.

To sum up, it is the combination of inspiration gained from Italian district research and theoretical and empirical observations gained through studies using an industrial network approach that is behind our ambition to investigate how all companies are embedded in the geographical dimension, i.e. that the geographical dimension is an integrated and unquestionable aspect of the life of all companies. But it is also a dimension that can be utilized to varying degrees. The aim is to take a first step in developing a theoretical framework in which the place dimension is analyzed as a strategic issue for companies/organizations. The development of such a framework will let us analyze how the place dimension influences and can be systematically used by companies/organizations. Such a framework might also give insights into the more complex dynamics observed in how companies/organizations of different geographical origin develop their networks. In this first step, we are going to use some short empirical illustrations from one investigation of the interference of the place dimension in resource development. We use as a focal unit a large Italian supplier of machinery for producers of wood, marble and glass products (Tunisini 2003) that is located in an industrial district in the center of Italy.

HOW TO APPROACH PLACE WITH A NETWORK TOOL

In order to investigate how place-related features are (more or less consciously) utilized by companies/organizations, we will use a research tool based on the distinction between four types of resources (see Figure 1 below). Two are mainly social: *organizational units* and *inter-organizational relationships*, and two are mainly physical: *products* and *production facilities* (Håkansson & Waluszewski 2002). The value of each resource is considered to be dependent on how it is combined with established or emerging solutions on both the supply and user side. Thus, the value of a resource is created from "outside"

Organizational unit (a)   **Organizational unit (b)**

Figure 1.   A tool-kit to investigate resource interaction among four types of resources. *Source:* Adapted from Wedin (2001, p. 168) and Håkansson & Waluszewski (2002, p. 38).

in combination with other resources. What this tool allows is the investigation of how resources are related, confronted and remodelled in relation to each other—including the issue of how place is embedded into them.

Facilities and Place-related Features

A facility or equipment has one obvious place-related feature: this is a resource that is in general both visible and fixed in the physical landscape. The fixed location of a facility is also an aspect that dominates the way in which the company deals with the place dimension. The location and its effect on logistics, access to skilled personnel, and access to local support in terms of skilled suppliers and customers, are some examples of frequently used reasons for locating a certain facility in a specific place. This may explain why a certain facility was placed in a specific place but it cannot be used to explain how the same facility later comes to be used. The main reason is that there are always changes taking place that will be taken into account by the company utilizing the facility over its lifetime.

The combination of resources that constitutes facilities means that they are most often characterized both by a certain economic and physical size and a certain lifetime. But facilities are more than technical devices, they are also embedded with images, ideas and knowledge of how to utilize them. In both these dimensions of a facility, its technological and its image level, place-related features might successively become embedded. Besides the place-related features that are embedded in the facility due to its primary location, the facility is also charging or being charged with place-related features during its interaction with other resources, such as other facilities, products, organizational units and relationships. In other words, a facility can be seen as a kind of coupling device, where related resources are charged with place-related features. By actively searching for and taking advantage of such features, both the cost of using the facility and the value of its outcome can be affected.

Products and Place-related Features

Compared to facilities, products are equipped with an almost opposite type of place characteristic—instead of having a fixed location, products are most often produced and used at different places. This means that a product can be regarded as a kind of geographical glue, holding together resources such as products, organizational units, facilities and relationships—their place-related features included. Some of these place-related features are embedded in the product while it is still being produced. These features may be given by nature, due to climate or other special geographical conditions, but they can also be created by man, by technological means or historically. When the product is used, it is most often combined systemically with other resources: other products, facilities and/or specific attributes of organizational units. In this combining process, place-related features are always present, and have to be dealt with. Natural or created place-related features may make demands on the input products, or may influence the possibility of using the end products. Consequently, it is in the interface between a product and the resources with which it is connected on the supply and user side that certain place-related features are activated. By actively searching for and taking advantage of such features, the cost of production or the benefits of using the product may be affected.

Inter-organisational Relationships and Place-related Features

Considering a business relationship as a resource means focusing on its content and function as a tool to connect two business units with each other. A relationship can be seen as a quasi-organization built up through exchange episodes during which personnel from the parties concerned get to know each other as well as each other's resources. During this process, resources become systematically related to each other—these involve all facilities and products. As the organizations and resources involved are situated in specific places, the relationship itself can be seen as a bridge tying resources in two (or more) places to each other. In this way a relationship becomes a distinct part of a geographically based resource pattern.

Thus, business relationships do not just connect resources in different places to each other: they also become roads, bridges or links, i.e. resource elements in a larger resource constellation. These bridges are multidimensional. Firstly, they are bridges between places that may be distributed in the geographical dimension in different ways, creating a systematic pattern. Secondly, the content of each relationship may be more or less featured by the place dimensions related to specific products, facilities, business units and other business relationships.

By actively searching for and utilizing these geographical features of relationships, costs and benefits of utilizing the resources may be affected.

Organizational Units and Place-related Features

Considering organizational units not only as actors, but also as resource units that can be used in combination with other resources, involves focusing upon the knowledge and experience features that such units may include. Over the years there is often a considerable amount of experience built into an organizational unit: in how to combine the company's own products with external ones, how to utilize internal and external facilities and how to handle, balance and combine relationships. This means that the organizational unit is related to geography in several ways. Firstly, it is placed somewhere, but secondly it also has, embedded in it, place-related features through the resources of which it is composed, and thirdly, the kind of such features that are embedded depends on the nature of the resource combinations. Two organizational units, located side by side and working in the same kind of business area, may include rather different place-related features, if one is mainly using local products, local facilities and local relationships, while the other is mainly using global products, facilities located at distant places and international relationships. Thus, a closer look at a company with a strong local image may reveal a collage of different national and international place-related features, in the same way as a unit with an international image may be charged with local place-related features. To this may be added that the process of embedding place-related features may be more or less conscious and skilful. However, by actively searching for and taking advantage of such features, the knowledge and experiences of an organizational unit can increase.

A CASE STUDY: BIESSE CORPORATE

Biesse Corporate is one of two Italian world-leading companies in wood/marble/glass working equipment. The company was born in 1969 in Pesaro in the Marche region. In 1977 Biesse introduced the first numerically controlled boring machine for panels and quite rapidly became a world leader in this business. It is still the leader today and it has also greatly broadened its range of other applications and processes. Since the mid-nineties, the company has had a very rapid growth: turnover has increased from 148 million euros in 1996 to 346 million euros in 2001; the number of employees has risen from 1040 to 2000; its offering has also been much enlarged by the acquisition of both Italian and foreign companies.

Biesse was established by an entrepreneur who specialized in machining processes. Before starting Biesse, he had in 1959 founded Cosmec, a small company producing mechanical components and selling to medium-sized and large public and private companies, whose factories were located in the Pesaro area. In this respect, the original location of Biesse has a particular significance. Historically, the geographical location was dominated by a large number of engineering factories owned by large Italian groups and by an extensive variety of small sub-contractors. The geographical area where Cosmec, originally, and Biesse, later, were set up thus has a long engineering tradition. The founder of the company developed it in this cultural and technical setting. Secondly, and very important, the Pesaro area also has a historical concentration of large Italian furniture companies. They were all born in the sixties and rapidly developed in the seventies and especially in the eighties. Besides a large number of small and medium-sized furniture suppliers, three of the most important Italian furniture producers are located in the Pesaro area. Altogether there are more than 340 small and medium-sized companies in the furniture industry located there. The close connection between both the producers of woodworking equipment and its users has always given a great impulse to the development of both kinds of companies.

The circulation and exchange of both technical and commercial knowledge, and the combination of small incremental innovative experiences among the different local players, developed a cultural "micro-climate" that recalls the Marshallian "industrial atmosphere." Co-location of both equipment producers and their users permitted an intense exchange and circulation of application and production know-how, facilitating continuous incremental innovations in the products and in the production processes, giving rise to the diffused perception of the value of these "made in Italy" products. We may say that there was a fruitful combination of different resource elements that made the geographical area particularly rich and full of promising business development.

In its own development, we can observe different ways in which Biesse Corporate has used place-related features and combined them with resource elements.

Biesse uses *facilities* that have a very concentrated location. As already remarked, the founder and owner of the company has strong cultural, historical and personal connections with the territory and he adopts a very localized production strategy. In his mind, place is really a constellation of resources to be utilized because of its potential or the value rooted in its historical mechanical tradition and in its historical texture of personal ties, shared experiences and joint developments. Biesse's production facilities are thus highly concentrated and close to the set of local suppliers. Recently the company completed the building of a large assembly and exhibition site that is located very close to its own factories and a few hundred meters from those of some of its long-term customers. This significantly reduces logistic costs but is also a huge investment in the territory that reflects a conscious strategy to promote and leverage on its own personnel, infrastructure, services and other kinds of resources.

Biesse had invested in a second production site, in Austria—the consequence of the acquisition of a company specialized in engineering processes with good connections with the German market. The goal of the acquisition was both the extension of the range of skills through the access to more customized engineering capabilities and the use of the acquired company as a bridge to a new difficult market—the German one; as a result, the location of the company and of its facilities had been viewed as a resource with which to access and make use of other resources singly and in combination. However, the results of this investment were not very positive and Biesse has benefited little from the complementary, technical resources and assets originated and developed in a different place and not much improved its position in the German market because of the cultural barriers perceived by many local customers against Italian manufacturers.

A varied approach to place-related features is also developed by the company in relation to its own organisational units, product items and relationship features.

Focusing on *the product* dimension, Biesse designs and assembles woodworking machines as well as machines for working marble and glass. The product is made up of 10 000/30 000 components giving a finished product structure of about 700/2 000 different items. Some of the product's strategic parts are developed internally by the company. In particular, the company designs and develops numerical control systems and engines. Other items, partly customized and partly standardized, are developed by Biesse's suppliers. The customized ones are mostly developed by closely related local companies; the standardized ones are supplied by international actors. In respect to local suppliers the company acts as a strategic center and leverages on the product-specific competences developed within the mechanical local cluster of companies; these have developed high product-specific competences. Moreover, they own a historical culture in the design and the development of such a mechanical product and Biesse invests and leverages in the shared sub-culture, giving it additional impetus.

On the other hand, an increasing number of product items are acquired from internationally located suppliers. This occurs when the standard content is high in the product and "stateless" suppliers are looked for as they are considered "best in class."

Biesse's competence in product design and development thus grew from a long-term mechanical tradition in its geographical area. The company makes extensive use of such local advantages in relation to product-development culture. Moreover, it also takes advantage of experiences stemming from the use of the product by local users. Dealing with place and relationship features, such advantages are exploited by intensive and constant contact and exchanges with local counterparts. However, these exchanges are not the result of some kind of spontaneous process. They are consciously and deliberately organized within the limits set by historical structures and processes. They are therefore approached with the intention of promoting the company's joint development with its own related partners and exploiting a shared "made in Italy" image all over the world. That implies the need for continuous control of the product by the company and the keeping of a product culture that is strongly rooted in the Pesaro area.

In the case of *organizational units*, Biesse has a very international orientation. About 83% of its revenue stems from international customers, and 11 commercial subsidiaries and 250 agents and distributors are spread all over the world in the most important markets: Germany, France, Spain, Scandinavia, the UK, the USA and Canada. Placing subsidiaries and commercial business units responsible for the image and the development of the company's products in the different local markets is viewed as a basic strategy. These commercial units are mostly charged with the organizing of local resellers and sales representatives who develop a strong connection with local customers and local application culture. They have to combine the Biesse offering, which is mostly based on the "made in Italy" image in the mechanical product, with the country-specific uses of the products and expectations of their functioning, which are also country-specific. In this respect, the use of place features rooted in the "made in Italy" image in relation to business units is thus intensive, with some exceptions. In Germany, where the main competitors are located, the "made in Italy" image suggested by Biesse has negative impacts when viewed in contrast with the German historical mechanical tradition. Consequently, Biesse's business units located and utilized in that country for product diffusion have to choose a different combination of place-related features—one that refers to the German tradition rather than to the Italian one.

Taking the *business relationship* as the primary resource dimension, we can observe how Biesse, born out of intensive interconnections primarily with local mechanical suppliers and local furniture companies as customers, today combines close long-term relationships with local suppliers and leading customers with extensive business relationships with global suppliers and international customers. Its approach to the use and the reinforcement of its business relationships with its own original location is aimed to promote and improve the advantages and competences of its original place-related features. However, this approach is not viewed as absolutely self-sufficient. So the company tries to use both its local and global dimension through the combination of both local and global suppliers and customer relationships, taking advantage of the combination of different place-related features.

Biesse has always made great use of its historical relationships with local partners. Frequently, they are the source of innovative ideas and of incremental innovation in the machines. As concerns supplier relationships, local suppliers of customized product items are regarded as a company's extended factory. Biesse has implemented an "assemble to order" model that implies a tight integration with supplier companies. In this respect the historical tradition of long-term relationships with local suppliers assisted the development of the new supply model.

As for user relationships, Biesse's customers are all over the world and their concentration is not high. However, local user relationships, even if not necessarily accompanied by a sale, are used intensively to gain experience of and enhance product innovation and to promote new uses of the product. Moreover, local users' factories are utilized to show the functioning of new equipment to other customers that are periodically hosted in Biesse and taken to visit different show rooms. In these terms, Italian and foreign customers are invited to experience the real application and functioning of Biesse products and systems by their own competitors.

The historical concentration of both suppliers of woodworking machines and users, that is furniture producers, in the same area has given a great impulse to the development of both. Localized users and suppliers represented a great advantage, especially because of technological innovation. Numerically controlled machines were tested and enhanced by nearby users. The evolving needs of the latter have given a great impulse to innovation, perfection and technical advance of equipment. There is also another dimension to business relationships that is important in connection with place. In the observed area, two competing companies are very closely situated. More precisely, Biesse is a few kilometres from its main Italian competitor. The two companies are both world leaders and they are closely located in an area where a large number of Italian customers are based. This conflict dimension to business relationships in the area has given a great impulse to Biesse's development and it has been indirectly a positive resource whose value has been the enhancing of innovation and development of new resources. Through their connection with common customers and the continuous shifting of personnel from one company to another, the two companies exchange resources and knowledge, learn about each other and develop themselves; they are both continuously pushed to innovate and search for new, more efficient uses and applications.

Biesse, we can conclude, makes a *heavy* use of place-related features, mostly consciously and partly as the result of a way of "doing business." We have also observed a *varied* pattern of place-related features but *we cannot conclude that it plays a solely positive role in the resource constellation.* Taking business relationships with local suppliers, they also act as a barrier to change and to possible improvements. In fact, the historical ties and texture of business relationships with many local suppliers have sometimes made it difficult for Biesse to interrupt relationships, change their content and turn them in new directions. Secondly, geographical closeness to the main competitor focuses the company's main attention more on how to differentiate itself from its own competitor than on the synergies and benefits that may stem from the combination of its own resources with the latter's.

Finally, taking the facilities dimension, the huge investments in local facilities demand high-quality services and supports by local infrastructures that are not always guaranteed. Moreover, that increases the company's dependence on local sub-suppliers while losing the advantages connected with the setting of production facilities in other geographical areas where other resource elements (cost of labor, services, suppliers' capabilities) can be combined and mobilized in more efficient and effective ways.

PATTERN OF PLACES EMBEDDED INTO SINGLE RESOURCES

Although the empirical illustration presented above is just one example of how place-related features have been embedded into one resource constellation, it underlines how place-related features always influence companies and their resources. The usefulness of the resources of the company is clearly influenced by other resources at the place where they themselves are located—but also by resources organized by partners in other places. Thus, the place or geographical dimensions are in other words not at all simple or one-dimensional. Instead an organizational unit situated in one place can be the channel to another resource situated somewhere else. Different patterns in technology, industrial and business activities, culture and other dimensions are embedded into the places where organizational units are located. As the same is the case for all the partners, we get a total pattern where places are systematically combined in a large number of different ways. One important consequence is that every company will be based on a unique combination of place-related features. Some of these might be common to its neighbors—others might be more similar to more distantly located units. Some of the neighbors might for the same reason be completely different. Another consequence is that even when the companies have international contacts these are with specific other places. The "room" is still limited; it is only divided into several pieces distributed over a larger geographical area. The geographical dimension is still very basic and influential. The question is whether and how these circumstances are taken advantage of by the company—or by its partners. Thus the pattern outlined underlines the importance of considering the place or geographical dimension as patterns of place-related features instead of as features of places in themselves.

The case also underlines the fact that the four types of resources identified are all related to geography in different ways. This creates a huge variety in how place can be utilized in the combining of resources. Any company may be more or less aware of the possibility of utilizing the synergies that may stem from these different combinations. There might be companies that make no conscious effort at all to utilize these possibilities, whereas there are others making a lot. Among the latter there will later be a large variety in what they are doing. They can choose to prioritize local resources or highly international ones or to combine local and international systematically. Furthermore, they can choose to do it for products or for facilities or for the location of business units or important partners. Thus, they have the opportunity to try to be more or less heavy in relation to the chosen places and they can also differ in the degree of variety in how the places are combined.

Why then should companies actively use place? What can they achieve from systematic utilization of place? Which are the main benefits? In order to discuss this point, we have to go back to the concept of network position. A company within a network is assumed to have a position in an enacted constructed environment. Being formed by nodes and strings—the network consists of something substantive—it has to exist in the space dimension with identifiable locations. The single actor, in order to be identified by others, needs a position that is made up of a set of resources, where the geographical dimension is included. In order to have a position in this kind of structure there is a need for investments. The heaviness of the position in a network context is dependent on the investments that the company has made and these investments are made in the resources discussed above, which all have a geographical identity. In these terms, investing in geography is a way to gain or reinforce a company's own position with respect to other companies and relationships. As the latter also have a geographical dimension, it is possible to find complementarity and combinatory effects in the geographical dimension. The more the company invests in a certain geographic pattern—through specific products, facilities, business units and relationships—the more it increases the weight of its position vis-à-vis other products, facilities, business units and relationships existing in or close to this pattern. In some cases of high investment the geographical dimension may become so dominant that it gives the identity to the company. Sometimes a specific set of companies will dominate a specific and concentrated geographic pattern (such as the Third Italy), especially when their investments are closely connected. Internationalization is, as a consequence, often a combination of a specific set of geographical places located in several countries.

So, by utilizing geography, companies can reinforce their own positions in relation to some specific others. But there is another partly complementary and partly contradictory aspect. By investing in a certain geographic pattern, the company can find new ways to combine resources located in different places with each other. A specific variety can give both positional and knowledge advantages and other benefits that come from companies' successful leveraging on the combining of their investments in different places. Combining heaviness and variety in the geographic dimension can improve the ability to become unique both as a participant in different development processes as well as in creating structural advantages. Investments in a geographic pattern, in fact, give opportunities of a better utilization of context-specific resources. Thus, in contradiction of the research fields that underline the importance of overcoming "friction of space," investigating geography from a resource interaction perspective points in the opposite direction, namely to the importance of taking advantage of friction of space. The role of place in the creation of friction between resources and furthermore, how this friction between directly and indirectly related resources can create new resource combinations that take advantage of existing solutions, is a challenging issue for future research.

NOTES

1. An interesting remark on the globalization debate is made by the Japanese management strategist, Kenichi Ohmae (1985), who instead of a general globalization process draws attention to the *global triad*, a tripolar macroregional structure around the North American, European, and East and Southeast Asian economic spheres.
2. See e.g. Håkansson and Snehota 1995, Håkansson and Waluszewski 2002 for an overview, or the website www.impgroup.org.

REFERENCES

Arthur, W. B., 1986, *Industry Location Patterns and the Importance of History*, Publication 84, Centre for Economic Policy Research, Stanford University: Stanford.

Becattini, G., (ed.), 1987, *Mercato e forze locali: il distretto industriale* [Market and forces at local level: the industrial district], Il Mulino: Bologna.

Boari, C., & Lipparini, A., 1999, Networks within Industrial Districts: Organising Knowledge Creation and Transfer by Means of Moderate Hierarchies, *Journal of Management and Governance*, Vol. 3, Issue 4, pp. 339–60.

Brusco, S., 1989, *Piccole imprese e distretti industriali* [Small firms and industrial districts], Rosenberg & Sellier: Torino.

Caroli, M., & Lipparini, A., 2001, *Piccole imprese oltre confine* [Small firms across the border], Carocci: Roma.

Castells, M., 1996, *The Rise of the Network Society. The Information Age. Economy, Society and Culture. Volume 1*, Blackwell Publishers Ltd: Oxford.

Corò, G., & Grandinetti R., 1999, Strategie di delocalizzazione e processi evolutivi nei distretti industriali italiani [Outsourcing strategies and evolution processes in Italian industrial districts], *L'industria*, n° 4, oct–dec. 1999.

Corò, G., & Micelli, S., 1999, Distretti industriali e imprese transnazionali: modelli alternativi o convergenti? [Industrial districts and transnational enterprises: two converging or opposing models?], *Sviluppo locale*, VI, 10.

Dicken, P., 1998, *Global Shift. Transforming the World Economy*, Paul Chapman Publishing: London.

Edgerton, D., 1996, Science in the United Kingdom of Britain and Northern Ireland: a case study in the nationalisation of science, In: Krige, J., & Pestre, D., (eds.), *Science in the Twentieth Century*, Harvard Academic Publishers: Boston.

Grandinetti, R., & Rullani, E., 1996, *Imprese transnazionali ed economia globale* [Transnational enterprises and global economy], NIS: Roma.

Henders, B., 1992, *Positions in Industrial Networks. Marketing Newspring in the UK*, Doctoral Thesis, Uppsala University, Department of Business Studies.

Håkansson, H., (ed.), 1982, *Industrial Marketing and Purchasing of Industrial Goods: An Interactive Approach*, Wiley: New York.

Håkansson, H., & Snehota, I., 1995, *Developing Relationships in Business Networks*, Routledge: London, New York.

Håkansson, H., & Waluszewski, A., 2002, *Managing Technological Development. IKEA, the environment and technology*, Routledge: London, New York.

Hoover, E. M., 1948, *The Location of Economic Activity*, McGraw-Hill: New York.

Johanson, J., & Mattsson, L-G., 1985, Marketing Investments and Market Investments in Industrial Networks, *International Journal of Research in Marketing*, Vol. 2, pp. 185–195.

Johanson, J., & Mattsson, L-G., 1988, *Network Positions and Strategic Action— An Analytical Framework*, Working Paper, Uppsala University, Department of Business Studies.

Johanson, J., & Wiedersheim-Paul, F., 1975, The Internationalization of the Firm—Four Swedish Cases, *Journal of Management Studies*, 12, October, pp. 305–322.

Krugman, P., 1991, Increasing returns and economic geography, *Journal of Political Economy*, Vol. 99, Issue 3, pp. 483–499.

Lindqvist, S., 1984, *Technology on Trial: The Introduction of Steam Power Technology into Sweden, 1715–1736*, Almqvist & Wiksell: Stockholm.

Lipparini, A., & Lorenzoni, G., 1999, The Leveraging of Inter-firm Relationships as a Distinctive Organizational Capability. A Longitudinal Study, *Strategic Management Journal*, Vol. 20, Issue 4, pp. 317–339.

Lorenzoni, G., & Baden-Fuller, C., 1995, Creating a Strategic Center to Manage a Web of Partners, *California Management Review*, Vol. 37, No. 3, Spring 1995, pp. 146–163.

Malmberg, A., Malmberg, B., & Lundequist, P., 2000, Agglomeration and firm performance: economies of scale, localisation, and urbanisation among Swedish export firms, *Environment and Planning A.*, Vol. 32, Issue 2, pp. 305–321.

Markgren, B., 2001, *Är Närhet en Geografisk Fråga? Företags affärsverksamhet och geografi—en studie av beroenden mellan företag och lokaliseringens betydelse* [Is Closeness a Matter of Geography? Companies' Business Activities and Geography—A Study of Dependencies between Companies and the Significance of Location], Doctoral Thesis, Uppsala University, Department of Business Studies.

Marshall, A., 1890, *Industry and Trade. A study of industrial technique and business organisation, and of their influence on the condition of various classes and nations*, Macmillan: London.

Maskell, P., Eskelinen, H., Hannibalsson, I., Malmberg, A., & Vatne, E., 1998, *Competitiveness, Localised Learning and Regional Development. Specialisation and Prosperity in Small Open Economies*, Routledge: London, New York.

Myrdal, G., 1957, *Economic Theory and the Underdeveloped Regions*, Ducksworth: London.

Ohmae, K., 1995, *The end of Nation State. The rise of Regional Economies*, Harper Collins Publishers: London.

Penrose, E. T., 1959, *The Theory of the Growth of the Firm*, Oxford University Press: New York.

Pilotti, L., 1998, I distretti innovativi del Nord Est [The innovative districts in Italy's North-East], *Sviluppo & Organizzazione*, n° 167, may–june 1998.

Piore, M. J., & Sabel, C.F., 1994, *The Second Industrial Divide*, Basic Books: New York.

Porter, M., 1990, *The Competitive Advantage of Nations*, Macmillan: London.

Porter, M., 1994, The Role of Location in Competition, *Journal of the Economics of Business*, Vol. 1, Issue 1, pp. 35–39.

Ricardo, D., 1817, *On the Principles of Political Economy and Taxation*, John Murrey: London (Reprinted in 1990 by Cambridge University Press:- Cambridge).

Tunisini, A., 2003, *Supply chains e strategie di posizionamento* [Supply chains and positioning strategies], Carocci Editore: Roma.

Törnroos, J-Å., 1991, *Om företagets geografi—en teoretisk analys* [On the Company's Geography—A Theoretical Analysis], Åbo Akademis Förlag: Åbo.

Varaldo, R., & Ferrucci, L., (eds.), 1997, *Il distretto industriale tra logiche di impresa e logiche di sistema* [The industrial district framed between the firm's and the system's logics], Franco Angeli: Milano.

Waluszewski, A., 2002, *How Social Science is Coloured by its Research Tools. Or What's Behind and Growing "Biotech Valley"?*, Paper presented at Nobel Symposium, 123: "Science and Industry in the 20th Century," Stockholm, November 2002.

Wedin, T., 2001, *Networks and Demand. The Use of Electricity in an Industrial Process*, Doctoral Thesis, Department of Business Studies, Uppsala University.

Widmalm, S., 2001, *Det öppna laboratoriet. Uppsalafysiken och dess nätverk, 1853–1910* [The Open Laboratory. Uppsala Physics and Its Networks, 1853–1910], Atlantis: Stockholm.

COMBINING SCIENTIFIC KNOWLEDGE AND VENTURE CAPITAL ACROSS PLACES AND NETWORKS OF RESOURCES

ENRICO BARALDI AND TORKEL STRÖMSTEN

". . . the production of facts and artifacts will not occur everywhere and for free, but will occur only at restricted places at particular times."

(Latour, 1987: 179)

1. INTRODUCTION: SCIENTIFIC KNOWLEDGE AND OTHER KEY RESOURCES

Scientific innovation is today considered such an important driver for economic growth as to induce public agencies to strongly promote the commercialization of scientific discoveries. Some geographical locations or regions appear more proficient than others in creating economic value out of their scientific innovations and the relevance of place-related factors in developing and exploiting scientific knowledge has been pointed out by several researchers. In relation to the biotech sector, Powell et al. (2002) formulate it in this way: "The relevant scientific expertise in biotech is, by now, broadly distributed throughout the industrial world, with major centres of scientific excellence in the U.S., the UK, Sweden, France, Germany and Switzerland.

The authors wish to thank their interviewees for so kindly providing the empirical material for this work, and in particular Mostafa Ronaghi, Ulf Landegren and Simon Fredriksson. Financial support was provided by Fondazione IRI and Svenska Handelsbanken/Jan Wallander's Foundation.

But the science is commercialized by firms in a significant manner
(. . .) in only a handful of locations worldwide." (Powell et al., 2002:
293). Further, Powell et al. (2002) discuss how the existence of specific
institutional arrangements and the availability of specific resources,
such as venture capital, in certain locations make it likely that scientific discoveries will be commercialized by companies within these locations, rather than in other locations.

Scientific knowledge can be seen as a resource, whose value depends upon how it is combined with other resources (Penrose, 1959:
25, 74–75). The other resources in the network around a scientific discovery (and the firm hosting the emerging innovation) are crucial to
its commercial success. This switches the focus from the innovation to
the significant actors that control resources important for *buying and
selling* the scientific idea and that embed it in a *production and use*
system (Håkansson & Waluszewski, 2002). Further, the relationships
that an actor uses to access and mobilize others' resources are themselves an important resource (Håkansson & Snehota, 1995). Thus, the
changes in the value of a scientific idea when it is progressively related
to different places will be looked at from a perspective that emphasizes networks and resource heterogeneity (Håkansson & Snehota,
1995; Håkansson & Waluszewski, 2002).

Entrepreneurial finance (see Gompers & Lerner, 1999) attributes
a rather straightforward role to venture capitalists in the commercialization of scientific knowledge: they provide valuable resources such as
capital, contacts and competence. There is no real downside to venture
capital. However, from the funded firm's perspective, the room to ma-
neuver certainly increases in some dimensions, but it also decreases in
others, as the investor will have a say in strategic questions. From a societal perspective, too, such as that of a region or a city, venture capital
is viewed as critical for the commercialization of scientific discoveries.
Swedberg (2002) stresses that there must be more to a place than
merely having the right *institutions* for it to prosper. To be successful in
the biotech industry, a region should have a university with high-class
research, regulatory authorities, and hospitals; but without venture capital, the chances will be small that a biotech industry will develop in the
region.[1] But there is also something else that is harder to grasp: relationships and networks. Relationships may span several places and
create network-like configurations. Thus, one place may be intimately
dependent upon development work in another, and vice versa.

The above literature implicitly focuses on commercialization of
scientific knowledge within the region where it originates: the actors

Enrico Baraldi and Torkel Strömsten **249**

within a given location commercialize a discovery, investing in it and making it a real product hosted by a firm. This chapter focuses instead on how different places influence the value of a scientific discovery within the biotech field. Using as an illustration the case of an innovation that relates Uppsala (Sweden) and Silicon Valley, the aim of this chapter is to examine how the *commercial* value of this particular type of resource is built up when it is concretely related to *several* geographical places. What happens when different pieces of scientific knowledge and other key resources, such as venture capital, in widely separated places "meet" and combine? What are the strategies of the actors in the network for creating value out of this innovation and how do these actors use the different places? Such a discussion contributes to a re-evaluation of the importance of *specific places* in techno-scientific development by comparison with today's emphasis on globalization. In doing so, this paper also provides a nuanced and deeply interactive view of the interplay between places and scientific, technical and economic resources.

The chapter proceeds now in section 2 to a conceptual discussion of the links between the two key resources of scientific knowledge and venture capital. Section 3 then presents a methodological note on how the empirical material was collected and the case study was constructed. Section 4 includes the ParAllele case, which section 5 discusses in the light of networks and spatial issues. Section 6 finally summarizes the chapter.

2. THE LINKS BETWEEN SCIENTIFIC KNOWLEDGE AND VENTURE CAPITAL: MARKETS, HIERARCHIES OR NETWORKS?

Two key resources in the commercialization process are knowledge and money. Policymakers, scientists and industrialists in the biotechnology field consider these two resources so important that they strive to provide them in abundance within their regions. In fact, science-based ventures entail high technological and commercial risk: a lot of money needs to be invested long before a viable product can be created and a firm can develop the relationships necessary to exploit it commercially. Here venture capital is often needed. But not all *combinations* between venture capitalists and scientists work well: a good capital-science match seems to let everything go smoothly, whereas its absence blocks even promising discoveries from materializing and delivering value.

However, it is too simplistic to assume that it is enough to combine a little scientific knowledge and a little venture capital (VC) to spur development and, especially, that this combination is easier to obtain in certain places *simply because* they contain plenty of both resources, knowledge and capital. It is too simplistic because these two resources do not automatically attract each other, nor will they necessarily produce value if combined with any other piece of complementary resource: their detailed features matter! In fact, the actors behind these two resources (knowledge and capital) search constantly for opportunities and *discard* many potential "matings" of knowledge and capital, as if there were better and worse knowledge and capital. This issue highlights the heterogeneity and qualitative differences between pieces of scientific knowledge, on the one hand, and also between pieces of venture capital, on the other.

At any time, there is a wealth of scientific knowledge and venture capital that does not get combined with a corresponding piece in the "commercialized scientific knowledge" puzzle. And probably certain pieces never will be combined with any complements or, if they do get combined, it will not be in the original form, but some change in them will be required. For the scarcer resource—capital—what counts most is finding a *proper* complement: despite the abundance of scientific ideas, the really good ideas are even scarcer than capital, so that much capital is not combined at the expected rate of return or, which is the same, more capital than expected needs to be poured in, or—what is worse—the expected commercial leverage of an innovation is never reached.

One may choose to explain these mismatches between scientific knowledge and venture capital as *market imperfections*. One can add to this explanation a *geographical dimension* and claim that, because some pieces of knowledge and of capital are located far apart, achieving a matching between scientific ideas and venture capital becomes very demanding. Therefore, in order to achieve this market matching, either knowledge must move to meet venture capital in another location or vice versa. The risk remains, however, that, despite their will to be mobile, either capital or science end up not really "liking each other" and no deal can be made to combine them. Certainly, no author would ever dare claim that the markets in which knowledge and venture capital change hands are "perfect." But some authors suggest that the *exchangeability, transparency, mobility* and *combinability* of these two resources have increased in the last decades. For instance, Arora & Gambardella (1994) and Arora, Fusfuri & Gambardella (2001) stress how specific markets for scientific knowledge (patents, etc.) are being established, relying on stronger enforcement rules and on the increased transparency of the pieces of knowledge exchanged. Likewise, other authors stress similar developments in the VC market.

Irrespective of whether exchangeability, transparency, mobility and combinability of knowledge and venture capital are increasing, such trends are far from producing anything near a *real* market for these two resources. Maybe a full "marketization" may happen for some very few selected pieces of knowledge and capital, that is, for the most *homogeneous* and *superficial* elements (e.g., the bare patent or the cash transfer), but certainly not for the most heterogeneous, hidden and underlying elements (e.g., tacit knowledge or venturing experience).

Creating markets for knowledge and VC is perhaps a contradiction in terms, for reasons that involve both resources. Knowledge is largely tacit or sticky (von Hippel, 1998) and contextual (Lundgren, 1994). On the other hand, venture capitalists are risk-averse: they only invest in scientific ideas that they strongly believe can make it to a flotation or a trade sale, giving investors a high return. These investments often take the form of syndication networks, that is, several VC firms invest jointly in a project (e.g., Lerner, 1994; Lockett & Wright, 2001; Wedin, 2002). To further stress the non-market nature of the science-venture capital link, it may be noticed that behind science-based firms there are often serial entrepreneurs, that is, scientists who have a proven record of commercial success, often with the same venture capitalist as investor.

An alternative to a market-like science-capital link is a *planned* combination: there are numerous examples of the design of science parks, clusters, etc. The two main ingredients in these planned recipes are public capital and local knowledge; but the hierarchically steered combinations of knowledge and money rarely succeed, even when they claim to rely on "market forces," such as frictionless technology transfer or attraction of foreign investors. The reason behind such failures is probably that completely different mechanisms from either market prices or hierarchical plans are involved in making the combinations of science and VC work. Moreover, there is a need not only to combine capital and scientific ideas, but also to find users for the resulting innovation. Thus, the science-capital link that connects a start-up firm and its financiers is closely related to the market into which the production and use of the firm's product must fit.

Considering the nature and complexity of their configuration and mechanisms, the arenas where knowledge and capital are exchanged and combined would be better described as *networks*, rather than markets or hierarchies (see Powell, 1990: 300). And within networks, transparency, homogeneity, mobility without corruption and free combinability are the exception to a rule of required specific adaptations, rigidity of movements, heterogeneity and information accumulation in a few centers (Latour, 1987). Therefore, the combinations of science and capital do not happen on perfect markets capable of instantaneously cutting distances, but are forged within networks that are heavy, corrugated, bent and entrenched in specific locales: thus, no matching of science and capital can ever occur smoothly or automatically, by virtue of generalized demand and supply relations. Talking of networks, instead of markets, makes specific, well-identified places even more prominent.[2]

3. A METHODOLOGICAL NOTE: BUILDING THE CASE STORY

This chapter presents a story of how a scientific discovery finds its way from one place to another, where it is combined with another scientific innovation and with venture capital into a start-up firm. We present how the first discovery, not commercialized in its "birthplace," travels and meets new people who include it in a product ready to be sold. To trace these processes is a journey in itself, and it is never possible to capture the "true" or "real" story. What we offer is our synthesis and interpretation of several accounts that we collected through interviews with the people involved in the research and commercialization of the focal innovation(s). We have let the key informants read the story and comment on it. However, the present version of the case story is our own.

The empirical material was gathered primarily from in-depth and informal interviews, fifteen in all, conducted in Uppsala and in Silicon Valley. The first interview was held in late 2001, while all the others took place in early 2004 (see appendix). These interviews aimed at having interviewees tell their part of the story: how they got involved with the innovation process and what their role was in developing and commercializing it. One of the interviewees did not have an active role in the process, but witnessed most of its steps and was therefore used to validate the other personal sources. In addition to interviews, we relied on such documentary sources as company presentations and press releases for further evidence. However, since these publications originate from actors who strive to protect their interests, we also used other sources such as patents, scientific articles in biotech journals, and several organizations' websites. This helped us better understand the focal technology, the innovation, and the context where it was developed and used.

This is a real-time story, still unfolding: the technology has not yet reached what can be called a "closure" (Bijker, 1995). Thus, the time when the story is told is important. A year from now the story might look different: other key informants might be identified and another story be told. This is of course important to keep in mind when reading it. Nevertheless, the case provides us with an illustration that helps us (1) to see the complexity in the process of combination of science and capital and (2) to discuss in the concluding section the role played by places and spatial issues.

4. PARALLELE: COMBINING UPPSALA AND SILICON VALLEY

"Do you want to start a company?" That was the question Mostafa Ronaghi, as a newly employed researcher at the Stanford Genome Technology Center (SGTC), asked a few of his colleagues at a get-together at Lake Tahoe (California). The firm he wanted to start was to be based upon several technologies, some of which he had come across when he was a Ph.D. student in Sweden, whereas others were ready or would be developed at SGTC. The colleagues listened carefully and with interest to Ronaghi, who had an impressive scientific track record and had been involved in a successful biotech start up in Sweden before joining SGTC.

4.1 Identifying an Opportunity

Ronaghi had been doing research in biochemistry and genetics in Sweden for almost a decade before moving to Stanford University in 1999. A trained enzymologist, his speciality was the development of chemistry-based methods for DNA sequencing and analysis. During his research at the Royal Institute of Technology, Stockholm, he was part of the team that developed the "pyrosequencing" technique for DNA sequencing. Around this technology, a homonymous firm was

founded and received venture financing leading to a flotation in Sweden. Scientifically, Ronaghi would go on to publish more than 20
peer-reviewed articles on pyrosequencing methods in such journals
as *Science*.

In the meanwhile, Ronaghi continued his research in the field of
analytical biochemistry for the purpose of developing new methods of
gene detection and analysis. During this search, Ronaghi came in contact with Ulf Landegren's research group at the Genetics & Pathology
Department (GenPat) of Uppsala University, Sweden. This research
group had realized that short DNA strings form a circle around a target DNA sequence, opening the way for a method that could be utilized for genotyping (i.e., the analysis of specific DNA regions).

Landegren had himself already had close contacts with California: he had spent five years as a post doc at Caltech. During this stay,
he worked with Lee Hood, one of the most prominent scientists in genetic research, and he developed a method of genetic analysis, the
oligonucleotide ligation assay (OLA), which was then licensed by Applied Biosystems and is one of the most actively sold tests for cystic
fibrosis today.[3] In 1989, Landegren moved home to Uppsala University, where a SKr 100,000 research grant was waiting for him. It then
appeared clear to Landegren how limited the economic resources in
Uppsala were when compared to those at Caltech, where he had had
two post docs and two laboratory assistants working for him. Things
would later improve in Uppsala, but Caltech's resources would remain significantly larger.

During the early 1990s, Landegren started working as a consultant for Pharmacia Biotech, a large biotech equipment supplier located in Uppsala. One of the methods that Pharmacia patented for
Landegren was a further development of the OLA technology. This
method builds on the fact that the two ends of synthetic DNA strands
hybridize to DNA molecules close to each other. If this is done cor-
rectly, the ends can be joined enzymatically, converting the probes
into DNA circles. The fact that there are two DNA segments that
must fit increases the *specificity* of the test: "It is just like when there
are two keys that have to be turned around in order to open a safety
vault," Landegren explains. When the ends of the probes are joined,
the probes are converted into circles of DNA, wound around, and
thus linked to, the target DNA molecule—hence the name of the
technology: "padlock probes."

In 1994, Landegren first patented the padlock probe technology and then published a paper on it. Even if the development of

padlocks can be traced back to Caltech and OLA, the modification made by Landegren in Uppsala, although small, had important consequences. The padlock method needs only *one* synthetic DNA string. By comparison, a technique that uses two separate recognition probes, such as the PCR method, makes it difficult to look at several genetic sequences in the same reaction, since the large number of recognition probes tend to cross-react and give rise to false reaction products. This was a problem that the modified OLA method, the padlock probe, could solve. In fact, this method made it possible to run many analyses *in parallel*. Whereas the PCR method can run ten or a dozen analyses simultaneously, padlocks opened the possibility of running 10,000 analyses, with good results. This would certainly save *time, costs* and *sample material*—all increasingly important parameters in genetic research.

Landegren and his team had published a few articles[4] on the use of padlock probes for genetic analysis. The Swedish team had also been trying since the mid-1990s to utilize the padlock probes to analyze simultaneously multiple DNA samples on a single array, and they had presented this work at an international meeting, attended by scientists from Stanford. However, the researchers at GenPat were proceeding very slowly in their attempts to scale up the analytical power of padlock probes. It was at this time that Ronaghi came across Landegren's padlock probes: he was immediately fascinated by the possibility of using this method to conduct large-scale and high-throughput DNA analysis, especially for the purpose of detecting and mapping "genetic diversity."

In fact, while the map of the human genome was being completed,[5] it appeared relevant to go deeper into the genomic material of single individuals, in order to identify that 5% of DNA responsible for all diversity in humans, such as physical appearance, risk of developing diseases, and reaction to pharmaceuticals. Understanding which variations (i.e., mutations) in a person's genome caused a specific disease or an adverse reaction to a drug would require going very deeply into each of the 3.2 billion nucleic bases composing the human genome, in order to identify the so called "single nucleotide polymorphisms" (SNPs), that is, the individual differences in the sequence of single nucleic bases. Clearly, this endeavor would require high measurement capacity, efficiency, sensitivity (i.e., how much genetic material is needed for running an analysis), and precision.

Landegren's padlocks promised the above advantages of high throughput, precision and sensitivity, *but only if further developed.*

These were some of the ideas that Mostafa Ronaghi took with him when he moved from Sweden to California in 1999. Further developing the padlock probe method into a viable tool for large-scale and efficient genotyping was, in particular, something that Ronaghi immediately started working on at SGTC. More precisely, reliability and high throughput required the padlock method to achieve repeatability and measuring accuracy, while being run *in parallel*: in other words, Ronaghi was looking for a way to achieve "multiplexing," that is, the possibility of simultaneously analyzing many DNA sequences in a sample. He started experimenting by himself, interacting with the GenPat group in Uppsala, but SGTC would soon prove a perfect environment to add this multiplexing capability.

4.2 Starting the Journey towards ParAllele

In 1999, Ronaghi was hired by the Stanford Genome Technology Centre (SGTC). Founded in 1993 with a grant from the American National Institutes of Health (NIH), SGTC is a large laboratory employing about 50 researchers under the leadership of Professor Ron Davis. Although related to the Biochemistry Department of Stanford University (to which it formally belongs), SGTC deals mostly with applied research and the development of *methods and technologies* supporting research in the Life Sciences.

Since his arrival in Stanford and at SGTC, Ronaghi had been considering starting a company to develop and commercialize a method for high-throughput genotyping relying on the padlock probe idea. But it would take a special episode to set this process in motion: it was in November 1999, during a trip to the resort at Lake Tahoe arranged for the SGTC staff, that Ronaghi confronted four of his colleagues with the suggestion of developing and commercializing such a method. These four colleagues—Paul Hardenbol (molecular biologist), Maneesh Jain (optical physicist), Eugeni Namsaraev (chemist) and Tom Willis (astronomer and geneticist)—were thrilled by Ronaghi's proposal to enter into business, while working on a breakthrough technology that could also help their scientific careers.

Back at Stanford, Ronaghi called a brainstorming meeting with his four colleagues to evaluate the technical possibility of achieving multiplexing with padlock probes. The result of this meeting was that all five researchers agreed to leave their other current projects and to focus on Ronaghi's proposal. These individuals had different scientific backgrounds and experience that were to play a key role in the following development. They all had the necessary common knowledge base to understand what this technology was about, but in particular they had a very valuable set of *complementary* competences.

These five scientists had also an interesting trait in common: they had all been involved in starting up companies based on their research and shared a basic understanding of the market potential of the invention that they were envisaging. Moreover, this research team seemed technically capable of achieving the consistency and precision in large-scale DNA analysis forming the basis for multiplexing.

And multiplexing was exactly what needed to be applied to the padlock probe method in order to make it easily repeatable, to be run in parallel and with measuring precision: this is what the team at SGTC started eagerly working on in late 1999. Multiplex analysis means *looking simultaneously at more than one DNA sequence in a sample.* Multiplexing would not only allow much faster DNA analyses (precisely those required to detect and map SNPs, see above), but also dramatically reduce the cost of analysis in terms of the consumption of plastic tubes and of such reagents as enzymes. For these reasons, multiplexing would add a commercial potential to Landegren's padlock method, by addressing concrete and widespread needs in public and private research labs, both at universities and in industry. A growing market (that of genetic diversity analysis, which in turn was expected to cater for the needs of such new fields as personalized therapeutics) therefore stood open for the technology that the SGTC team was about to start developing. Consequently, the five scientists were from an early stage explicitly aiming at creating a company— the soon-to-be ParAllele—dedicated to exploiting commercially this new technology.

4.3 Adding Multiplexing to Padlocks: "MIP"

Padlocks are certainly an important new method for the biotech community, but taken alone, without multiplexing, they provided a limited commercial value. It was instead the addition of multiplexing to padlocks that opened the way to exciting technical applications, of great commercial value. Achieving this combination was however an endeavor difficult to accomplish. In fact, in order to perform multiplexing, the SGTC researchers had partly to chemically *re-engineer* the padlock probe, which was originally only adequate for analyzing one DNA sequence at a time. This required the padlock probes to be equipped with a lot of new features: these probes are very difficult to create, but the SGTC team was able to develop a robust method of obtaining them inexpensively. After only three months of development, by early 2000, Ronaghi and his colleagues, through the Stanford Office of Technology Licensing (SOTL), filed for a patent,[6] whereby they combined padlocks with multiplexing. But in order to have a complete method, the SGTC team had to further improve the multiplexed padlock probe by developing another technique for chemically enhancing its *sensitivity* of detection. This step would take longer, but the complete technology for multiplex genetic analysis with padlock probes was practically ready by 2001, one-and-a-half years after the informal discussions at Lake Tahoe: its official name was MIP, that is, "molecular inversion probe."

Whereas it was not possible to patent the whole MIP genotyping method, pending Landegren's patents, Ronaghi and colleagues also filed a patent for the method for chemically enhancing sensitivity. Specialist lawyers located around Stanford's Campus (Fish & Nieve and Morrison & Foerster) helped the five inventors to draft their patents, but SOTL became the official owner of the patents on the two technologies, officially known as (1) "Direct Multiplex Genotyping on Genomic DNA" (that is, the *multiplexing* function) and (2) "Method for Renaturation, Reassociation, Association and Hydridization of Nucleic Acid Molecules" (the supplemental method to enhance *sensitivity*). Figure 1 relates the above pieces of technology.

Even at this early stage, the SGTC inventor team decided not to develop a machine embedding the functionalities of MIP: instead they aimed to develop a method that would be as light as possible and that could be run on most existing equipment, performing millions of analysis at the cost only of reagents and consumables.

Meanwhile, the very positive results achieved with the MIP method helped the five researchers overcome the initial skepticism of Ron Davis, SGTC's chief. When MIP received great interest and positive feedback at several academic conferences, Davis became even more convinced of its potentials. He then became an important support for MIP because of his reputation and widespread contacts both in the academic and in the biotech business community in the Bay Area.

4.4 A First Encounter with Venture Capital

Even before founding their company, the five inventors had come into close contact with the Swiss venture capitalist Index Venture.

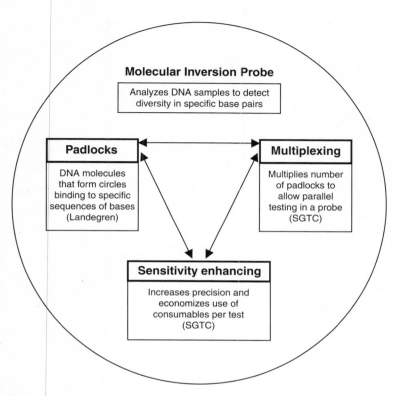

Figure 1. The MIP technology and the three methods that compose it.

Tom Willis, who had worked for many years as a technical consultant for Index, presented in 2000 the emergent MIP technology to Index's Francesco De Rubertis, a geneticist with a background from Massachusetts Institute of Technology (MIT). De Rubertis saw the technical and commercial potential of MIP and started providing business advice to the five inventors. Based on (1) a strong personal trust in Tom Willis, (2) the belief that the SNP market would grow even further and (3) the fact that MIP was practically ready and did not need any further expensive development, Index went even further: in April 2001, Index provided "seed funding" for the newly founded ParAllele.[7] In this way, Index became an early partner, strongly motivated to help ParAllele through successive rounds of financing. Seed funding was provided on a very informal basis, with only the promise of receiving a better price than any other VC on ParAllele's shares in an envisaged first round of financing.

The team decided to locate ParAllele's office in South San Francisco: this very place was chosen despite much higher real estate costs there than in Palo Alto (SGTC's location), because South San Francisco hosts many biotech firms, which the founders expected would facilitate cooperation and recruitment of qualified personnel. Moreover, many of ParAllele's potential customers were located in this area, within a couple of kilometres.

4.5 IPRs: Contacts between Ulf Landegren and the SGTC Team

Index soon raised the IPR issue that MIP was dependent on the padlock technology (see Figure 1) patented by Ulf Landegren. It was clear that this patent[8] was necessary in order to commercialize MIP through ParAllele and especially in order to collect further venture capital. No VC firm would invest in the company without a valuable and safe patent portfolio. Index was therefore ready to support the five inventors in the negotiations to come with the Swedish professor.

Landegren had already been approached by the SGTC team in 2000, at an important Biotech conference at Cold Spring Harbor. The five SGTC inventors had presented him with the idea of using the padlock technology together with tag arrays (the key idea behind multiplexing). According to Landegren, the basic point in their message was: "Do you want to compete or do you want to collaborate?" Landegren was not totally happy about this development, since he had hoped that the Uppsala group could continue to work on padlocks in peace and quiet, and improve the technology by themselves and maybe later commercialize it. However, SGTC seemed to be at an advantage. The GenPat Group at Uppsala University included only ten people and had fewer financial resources compared to SGTC, even if it provided a very dynamic environment with strong engagement in each doctoral research project by the supervisors, Landegren and Nilsson. Moreover, the Uppsala group had only one doctoral student working on this project.

Even if Landegren was aware of the importance of his padlock innovation, he was unable to exploit it commercially in Sweden. One reason was that in the early 1990s he was working as a consultant for Uppsala-based Pharmacia Biotech. The company financed his patent on padlocks and had some legal rights to the innovation, but showed no interest in exploiting it. This connection with Pharmacia prevented

Landegren and his group from commercializing padlock probes because this firm had the legal rights to what Landegren was developing. Moreover, they had the "first right of refusal," as Landegren puts it. To get help with patenting, Landegren needed to present an invention to Pharmacia first, which made other contacts difficult: Pharmacia's lack of interest made it hard to get others interested. But when British Amersham took over Pharmacia Biotech, many molecular biology projects in Uppsala were set aside and, in 2000, Landegren was granted the rights to his innovations.

4.6 Uppsala Grants the Right to Exploit Padlocks within MIPs

The negotiations with Landegren to obtain the licence for the padlock technology became increasingly intense. The venture capitalist Index took part in several meetings, arguing that, since the padlock technology alone would not sustain a company, the best thing for Landegren to do was to license his technology to ParAllele. But the Swedish researcher was not anxious to do so, because he still had some plans to commercialize his method himself, now that the Pharmacia rights were no longer in his way. In fact, when ParAllele's official request came, the Swedish team at GenPat Uppsala had been engaged for several years in the development of multiplexed padlock probes.

However, the resources and the connections available at the Uppsala lab were nowhere near those available at the Stanford lab. For instance, such essential materials as industrial tag micro-arrays were not available at the GenPat lab: the group relied on home-made micro-arrays, but these gave unsatisfactory results and caused considerable delays. By contrast, in their search for a multiplexing and sensitivity-enhancing method, the SGTC team could rely on a strong group composed only of post-docs with strong and complementary expertise. Moreover, SGTC was a world-renowned micro-arrays center, with close cooperation with the industry leader Affymetrix and with a chief, Ron Davis, boasting extensive experience in this field.

The result of tough negotiations was that Landegren became bound to ParAllele by a licensing agreement earning him periodic royalties, a position on the firm's advisory board, but also containing a clause requiring him to disclose to ParAllele any of his future developments of the padlock technology. Moreover, Landegren and his co-worker Mats Nilsson were de facto included among the founders of ParAllele, with an equity share.

4.7 ParAllele's Interaction with Venture Capitalists

Since they had started searching for financing, at the end of 2000, the five inventors had been working on a business plan. They also nailed down some figures for ParAllele's expected market, broadly defined as the "SNP market." ParAllele's founders expressed this market as a technical application area, rather than as a specific group of customers. But this market (i.e., all public and private labs dealing with mapping genetic diversity) seemed to be (1) very promising, in terms of growth (after the completion of the HUGO project) and (2) in search of new more cost-effective solutions for genotyping.

In early 2001, ParAllele's founders were still speaking in *general* terms of an SNP analysis market, but they started looking more concretely at the existing competitors and at the likely market size (roughly assessed at $500 million). From a user's perspective, it appeared evident that any new SNP genotyping technique should address the problem of the high cost of performing massive high-throughput analysis and the scarcity of a key process material for labs such as phenotyped human DNA tissue (connecting genetic code to a specific functional characteristic of a human being, such as diabetes or blue eyes). And the MIP method appeared very well equipped to address both of these pressing problems.

The seed financer Index also had an effect on the business model envisaged by ParAllele's founders, who were aiming at providing simply a service platform for a mere for-service fee. Index's suggestion was instead *also* to create a *proprietary kit*, where the technical platform could be embedded. This required also having software and electronic components perfectly functioning before any product release. At the same time, Index explicitly requested that other VC firms from Silicon Valley and the Bay Area be involved in the following stages, because Index felt it could not handle the process from Switzerland. It was considered very important to be located near the funded firms: at least one VC firm should ideally be within driving distance in order to assist and supervise the start-up, and also deal with everyday problems, including interviewing job candidates.

The five inventors focussed on a list of 10 venture capitalists, those having a deep knowledge both of ParAllele's potential market and of its technical field—a requirement the founders stipulated in order to receive effective support for the company development. They directly approached four VC firms and three presented a "term sheet" (i.e., a pricing offer on a quote of ParAllele's shares). When two of these, Abingworth and Versant, jointly presented a term sheet together with Index, this was accepted by ParAllele's founders. This deal brought $7.5 million to ParAllele and was completed in October 2001, signaling the first round of financing with three VC firms that shared a high technical and business competence in the biotech field and that had financed several early-stage biotech ventures, many of which were still in their investment portfolios. These three VC firms had instead different geographical locations, contributing to spreading also internationally the interest in ParAllele: Versant Ventures was based in Palo Alto, just a few kilometres from SGTC; Abingworth Management is British, but had offices in Palo Alto (just three kilometres from SGTC); and Index Ventures was located in Geneva (Switzerland). The presence of two local VCs thus also satisfied Index's initial request.

4.8 Venture Capitalists Influence ParAllele's Market Definition

The new VC firms further steered ParAllele's business model towards "providing a complete genotyping solution" and selling a *kit* including the MIP technology. These firms also pushed for the provision of highly qualified *services* in close *collaboration* with large pharmaceutical firms. Moreover, the VC firms pushed for a further definition of ParAllele's target market, with regard to numbers of potential actors (buyers, competitors and partners) and potential size: clearly identified technical needs were specified, also to distinguish ParAllele from its competitors and from other firms doing similar things. It appeared that the value of the MIP technology could be best exploited in two segments: *SNP genotyping* (the analysis of *already identified* SNPs) and *SNP detection* (the search for and discovery of new, *previously unmapped* SNPs). The two selected segments were expected to be worth $500 million (an estimate still valid today, even if the expected growth has yet to come). ParAllele divided its potential customers into two categories:

(a) "high-end": maximum 20 large laboratories at government sites, big pharmaceutical and a few genotyping contractors, all characterized by daily needs up to 500,000 genotype analyses;
(b) "low-end": up to 2000 smaller laboratories, with daily needs as low as 50 analyses.

ParAllele chose however to focus primarily on the large-scale-reactions market, requiring 1000 or more reactions each time, leaving aside momentarily clinical diagnostics, which needs one analysis each time. Thus, ParAllele's target customers are (1) those very few large research labs that conduct genetic mapping to localize the genes responsible for a disease,[9] and (2) big pharmaceutical firms that try to characterize genetic variations that affect how individuals react to a certain drug.

4.9 ParAllele Develops Business Relationships

Before acquiring the above customers, ParAllele had an even greater need to acquire legitimacy for itself and for its technology. An important step towards legitimacy was taken in October 2002, when ParAllele received a large grant from the NHGRI (National Human Genome Research Institute) for cooperating with Baylor College of Medicine on the advanced Hap Map project.[10] The large grant ($37 million) was divided among a total of ten organizations. The collaboration with Baylor College was particularly important for ParAllele, because this public institute also acted as a beta-customer, testing and helping further develop the MIP technology. Subsequently, other important potential customers were contacted and they agreed to test the MIP method under the supervision of and in cooperation with ParAllele's personnel. Some eventually decided to purchase the method: this opened the door for establishing continuous relationships with customers for the supply of reagents and consumables to be used during SNP genotyping and for the provision of consulting services.

In fact, in July 2003, ParAllele obtained the first high-profile collaboration with a large pharmaceutical firm, Merck, which funded an extensive study based on the MIP method. Shortly afterwards, in September 2003, ParAllele started with another big pharmaceutical firm, Roche, a joint project to investigate the genetic variation behind Type 2 diabetes: while ParAllele provided its MIP platform, Roche financed the study and provided clinical DNA samples for the genotyping analysis. Even if VC firms were not actively involved in recruiting ParAllele's customers or partners, they still helped to create "goodwill" around ParAllele: they strongly advertised ParAllele and its technology through their contacts at pharmaceutical firms, with presentations and informal talks with the executives in their contact network. This helped create interest in and a good reputation for ParAllele, which favored obtaining actual cooperation contracts with the above customers/partners. Moreover, VC firms offered advice on which specific customer to contact (especially Merck) and which particular person one should talk with to "enter" a customer.

4.10 A Late Entrant

When ParAllele's MIP technology was ready to be commercialized, it was a very *late entrant* in the genotyping field: being perfected in 2001, MIP was born almost a decade after the first genotyping techniques and ParAllele was the last entrant in a field already occupied by a dozen firms (e.g., Orchid, Luminex, ABI, Perlegen, Illumina, Sequenom, Third Wave, Qiagen's Masscode). But being late was not an absolute disadvantage to ParAllele: it enabled the inventors at SGTC to see the other technologies at work, even to use some of them, and to evaluate their advantages and disadvantages (e.g., the huge DNA sample consumption required by some of them).

This allowed the MIP group to address the existing technologies' problems and to solve some of them. This led to a recognition of the importance of providing *high sensitivity* to reduce tissue consumption and also relates to one of the key features of ParAllele's offerings— a method *without* an expensive machine. By contrast, most of ParAllele's competitors provided methods requiring equipment costing up to $2 million (to which the costs for reagents, consumables and DNA tissues must be added): instead the MIP method is hardware-independent and can also be run on these machines.

Moreover, the market and strategy problems (see Orchid's failure) of the earlier entrants induced ParAllele's founders to take a more sober approach to the marketing of genetic analysis, resulting in a more focused strategy, regarding target customers, applications and actual offerings: no longer complex and expensive machines, but simply a method and a set of reagents eventually included in a *microarray* usable on any of the existing large machines. In fact, Index's suggestion to create a kit and a concrete product embedding MIP became concretized when ParAllele became related to Affymetrix, a major producer of micro-arrays for genetic analysis, located just a few kilometres from SGTC. Affymetrix started providing ParAllele with both standard and customized micro-arrays, on which ParAllele analyzes their MIP reactions.

4.11 Back to Uppsala and GenPat

While MIP developed in Silicon Valley, with several actors entering the scene, things did not stop in Uppsala. Indeed some interesting developments happened in the birthplace of padlocks. First of all, the connections between the Swedish research group and ParAllele expanded from the formal licensing contract to more informal research interactions: for instance, in 2003 an article was published on Nature Biotechnology by all the researchers from Sweden and Stanford mentioned in the previous sections: Hardenbol et al. (2003). Moreover, Landegren kept visiting ParAllele twice a year and remained a member of its scientific advisory board. However, as ParAllele people increasingly learn about padlocks, Landegren expects his involvement to fade, unless more technologies are added to ParAllele's current business concept.

The content of the contacts is information-sharing. Landegren informs on what is going on research-wise in Uppsala and the ParAllele group informs all members in the Scientific Advisory Board on the commercial and technical development. Currently, the group in Uppsala continues to develop the padlock probe technology, and ParAllele has some, but not all, rights to further developments of padlocks.

5. DISCUSSION AND CONCLUDING REMARKS: NETWORKS, PLACES AND COMBINATIONS OF SCIENTIFIC KNOWLEDGE AND VENTURE CAPITAL

The combination of *scientific knowledge* with *venture capital* is pivotal for its commercialization. Reflecting the theoretical section 2, the empirical material showed how this combination happens in *networks* that can stretch across and connect several places. Figure 2 provides an overview of the network that emerged around the MIP technology and ParAllele. The lines connecting the key actors show the type of resource exchanged or combined: equity shares, capital ($), advice, reputation, and licences.

The case study showed how different pieces of scientific knowledge (padlocks and multiplexing) and other key resources (capital, advice, qualified personnel, relationships with big pharmas) were combined, despite being in widely separated places, such as Uppsala, Stanford and Switzerland. These combinations do not happen in an impersonal market-like setting, but result from the efforts of actors who closely interact with each other. Both combinations and the exchanges of the two key resources of science and capital require intense and complex negotiations that *simultaneously* involve many actors belonging to the domains of science, industry and venture capital: for instance, Ulf Landegren, ParAllele and Index for the licens-

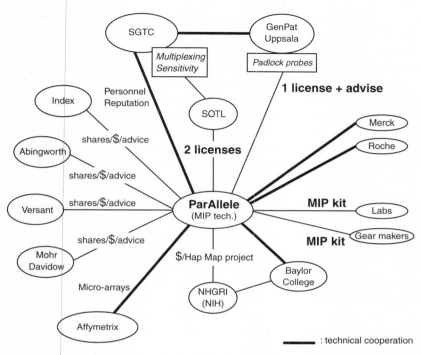

Figure 2. The network emerging around ParAllele and the MIP technology.

ing of padlocks. Close interaction, shaping alliances and negotiation are the key traits of all the involved actors' strategies in defense of their interests as scientists, entrepreneurs and venture capitalists.

The case of ParAllele also demonstrates that the combinations of pieces of scientific knowledge with each other and with venture capital are affected by factors outside the strict intellectual property rights or financial domains, with their rigid contracts and methods of evaluation: these factors are instead *contextual* and tightly related to the environment in which each piece of knowledge is developed and where it can be exploited. But why should place-related factors intervene and interfere with the automatic functioning of science and of capital flows? The reason is that *all local contexts* to which a piece of knowledge is directly or indirectly exposed affect its value and potentials. An example from Section 4.5 helps stress the influence of such contextual, place-related factors on science's commercial value.

If Pharmacia Biotech, a dominant player in the biotechnology tool field, in the local context of Uppsala in the 1990s, had considered padlocks more interesting and decided to exploit this innovation commercially, it is very unlikely that ParAllele could have obtained the licence to include it in its MIP. It is likely that ParAllele would have had to pay such a large amount of money to make its own venture probably unviable. Thus, a potentially advantageous local feature of the Uppsala GenPat lab, that is, the near presence of a strong potential customer and partner, turned into a disadvantage to the *local* value and possibilities of exploitation of padlocks. It is only a few years later that a place far away, Silicon Valley, came with a proposal for immediately exploiting padlocks, but this time in combination with a broader technology.

It is, however, important to note that things had changed in the period 1994–2001: firstly, some other techno-scientific progress had been necessary to increase the value of padlock probes (now combined with multiplexing and enhanced sensitivity) over a threshold to attract venture capitalists; secondly, this progress had been accelerated in a place, SGTC, which, although having had nothing to do with the invention of padlocks, had *all the necessary resources and connections* to perform fast enough the further development of padlocks to "win the race" with the much poorer GenPat lab in Uppsala. But it took the "network connector" Ronaghi, with his experience of the Swedish context, to revamp the interest in padlocks across the ocean and to set in motion a strong development effort. Often the local context prevents inventors from seeing possibilities of improving and combining their own inventions: and Landegren was certainly not helped by the option right on his discoveries that he had granted to Pharmacia Biotech. Ronaghi and his colleagues at SGTC did not have such burdens and could more freely see the possibilities of padlocks. Most importantly, they soon realized that in order to make padlocks a more easily commercializable technology, meeting also the wishes of venture capitalists, it needed to be combined with other pieces of knowledge (e.g., multiplexing). Thus SGTC set out to develop these pieces.

When the SGTC team started developing the complements for padlocks, the *commercial value* of this scientific resource became greater in Silicon Valley than in Uppsala. Several other resource combinations that the context of Silicon Valley and Stanford could offer to padlocks greatly outbid Uppsala's. Thus, even if the GenPat lab could potentially develop the complementary technologies, these could be developed far faster at Stanford University than in Uppsala.

Another important aspect emerging from the case story concerns the *shaping of science*. We already stressed the importance of networks over markets in linking science and capital. These network links are so penetrating that VC firms can affect the scientific content of the venture they buy. Instead of purchasing a ready-made science basis in a biotech firm, all the VC firms involved, and especially Index which came in so early, shaped the object of their investments. Besides selecting scientific ideas depending on personal bonds to their inventors (as Index explicitly did), VC firms are also active in affecting the content of the scientific bases of their start-ups. For instance, Index strongly argued for having the license on padlock inside ParAllele's patent portfolio. Moreover, Index actively influenced ParAllele's business model, that is, the customer applications for MIP's science content. Whereas this did not affect the original techno-scientific solution, it affected the subsequent product development by pushing ParAllele towards certain specific types of collaboration partners (see Figure 2).

But VC was present even at the conception stage of the scientific innovation. Capitalists may not have specified how to conceive a micro-array or which enzyme to use, but they were present in the minds and goals of the researchers involved in the ParAllele story. To the SGTC team in particular it was clear from the very beginning that they needed to develop and/or combine all pieces of science and technology according to the likely requirements of VC firms. These scientists never developed science for science's sake, but always aimed at a technology that worked and would be given a higher value by the venture capitalist.

Finally, the case provides interesting but contrasting evidence of the importance of *proximity* in linking science and capital: (1) the fact that Index, ParAllele's seed financier, is located in Switzerland indicates that proximity, at least for the early science-capital linkages, is not necessary, whereas personal bonds play a much more important role; (2) the fact that the VC firms entering the scene later are located close to ParAllele stresses the importance of proximity in corporate governance and control issues (e.g., board meetings), and of specific places for instilling in the start-up a shared local business culture and for involving it in localized business contacts. The latter point explains ParAllele's search for a VC firm from Europe (Abingworth), in order to spread the network of potential commercial contacts to European customers and research partners.

The case stresses that specific places played an important role in how padlocks was eventually commercialized inside ParAllele's MIP technology. Thus, a main conclusion of this chapter is that *specific geographic places* greatly impact the *commercial value* of a resource generally treated as universal, namely scientific knowledge.

Focusing on the networks that link knowledge and capital also helps us see how places *interact* with each other. And, unless there is a full "migration" of resources, places continue to interact and enrich each other. Even if our case shows a partial migration of scientific knowledge to Silicon Valley, many other resources, namely the most tacit and deepest part of the "migrated" knowledge, are still in Uppsala at GenPat (see Section 4.11): these resources are ready to enrich and be enriched through the interplay with other places near and far.

NOTES

1. But such endowments of institutions, science and capital did not help Lombardy, Italy's most dynamic biotech region, to go beyond just a handful of biotech start-ups (Orsenigo, 2001). In fact, the cocktail that promotes and sustains a long-term regional development in biotech also requires other components, such as the presence of established firms, and big pharmaceutical companies that act as "anchors" (Feldman, 2003) or as "switchboards" (Waluszewski, 2004: 138).
2. Quite curiously, a core meaning of "market" is a physical, well-identified place: a square in a village, where people meet face-to-face to exchange things. This is very different from the markets referred to by economists, i.e., the commodity or stock exchange markets, which are totally impersonal and de-localized.
3. The patent is shared with Lee Hood. In 2002, Applied Biosystems sold the cystic fibrosis test for US$10,2 million.
4. Landegren, Kaiser, Sanders & Hood (1988) in *Science*; Nilsson et al. (1994) in *Science*; and Banér, Nilsson, Mendel-Hartvig & Landegren (1998) in *Nucleic Acids Res.*
5. The project HUGO (Human Genome Organization), completed by the year 2000, offers a *rough* sequence of the long chain of nucleotides (i.e., the A-C, G-T pairs) to be found in the genetic material of all humans.
6. Many of the innovations developed at SGTC have been *patented* and *licensed* with the help of SOTL.
7. ParAllele stands for *parallel* testing of *alleles* (i.e., natural variations in nucleic acid sequences).
8. The patent for DNA padlocks was written in February 1994. In May 1994, Mats Nilsson and Landegren presented a paper on padlocks at a meeting in Cold Spring Harbor. In August 1994, a paper on padlocks was published in *Science* (Nilsson et al., 1994). Today the group holds seven different patents or patent applications for this technology.

9. Sweden hosts only one lab for genotyping, the Rudbeck laboratory. The world's largest genotyping centre is the Sanger Centre (Cambridge) and the second largest is the Centre National de Genotyping (Paris).
10. This project was the first major effort to develop a comprehensive public catalogue of the genetic variations among diverse human populations. This should provide a basis for studies of an individual's inherited risk of such diseases as asthma, cardiovascular disturbances and cancer.

REFERENCES

Arora, A., & Gambardella, A., 1994, The changing technology of technological change: general and abstract knowledge and the division of innovative labour, *Research Policy*, Vol. 23, pp. 523–532.

Arora, A., Fusfuri, A., & Gambardella, A., 2001, Markets for Technology and their Implications for Corporate Strategy, *Industrial and Corporate Change*, Vol. 10, No. 2, pp. 419–451.

Bijker, W. E., 1995, *Of Bicycles, Bakelites, and Bulbs. Toward a Theory of Sociotechnical Change*, The MIT Press: Cambridge, MA.

Feldman, M., 2003, The Locational Dynamics of the U.S. Biotech Industry: Knowledge Externalities and the Anchor Hypothesis, *Industry & Innovation*, Vol. 10, Issue 3, pp. 311–328.

Gompers, P., & Lerner, J., 1999. *The Venture Capital Cycle*, The MIT Press: Cambridge, MA.

Håkansson, H., & Snehota, I. (eds.), 1995, *Developing Relationships in Business Networks*, Routledge: London.

Håkansson, H., & Waluszewski, A., 2002, *Managing Technological Development. IKEA, the environment and technology*, Routledge: London.

Latour, B., 1987, *Science in Action*, Harvard University Press: Cambridge, MA.

Lerner, J., 1994, The Syndication of Venture Capital Investments, *Financial Management*, Vol. 23, No. 3, pp. 16–27.

Lockett, A., & Wright, M., 2001, The syndication of venture capital investments, *Omega: The International Journal of Management Science*, Vol. 29, Issue 5, 375–390.

Lundgren, A., 1994, *Technological Innovation and Network Evolution*, Routledge: London.

Orsenigo, L., 2001, The (Failed) Development of a Biotechnology Cluster: The Case of Lombardy, *Small Business Economics*, Vol. 17, pp. 77–92.

Penrose, E., 1959, *The Theory of the Growth of the Firm*, Reprint 1995, Oxford University Press: New York.

Powell, W. W., 1990, Neither Market Nor Hierarchy: Network Forms of Organization, *Research in Organizational Behavior*, Vol. 12, 1990, pp. 295–336.

Powell, W. W., Koput, K. W., Bowie, J. I., & Smith-Doerr, L., 2002, The Spatial Clustering of Science and Capital: Accounting for Biotech Firm-Venture Capital Relationships, *Regional Studies*, Vol. 36.3, pp. 291–305.

Swedberg, R., 2002, *The Economic Sociology of Capitalism: Weber and Schumpeter*. Paper presented at Scancor, Stanford University, March 4, 2002.

von Hippel, E., 1998, Economics of Product Development by Users: The Impact of "Sticky" Local Information, *Management Science*, Vol. 44, No. 5, May 1998, pp. 629–644.

Waluszewski, A., 2004, A competing or co-operating cluster or seven decades of combinatory resources? What's behind a prospering biotech valley?, *Scandinavian Journal of Management*, Vol. 20, pp. 125–150.

Wedin, T., 2002, *Combinatory Resources and Weak Ties: The Development of an Investment Network Around the Stockholm-Uppsala Biomedical Sector*. Paper presented at the workshop on The Economics and Business of Biosciences & Biotechnologies: What can be learnt from the Nordic Countries and the UK?, Gothenburg, September 2002.

TECHNICAL REFERENCES

Banér, J., Nilsson, M., Mendel-Hartvig, M., & Landegren, U., 1998, Signal amplification of padlock probes by rolling circle replication, *Nucleic Acids Res.*, Vol. 26, pp. 5073–5078.

Dahl, F., Banér, J., Gullberg, M., Mendel-Hartvig, M., Landegren, U., & Nilsson, M., 2004, Circle-to-circle amplification for precise and sensitive DNA analysis, *Proceedings of the National Academy of Science*, Vol. 101, No. 13, pp. 4548–4553.

Hardenbol, P., Baner, J., Jain, M., Nilsson, M., Namsaraev, E., Karlin-Neumann, G. A., Fakhrai-Rad, H., Ronaghi, M., Willis, T. D., Landegren, U., Davis, R. W., 2003, Multiplexed genotyping with sequence-tagged molecular inversion probes, *Nature Biotechnology*, 2003, June, Vol. 21, No. 6, pp. 673–678.

Landegren, U., Kaiser, R., Sanders, J., & Hood, L., 1988, A ligase-mediated gene detection technique, *Science*, Vol. 241, pp. 1077–1080.

Nilsson, M., et al., 1994, Padlock probes: circularizing oligonucleotides for localized DNA detection, *Science*, Vol. 265, pp. 2085–2088.

APPENDIX

List of interviews:

Date of interview	Respondent	Affiliation
12 Dec. 2001, 17 Mar. 2004, 30 Mar. 2004 (telephone interview) and 18 Nov. 2004	Mostafa Ronaghi	ParAllele Bioscience, cofounder, and Stanford Genome Technology Centre, genomics and enzymologist.
6 Feb. 2004 and 17 Apr. 2004 (and several informal talks)	Simon Fredriksson	Stanford Genome Technology Centre, proteomics researcher.
31 Mar. 2004 and 9 Dec. 2004	Ulf Landegren	Professor, Genetics & Pathology Department, Uppsala University, and ParAllele Bioscience, cofounder.
30 Mar. 2004 (telephone interview)	Francesco De Rubertis	Index Ventures.
1 Apr. 2004 and 1 Dec. 2004 (telephone interviews)	Audrey Long	ParAllele Bioscience, external relations and marketing.

DEVELOPMENT AND TRANSFER OF INNOVATIONS IN MNCS

The "Local for Local" Imperative

FRANCESCO CIABUSCHI AND MATS FORSGREN

INTRODUCTION

In recent writings on globalization, it is often assumed that more global equals less local, in the sense that the "space of flows" drains all resources from the "space of places" (Stryjan, 2004; Castells, 1996). Both supporters and opponents of globalization seem to claim and agree on the fact that places as such will decrease in importance, even if not becoming totally marginalized. The basic idea behind this view is that globalization leads to a state of omnipresence due to a global informational network: one is in the center, wherever one is, and could in principle be anywhere. In line with this logic, proximity applies everywhere and the need for places is bound to vanish. This is a central line of thought among advocates and critics, except that the critics point out that this new world will be open only to a privileged portion of humanity (Stryjan, 2004).

This strong belief in the inherent logic and consequences of globalization is echoed in research on the role and structure of the multinational company (MNC). The MNC is not only supposed to be a main actor in the globalization process but also in itself reflects the core meaning of the information society. For instance, Castells—being an advocate of globalization—states that the (MNC) "network enterprise makes material the culture of the informational, global economy: it transforms signals into commodities by processing knowledge" (Castells, 1996: 188). A similar view is reflected in recent writings on MNCs, especially those with more of a management perspective. Bartlett, Ghoshal, and Nohria have suggested that the modern MNC is—or should be—a "transnational organization" or a "differentiated network" in which every unit is linked to every other unit in a complicated web of information and communication channels (Bartlett & Ghoshal, 1989; Ghoshal & Nohria, 1997). Although they recognize that subsidiaries of an MNC differ because of different local environments, the core of their message is the existence of the intra-organizational, informational, cross-country network that binds the units and their actions together. An even more obvious example of this idea of omnipresence is the MNC as a "holographic organization," in which information about the whole is stored in each part of the company. The metaphor of the "firm as a brain" (in contrast to the "brain of the firm"—the hierarchy) has been used to express the idea of the MNC as a "global network" (Hedlund & Rolander, 1990).

The basic perception underlying these perspectives, i.e., the MNC as transnational organization, differentiated network, and global network, is obviously in line with the reasoning earlier on the inherent characteristics of globalization: every subsidiary of the MNC is in the center wherever it stands, and the importance of the place is marginalized. Proximity applies everywhere and space becomes "slippery" (Markusen, 1996). The development of MNCs into global, informational networks is supposed to be an unavoidable process, something that happens through the dynamics of the system itself.

However, even though globalization obviously is a strong force due to factors such as the standardization of products and systems, new information technology (IT) and reduced transportation costs, the basic conclusions about the reduced importance of place and the dominance of the global network MNC may be questioned on several grounds. First, access to all kinds of information from every other place/unit (if possible) will probably lead to growing congestion, which in turn will be addressed by a much scantier, more superficial or selective management of the information and its sources. This can be partly looked upon as substituting old distances with new ones. Second, the decrease of traditional distances may very well lead to the creation of new place-dependent distances (Stryjan, 2004). For instance, if a subsidiary can do business with more distant sister units than before, this will not reduce the importance of the subsidiary's location; it only changes the geographic structure of the subsidiary's business network.

Third, the perception of the MNC as a global network does not seem to consider the importance of trust-building in business life and the need for face-to-face contacts in order to do that. Physical proximity and direct sensory inputs in face-to-face contacts cannot be fully replaced with new IT technology. That is just as relevant, whether or not one considers the business life inside the MNC or in relation to external markets. This latter issue points to the fundamental question of entrepreneurship and how business is created. The perspective of the MNC as a global network seems to underestimate the importance of place and proximity for the interplay between business actors in terms of their creating business relationships and starting new business ventures. In fact, the perspective seems to reduce business relationships between business actors, inside as well as outside of the MNC, to a question of communication in a web of "arm's-length" relationships. Thereby, an MNC subsidiary's information exchange with another unit does not differ in substance from its exchange with all other units. Hence, the global MNC resembles a (short-term) market for information exchange between equals, rather than between particulars.

Fourth, related to the last point, the MNC network is assumed to be a communication network in which information is shared rather than a network in which knowledge is created. In other words, it seems that the focus is much more on the transfer of information, for instance about new products, rather than about how these products are created in the first place. One reason is that the reduction of the network concept to a global communication network obscures the importance of how the business looks and how it is structured (Forsgren, 2004). For instance, how the subsidiaries of an MNC are related to each other as suppliers, customers, or competitors, as well as the question of what they actually produce, sell, or buy, is more or less ignored in the literature of international business. It is reasonable to assume that the more the core of the business and development of new knowledge is considered—and not only information-sharing in more general terms—the more important it is to consider place and specific relationships as important factors.

Fifth, the MNC-as-a-global-network perspective underestimates the point that "place" is also important because it produces partial interests and power. Even though there are new facilities and opportunities for sharing information over increased distances, this does not imply that such sharing will automatically occur. MNC subsidiaries may be unwilling to share information with other units or may even be reluctant to receive information from others, and sometimes they also have the power to resist extensive information exchange (Forsgren et al., 2000).

To sum up, there are theoretically based reasons to question the conceptualization of the modern MNC as a global network along the lines suggested by many scholars (Bartlett & Ghoshal, 1989; Ghoshal & Nohria, 1997; Hedlund, 1986). To some extent this also applies to researchers who have looked upon the MNC as a social community (Kogut & Zander, 1993; Tsai & Ghoshal, 1998). Empirically, observations that can support the view that the modern MNC is a real global network are limited, and they tend rather to indicate a relatively low degree of integration in MNCs in terms of product or knowledge flows (Kuetschker & Schurig, 2002; Andersson & Forsgren, 2000).

In this chapter, we will look more deeply into the last three points advocated in the foregoing discussion. Particularly, we will focus on the interplay between the *local place*, conceptualized as the individual subsidiary and its local business network, and the *global space*, in the form of the global system of subsidiaries within the MNC.

The aim of the chapter is to contribute to the discussion on place and innovation by stressing the criticality of the local place for innovation development and the local-to-local nature of the innovation transfer process within the MNC. Specifically, we will discuss the processes of innovation development and transfer in MNCs from a business network perspective and thereby analyze the impact that the development phase has on innovation transfer possibilities. Finally, we will construct a model to scrutinize how different types of relations between subsidiaries (a) affect the likelihood of transferring an innovation and (b) determine what kind of transfers may occur in different situations.

INNOVATION PROCESSES IN THE MNC

As advocated earlier, in the conceptualization of the MNC as a transnational firm (Bartlett & Ghoshal, 1989) or a differentiated network (Ghoshal & Nohria, 1997) it seems almost automatic and unproblematic for the firm to build and manage heterogeneous and intense knowledge and resource flows among the different subsidiaries. Additionally, the underlying implicit assumption seems to be that the more knowledge and resources are exchanged within the MNC, the better its competitiveness (e.g., Hedlund, 1986; Kogut & Zander, 1993); this somehow underestimates the actual complexity and cost of such practice.

Even though there are indications that the competitive strength of the MNC is linked to its geographical dispersion and to the flows of innovation and knowledge between units, limited consideration is actually given to how innovations are developed in the first place or to how the development process influences transfer possibilities. Moreover, it seems that in the transnational conceptualization of the MNC, subsidiaries are "invisible" in the sense that what they actually do, and how they relate externally to the market and internally to each other, is seldom taken into account, even though we can expect that these factors have a profound impact on the innovation transfer process. Although the MNC is believed to be the best organizational form for transferring knowledge and innovations (Kogut & Zander, 1992), this may still present serious challenges and may not be worth the effort. Discussing the limits of the "transnational form" we argue that (1) the innovation development process also has to be considered in order to analyze transfer possibilities, that (2) the nature of the relation between the units involved in the transfer is a critical factor for the understanding of what kind of innovation transfer may occur, and that (3) the effects of specific local places are essential for innovation development and innovation transfer processes.

In this chapter, we refer to innovation as the whole process of linking any new problem-solving ideas into use (Kanter, 1988) and we conceptualize the innovation process occurring within MNCs as the process of innovation development, transfer, and exploitation. This threefold distinction becomes necessary in the case of the MNC compared to a more traditional domestic firm due to the rather dispersed organizational structure of the former, both in geographical and functional terms. Thus, what is actually a direct and locally bound process in the case of domestic firms—i.e., local innovation development and subsequent local commercialization—is often not so in the case of MNCs.

In the work done by Rugman and Verbeke (2001), the significance of the interplay between local and global dimensions is put forward as characterizing the process of competitive advantage creation. They classify MNCs' places of innovation as local (home country or host country) and global (international company-wide network). Thus, if innovations can be both locally and globally developed, the ensuing transfer processes would be different and travel in opposite directions. Basically, provided that transfer occurs, globally developed solutions are subsequently diffused to local units for utilization, while locally developed ones are leveraged from subsidiaries at the global level.

A typical example of local development and global transfer is found in the Center of Excellence (CoE) phenomenon. CoEs are MNCs' units that develop through their local activities specific valuable competence that is utilized by the internal network of sister units within the MNC (Holm & Pedersen, 2000). On the other hand, a typical case of global solution development and local transfer is provided by the organizational form of transnational teams. Managers from different units gather for the purpose of joining efforts and competences to develop a global solution, which is then locally transferred and exploited (often by the very same team members).

In this chapter, we focus on innovations developed at subsidiary level and transferred to sister units located in other countries. Figure 1 illustrates our view of the innovation process unfolding throughout the internal network of subsidiaries. The innovation development stage represents the transformation of a problem-solving idea into an innovation by potentially interacting with a network of both internal and external counterparts (Andersson M. et al., 2001; Hillebrand & Biemans, 2004). The transfer stage is the sharing of the developed innovation from the focal unit with specific sister units. The exploitation phase starts with the adoption of the innovation by other organizational units and it proceeds with the local adaptation and implementation of the innovation for commercial purposes.

If we observe the representation in Figure 1 from a spatial point of view, it is possible to notice how the innovation process is characterized by the interplay between the "local place," i.e., exploration activities at subsidiary level, and "global space," i.e., exploitation practices at the intra-firm level. Each different phase of the process presents a cross-border process linking diverse locations. In the development phase, there is a cross-firm process involving internal subsidiaries and external local business counterparts. In the transfer phase, there is a cross-unit and cross-country process stretching from the focal unit, located in one country, to one or more receiving subsidiaries located in different countries. Finally, the exploitation process again crosses firm boundaries by embracing the local external market(s) of the receiving unit(s).

A unit's capability to develop innovations is to a great extent based on interactions with external local counterparts. In particular, studies show how the interaction and tight cooperation between the firm and its customers and suppliers in the local business context is

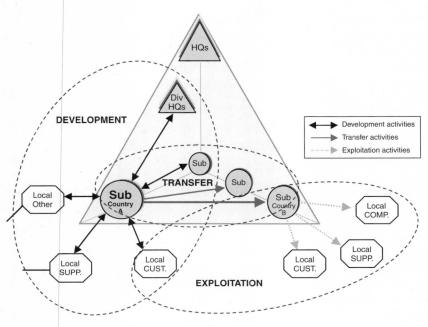

Figure 1. The innovation process within MNCs.

fundamental for the development of the competence of firms (e.g., Håkansson & Snehota, 1989, 1995; von Hippel, 1988). Innovations are aimed for the market, so external business relationships are a critical source of competence for the firm. By being active and absorbing from the various local environments, MNCs are potentially in a position to develop more radical and novel innovations (Cantwell, 1999). This capability leads to the conclusion that local processes of innovation and interaction represent an important source of competitiveness for firms operating in a global economic system. However, one might question whether all innovations locally developed by subsidiaries are always transferred to sister units. And if not, under which circumstances are innovations *not* internally transferred? Several studies in the field of international business suggest that there may be a negative association between a sister unit's utilization of a subsidiary's innovations and its degree of external (local) business embeddedness (Forsgren, 1997; Andersson et al., 2001, 2002). The intensity and depth of subsidiaries' local activities influence the local specificity of innovations developed, hence hindering their actual transferability. Additionally, the more resources and activities are committed to the local market, the fewer are left for the internal transfer activities due to time and resource constraints (Forsgren et al., 2000).

The MNC organizational context influences the transferability of an innovation. The firm's internal network of units (Grant, 1996; Kogut & Zander, 1992; Gupta & Govindarajan, 1991, 2000) is the typical arena for the transfer, and there may be integrative mechanisms in place facilitating or hindering the transfer process, such as routines, HQ control, incentives, and corporate culture (e.g., Doz & Prahalad, 1981; Grant, 1996; Tsai & Ghoshal, 1998). The effects of such organizational attributes on innovation transfer possibilities can be very strong. However, a fundamental issue for knowledge transfer is how the subsidiaries are operationally related. Or, expressed otherwise: "The business comes first, the integrative mechanisms later." Therefore, we need a model that can help analyze the relationship between the operational structure of an MNC and the existence or nonexistence of knowledge transfer. Such a model will be suggested in the following section.

THE RELATIONAL STRUCTURE OF THE INTERNAL SUBSIDIARY NETWORK

The activities carried out by different subsidiaries and their specific capabilities have a profound influence on the MNC organizational structure and on conditions for knowledge transfer. In order to understand what activities are going on in the MNC and how they relate to each other, we look upon the MNC as an industry of its own with more or less related activities and we apply models that are used to characterize industries. A valuable one is offered by Richardson (1972). In his seminal article about the organization of industry he writes:

> It is convenient to think of industry as carrying out an indefinitely large number of *activities*, activities related to the discovery and estimation of future wants, to research, development and design, to the execution and coordination of processes of physical transformation, the marketing of goods and so on. And we have to recognize that these activities have to be carried out by organizations with appropriate *capabilities*, or, in other words, with appropriate knowledge, experience and skill. The capability of an organization may

depend upon command of some particular material technology, such as cellulose chemistry, electronics or civil engineering, or may derive from skills in marketing of and knowledge of and reputation in particular markets. Activities that require the same capability for their undertaking I shall call *similar activities*. . . . But the organization of industry has also to adapt itself to the fact that activities may be *complementary*. I shall say that activities are complementary when they represent different phases of a process of production and require in some way or another to be coordinated. (Richardson, 1972, p. 888–889).

Therefore, if we apply this perspective to the MNC as a "loosely coupled" organization with a bundle of more or less interdependent subsidiaries, the "organizing of industry" metaphor seems fitting. This means that at any point in time the subsidiaries of the MNC represent different activities, products, markets, specialties, and capabilities more or less in the same way as a whole industry. The activities of two subsidiaries can either be built on the same type of capability or be related to each other in terms of product or service flows, e.g., as customers and suppliers. In the first case, the subsidiaries are dependent on a similar type of competence for their operations, but they are not dependent on each other in the ongoing business. In the second case, they are forced to coordinate their business, but the business in each subsidiary can be based on totally different types of capabilities.

The concepts of similarity and complementarity are independent of each other, which means that one unit can be more or less similar in terms of capabilities, yet complementary in terms of coordination with other sister units within the MNC. Figure 2 illustrates the model; it shows three MNC subsidiaries: A, B1, and B2. Subsidiary A serves as supplier to B1 and B2 and therefore is considered to have a complementary relation with both of them. Subsidiaries B1 and B2 instead are similar and base their operations on the same type of capabilities and technologies. This model implies that both similarities and complementarities can exist in MNCs and in different ways, including not existing at all, although most probably it is a matter of degree of similarity and complementarity between units.

We use this simple model of similar and complementary relations between MNC subsidiaries in order to shed some new light on the conditions for knowledge transfer in MNCs. We argue that these two different relational dimensions influence the possibilities for and the type of knowledge transfer process occurring in MNCs.

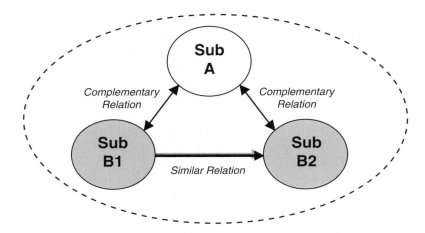

Figure 2. The MNC conceptualized as a network of subsidiaries having complementary and similar relations.

KNOWLEDGE FLOWS IN THE MNC

On the basis of the conceptualization presented in Figure 2, we argue that between two similar subsidiaries (B1 and B2) there is a *horizontal* relation and that between two complementary subsidiaries (A and B1/B2) a *vertical* relation exists.

The extent to which an MNC will actually function as a global network depends on several related factors. First, the extent to which innovations will be transferred horizontally between two similar subsidiaries is dependent on the ability of the subsidiary to create new knowledge in the first place, which in turn is dependent on the quality of the subsidiary's business network in terms of embeddedness. If nothing is created, there will be nothing to transfer. Second, the extent to which innovations will actually be transferred horizontally is dependent on motivational and communication factors as well as the absorptive capacity at the potential receiver side. In the case of vertical relationships between complementary subsidiaries, the problems are fundamentally different. Here, "innovation transfer" is not first of all transfer but "mutual problem-solving" between parties that are linked to each other business-wise, i.e., in a vertical relation along the value chain. To what extent this "transfer" will occur is heavily dependent on the characteristics of the relationships. By definition, close business relationships include adaptation of resources and activities on both sides (von Hippel 1988; Håkansson & Snehota, 1995), which in turn implies that mutual problem-solving is an important ingredient of the relationship. Or expressed differently: a more market-like or arm's-length vertical relationship between two subsidiaries contains less mutual problem-solving and consequently less "transfer" in the vertical relationships.

Along this line, we can point to certain factors within the MNC that explain why the existence of the global network MNC is less common than is usually assumed. We will illustrate our reasoning by some empirical examples.

Horizontal Flows: A Knowledge Transfer Process

Horizontal knowledge flows occur between similar units located in different contexts (such as different countries). Forces that drive and hinder the transfer are different in the horizontal and the vertical relationships. In the former case, the possibility of transferring an innovation from subsidiary B1 to subsidiary B2 is facilitated by the degree of similarity of capabilities on both sides. To the extent that the subsidiaries are operating with similar technology and in similar markets, the possibility of subsidiary B2 absorbing an innovation created in subsidiary B1 is higher. However, markets are seldom similar. After all, the fact that the MNC has subsidiaries within the same product range but located in different countries implies that the markets are different enough to motivate a duplicated structure.

The uniqueness of the local context, e.g., in terms of specificity and closeness of the customer and supplier relationships, can be quite high and therefore require rather *dissimilar* attributes. Consequently, the transfer of innovations between subsidiary B1 and subsidiary B2 can be quite difficult to carry out despite the fact that the subsidiaries belong to the same product line; this is because innovations developed in close cooperation with customer and or suppliers in subsidiary B1 can be difficult to apply in subsidiary B2's local market. As a result, both units' external business embeddedness, i.e., the degree of closeness and interaction with local business counterparts, can be a barrier to transfer. On one side external embeddedness impacts the ability to develop and the possibility of transferring the innovation, while on the other side it impacts the capacity to receive and use it.

The horizontal case, therefore, points to an interesting dilemma: the higher the subsidiaries' degree of external embeddedness, the higher the possibility of creating innovations and new knowledge at the subsidiary level, but the lower the possibility of transferring that knowledge horizontally to other MNC units.

The second problem in the horizontal case has to do with motivational factors. The structure as such implies that although the subsidiaries belong to the same corporation, they run their own business and are not connected in their daily operations. As a consequence, there are no inherent drivers for knowledge transfers due to dependencies in resource exchange. The extent to which transfer will occur is dependent on the willingness and motivation of both sides to invest time and resources in the transfer.

Thus, if we consider the alternative cases of two units (i.e., sender B1 and receiver B2) that were either embedded or unembedded within their markets, depending on their degree of embeddedness we would have four different configurations of the potential magnitude of knowledge flows, as illustrated in Figure 3 below.

In order to be transferred, an innovation has first to be developed, then made available for transfer (willingness and possibility of sending it), and finally potentially receivable (willingness and possibility of receiving it). By taking into consideration the alternative cases when the units are locally embedded or unembedded in their own markets, it appears that the highest potential for horizontal flows

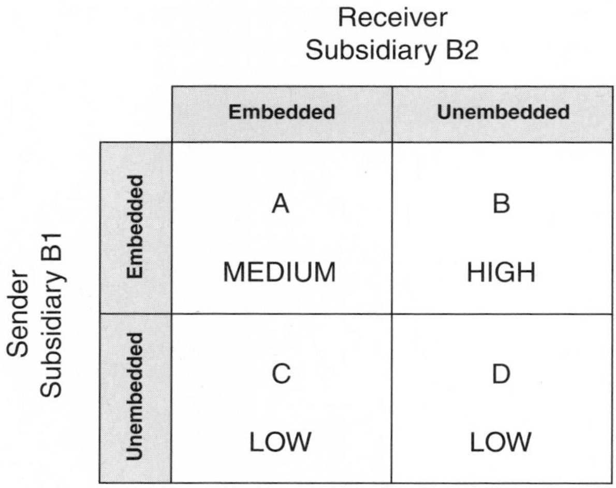

Receiver
Subsidiary B2

	Embedded	Unembedded
Embedded (Sender Subsidiary B1)	A MEDIUM	B HIGH
Unembedded	C LOW	D LOW

Figure 3. Knowledge transfer potential between similar units.

of knowledge between similar units is when the sender (subsidiary B1) is embedded and the receiver (subsidiary B2) is not (case B).

Leveraging an innovation to an unembedded sister unit (case B) may be easier compared to leveraging to an embedded one (case A). The receiving unit's resources are not particularly committed to the market; hence they are ready to be utilized in the adoption process. Because the unit itself is not significantly innovative, the willingness to receive and adopt innovations from sister units is high. Typical cases are young subsidiaries established in countries new to the firm, units located in markets with extremely unsophisticated demand (e.g., developing countries and still some countries of the ex-Soviet bloc), and small local units characterized by modest resources.

An example illustrating this kind of knowledge transfer (case B) is found in Siemens Information and Communication (IC). Siemens IC is one of the five divisions of the German conglomerate Siemens AG, and one of the world's leading providers of information and communications technologies, operating with a wide network of local sales units stretching worldwide. These units are rather heterogeneous, and generally their size and resources resemble their local market characteristics. Some of the subsidiaries are located in large, more advanced countries and have for decades operated closely with stimulating customers and suppliers, while others are smaller and more inexperienced, and within marginal or even new markets. However, often a local subsidiary might not have enough resources or the right competence to handle local competition independently. This has been particularly true in recent years, which have been characterized by telecommunications market deregulation, i.e., new customers and new competitors for Siemens. Consequently, Siemens's local sales units are sharing competence with each other in order to increase competitiveness and particularly to support troubled sister units. Even specific knowledge-sharing tools such as "ShareNet" (Nielsen & Ciabuschi, 2003) have been developed and are employed for horizontal knowledge transfer between sales units. Due to the units' similar background, capabilities and activities, to a common language, and to the receivers' low local embeddedness and motivation to adopt new competence and solutions locally, the transfer process is straightforward and efficient.

In the case of horizontal innovation flow from an embedded sender to an embedded receiver (Figure 3, case A), difficulties could arise particularly due to motivational aspects (e.g., not-invented-here syndrome) and resource scarcity (e.g., resources already employed locally). For instance, the more a receiver is locally embedded, the higher is the possibility that it is already engaged in development activities on its own with its local partners. This means that only a limited amount of resources would be available to receive competence from sister units. Thus, the potential for leveraging innovations from an embedded unit is high, but if the receiver is equally embedded in its market, then the resulting knowledge flow could be much lower (i.e., medium flow). In other words, the local innovation tends to remain local.

An example from the packaging industry may illustrate this case. Generally in this industry all operating units are very local in nature, highly embedded, and geographically very near (average 250 km) to the customers. Packaging suppliers are strongly driven by customers' problems and requests in their development of new solutions, which consequently result in highly customized products. Although packaging solutions are often categorized as incremental innovations, the modifications happen at very high rate; the key to success is to learn directly from the customers about their actual packaging uses in order to build together the best solution. These new solutions are extremely customer-specific; although potentially suitable to other customers and transferable to other units within the same organization, they need to be standardized or in some particular way significantly adapted by the receivers.

A very successful and well-known MNC in this industry is SCA Packaging,[1] leader in the European market and steadily growing with about 300 local production/sales units in more than 30 countries around the world. In the transfer of new solutions between two or more subsidiaries, although they may be highly similar in technology, processes, raw material employed, etc., their high degree of local embeddedness is often an obstacle that has to be overcome. For example, as a manager of a local SCA Packaging unit commented: "Units are highly embedded in their respective markets, so resources are not always available to commit to innovation transfers—they have to be taken away from somewhere else."[2] In addition, the fact that the receiver is also engaged in its own development activities with its own local counterparts might negatively influence the willingness to receive a solution developed by another unit (e.g., the "not-invented-here syndrome").

Finally, when the sender (B1) is not locally embedded and it keeps arm's-length relations with local counterparts, as already mentioned, it is assumed that innovation development is not favored. This means that subsidiary B1 is not in the best position to contribute to the MNC competence development (Andersson et al., 2002). Hence, in this case the potential for innovation transfer to either type of receiver (i.e., cases C and D) is very low. It could actually be assumed that an unembedded subsidiary B1 would be a better candidate to receive an innovation than to be a sender.

Vertical Flows: A Problem-solving Process

The vertical case is quite different from the horizontal one. First of all, here the actual outcome of the process is not the transfer of an innovation from one unit to another, but the development of a new one. Secondly, this kind of relationship by definition means that the parties are linked to each other through their common business (i.e., as buyer and seller) and therefore have economic incentives to coordinate their activities in different ways. Motivational barriers are relatively low because exchange of information is necessary for coordination to occur. However, such information exchange does not automatically imply "transfer" in terms of *mutual problem-solving* and creation of new innovations. On the contrary, it is reasonable to assume that many vertical relations are of arm's-length character due to economic drivers for standardization of products and production processes. That also goes for vertical relations inside the MNC. In fact, the more we look upon the MNC as a coherent production and marketing system designed by the headquarters, the less should occur any close, mutual problem-solving relationship between Sub A and Sub Bs, because we should at least expect that the existence of market-like vertical relations is as common inside the MNC as between independent firms.

If we think, for example, about the packaging industry, not much problem-solving takes place between "sheet plants," producing standardized raw material (sheets) for packaging, and "box plants," assembling the various materials and selling the specific packaging solution to its customers. In this case the relation between the two complementary units is a market-like business relation in which price and security of delivery is more important than cooperation or product development. This situation includes the case when units shift their supplies back and forth between internal and external sources.

An illustrative example of limited problem-solving in vertical relations internally to the MNC is the way new products are developed at IKEA. The IKEA organization is a worldwide leader in furniture

retailing, with a world network of 180 retail outlets. The IKEA strategic center, IKEA of Sweden, is responsible for developing each of its
products. IKEA of Sweden is directly and constantly involved in
problem-solving not with internal retail units but with external suppliers, and it develops products that are engineered for manufacturing
in order to obtain as low production costs as possible. This is, for instance, particularly important for a product manufactured in large
volumes such as the "Lack" sofa table, one of IKEA's absolute best-
sellers reaching 2.5 million units sold yearly (Baraldi & Ciabuschi,
2005). Lack was launched over 20 years ago, but its retail price has
been kept constant through all these years. The secret behind this success has been continuous product development, where IKEA of Sweden and its suppliers are constantly involved. Innovation efforts
around Lack aim at improvements of materials, production technology, and colors. The innovation process starts typically at IKEA of
Sweden, and the new technical solutions adopted emerge in the interaction between IKEA of Sweden and its various suppliers. To find
concrete solutions, face-to-face meetings are usually held, especially
on the factory floor. The innovated Lack (e.g., with a new type of ve-
neering material) is then transferred and locally utilized by all IKEA
sales units around the world in absolutely standard form. Over a certain period of time, the new Lack is specifically exploited by retailing
units to sustain their sales volumes. The only possibility retail units
have to affect product development is during the periodic meetings
with IKEA of Sweden. But retail units only give feedback on the Lack
modifications already introduced, rather than discussing future ones.
In fact, as stressed by managers of IKEA of Sweden, IKEA would
never be able to cope economically with all the requests for adaptations and new features suggested by local retail units.

CONCLUSION

In this chapter, starting from current discussions on globalization in
which it is assumed that more global equals less local, we question the
ideal picture of MNCs in today's business world presented as both an
actor of globalization and a global entity. This paper criticizes the
basic argument about the reduced importance of place and the dominance of the global network MNC, especially due to the bearing that
place has on the network. Particularly, we argue that the interaction
between the local place, conceptualized as the individual subsidiary
and its local business network, and the global space, conceptualized

as the MNC as a whole, influences the entire innovation process, i.e., innovation development, transfer, and exploitation.

The theoretical analysis builds on a relational view of the operational structure of the MNC internal subsidiary network. By distinguishing between similar and complementary relations, depending on the specific activities and capabilities of subsidiaries, we argue that horizontal as well as vertical flows of knowledge may occur between the different units within the MNC. Therefore we conceptualize horizontal flows of knowledge (between units of similar character) and vertical flows of knowledge (between units with complementary activities and capabilities) as two distinct phenomena.

The different character of horizontal and vertical relations manifests itself in different innovation "transfer" processes, i.e., transfer vs. problem-solving. Consequently, not only the motives driving the process but also the difficulties encountered will vary. As for the difficulties, factors hindering innovation transfer potential are found not only internally in the corporation but also externally, specifically in the subsidiary local context. In fact, the local embeddedness of subsidiaries is not only critical for innovation development but also impacts transfer possibilities. In other words, innovation transfer potential is influenced by the innovation development setting. Arguing for the significance of the "local for local" innovation transfer process, we posit that both the sender's and the receiver's degree of local embeddedness must be taken into account, as they influence the motivation and feasibility of transfer/adoption.

Our discussion, as illustrated by the empirical examples, leads to the important conclusion that knowledge transfer and problem-solving are neither always possible nor necessarily desirable. Specifically, we claim first of all that locally embedded subsidiaries are in better condition to develop innovations than unembedded units (i.e., those characterized only by arm's-length relations), and that the degree of local embeddedness of the receiving unit also influences the actual degree of transferability. Secondly, in the case of horizontal innovation transfer, only the case of an externally embedded sender (i.e., one able to develop innovations) and unembedded receiver (i.e., one eager to adopt innovations) presents a high potential for horizontal competence flows. Thirdly, contrary to the horizontal process, the outcome from problem-solving in vertical relationships is not the transfer of existing innovations, but the development of new ones. Finally, problem-solving situations among complementary units are not automatic or cost-free. MNCs tend to limit, often deliberately, mutual problem-solving from occurring, hence specific motives and settings have to be in place for initiating such processes.

In conclusion, further research is warranted on both the actual extent of innovations transferred within MNCs and on the impact that the adoption of innovations has on the receiver unit's local business. Moreover, based on the discussion on horizontal knowledge transfer and vertical problem-solving, a new conceptualization of subsidiary roles and MNC structure seems necessary, in order to move away from the view of the MNC as a brain and perhaps edge closer to the idea of the MNC as a federation of relatively loosely coupled entities.

NOTES

1. Svenska Cellulosa Aktiebolaget (SCA) is a Swedish-based multinational operating in the paper, packaging, and hygiene products industries.
2. This information was gathered through face-to-face interviews during 2002–03 as a part of a larger research project investigating the phenomenon of innovation transfer in MNCs: the TIME project (Uppsala University, Sweden).

REFERENCES

Andersson, U., and Forsgren, M. (2000). In search of centres of excellence: network embeddedness and subsidiary roles in MNCS. *Management International Review*, 40 (4), 329–350.

Andersson, U., Forsgren, M., and Holm, U. (2001). Subsidiary embeddedness and competence development in MNCs—a multi-level analysis. *Organization Studies*, 22 (6), 1013–1034.

Andersson, U., Forsgren, M., and Holm, U. (2002). The strategic impact of external networks: subsidiary performance and competence development in the multinational corporation. *Strategic Management Journal*, 23 (11), 979–996.

Andersson, M., Holm, U., and Holmström, C. (2001). Relationship configuration and competence development in MNC subsidiaries. In: Håkansson, H. and Johanson, J., *Business Network Learning*. Oxford: Elsevier Science Ltd. Pergamon, 185–205.

Baraldi, E., and Ciabuschi, F. (2005). IT and innovations in multinationals: experiences from product development at SCA and IKEA. Forthcoming in Sharma, D. and Johansson, J. (Eds.), *Managing Customer Relationships with IT and Internet*, Elsevier Science.

Bartlett, C. A., and Ghoshal, S. (1989). *Managing Across Borders: The Transnational Solution*. Boston: Harvard Business School Press.

Cantwell, J. (1999). Firms as the source of innovation and growth: the evolution of technological competence. *Journal of Evolutionary Economics*, 9, 331–66.

Castells, M. (1996). *The Rise of the Network Society*. Oxford: Blackwell Publishers.

Doz, Y. L., and Prahalad, C. K. (1981). Headquarters influence and strategic control in MNCs. *Sloan Management Review*, 23 (1), 15–30.

Forsgren, M. (1997). The advantage paradox of the multinational corporation. In Björkman, I. and Forsgren, M. (Eds.), *The Nature of the International Firm*. Copenhagen: CBS Press, 69–85.

Forsgren, M. (2004). The use of network theory in MNC research. In Mahnke, V. and Pedersen, T. *Knowledge Flows, Governance and the Multinational Enterprise. Frontiers in International Management Research*. New York: Palgrave Macmillan.

Forsgren, M., Johanson, J., and Sharma, D. (2000). Development of MNC centers of excellence. In Holm, U. and Pedersen, T. (Eds.), *The Emergence and Impact on MNC Centers of Excellence—a Subsidiary Perspective*. Macmillan: London, 45–67.

Ghoshal, S., and Nohria, N. (1997). *The Differentiated MNC: Organizing Multinational Corporation for Value Creation*. San Francisco, CA: Jossey-Bass.

Grant, R. M. (1996). Toward a knowledge-based theory of the firm. *Strategic Management Journal*, 17 (Winter Special Issue), 109–122.

Gupta, A. K., and Govindarajan, V. (1991). Knowledge flows and the structure of control within multinational corporations. *Academy of Management Review*, 16 (4), 768–792.

Gupta, A. K., and Govindarajan, V. (2000). Knowledge flows within multinational corporations. *Strategic Management Journal*, 21 (4), 473–96.

Hedlund, G. (1986). The hypermodern MNC: a heterarchy, *Human Resource Management*, 25 (1): 9–35.

Hedlund, G., and Rolander, D. (1990). Action in heterarchies—new approaches to managing the MNC. In Bartlett, C. A., Doz, Y., and Hedlund, G. (Eds.), *Managing the Global Firm*. London: Routledge.

Hillebrand, B., and Biemans, W. G. (2004). Links between internal and external cooperation in product development: an exploratory study. *Journal of Product Innovation Management*, 21 (2), 110–122.

Holm, U., and Pedersen, T. (2000). *The Emergence and Impact of MNC Centers of Excellence: A Subsidiary Perspective*. London: Macmillan.

Håkansson, H., and Snehota, I. (1989). No Business Is An Island: the network concept of business strategy. *Scandinavian Journal of Management*, 5 (3): 187–200.

Håkansson, H., and Snehota, I. (1995). *Developing Relationships in Business Networks*. Routledge: London.

Kanter, R. M. (1988). When a thousand flowers bloom: structural, collective, and social conditions for innovation in organization. *Research in Organizational Behavior*, 10, 169–211.

294

Kogut, B., and Zander, U. (1992). Knowledge of the firm, combinative capabilities, and the replication of technology. *Organization Science*, 3 (2), 383–397.

Kogut, B., and Zander, U. (1993). Knowledge of the firm and the evolutionary theory of the multinational corporation. *Journal of International Business Studies*, 24 (4), 625–45.

Kuetschker, M., and Schurig, A. (2002). Embeddedness of subsidiaries in internal and external networks: a prerequisite for technological change. In Havila, V., Forsgren, M., and Håkansson, H. (Eds.), *Critical Perspectives on Internationalization*. Elsevier Science.

Markusen, A. (1996). Sticky places in slippery space: a typology of industrial districts. *Economic Geography*, 72 (3), 293–313.

Nielsen, B. B., and Ciabuschi, F. (2003). Siemens ShareNet: knowledge management in practice. *Business Strategy Review*, 14 (2), 33–40.

Richardson, G.B. (1972). The organization of industry. *The Economic Journal*, September, 883–896.

Rugman, A.M., and Verbeke, A. (2001). Subsidiaries' specific advantages in multinational enterprises. *Strategic Management Journal*, 22 (3), 237–250.

Stryjan, Y. (2004). Spanning the local and the global: entrepreneurship and the production of place. Unpublished paper, Södertörns Högskola (University College), Stockholm.

Tsai, W., and Ghoshal S. (1998). Social capital and value creation: the role of intra-firm networks. *Academy of Management Journal*, 41 (4), 464–76.

Von Hippel, E. (1988). *Sources of innovation*. Oxford: Oxford University Press.

PART IV

Across and Beyond Spatial Scales

Directions on how to reach the IKEA furniture store in Jeddah, Saudi Arabia.
From http://www.ikea.com.sa/stores/?store=2&language=1, last visited 2006-02-08.

THE PLACES OF IKEA

Using Space in Handling Resource Networks

ENRICO BARALDI

1. INTRODUCTION: PLACE, RESOURCES AND IKEA

Places are central to the life of every company, from the moment when it is born and throughout its various developmental stages. A relocation, the opening of a new branch office or store, maybe abroad, and the start of a relationship with a supplier from a certain region: any of these may well signify an important moment in a company's life or even a turning point in its history. But these moments are just the tip of an iceberg: companies interact *constantly* with various places, even without being fully conscious of doing so. Places affect companies' lives, but companies, alone or in interaction with others, also affect places. This interaction with places happens through the *resources* that firms handle daily, such as *products*, *facilities*, business *units* and *relationships* (Håkansson & Waluszewski, 2002). IKEA is no exception to this rule. But what makes IKEA peculiar is the *many ways* in which it relates to space and places.

Being a furniture distributor, IKEA "shapes" such places as our homes and the sites where it exhibits its products. Purchasing these products from fifty countries and selling them in thirty, IKEA binds together thousands of locations. Linking its 2,000 first-tier suppliers with 180 retail stores requires 20,000 transport corridors. In between this complex network of places is IKEA, with its own many "private" places, such as its large distribution centers, retail stores, and headquarters. All the space-related aspects of the resources mentioned above matter greatly to IKEA's costs, revenues and development. Accordingly, IKEA uses space and its various places to handle and affect several internal and external resources.

The purpose of this chapter is, firstly, to discuss the *importance of places* to a firm's effort to efficiently utilize and develop industrial resources and, secondly, to develop an *analytical framework* for considering the interplay between *resources* and *space*, including how a firm can shape and use space in order to affect resources. This framework, built on the example of IKEA's experience, permits a more interactive view and transcends theoretical approaches to space as a given or as an independent variable. The chapter is organized as follows. Section 2 provides a review of the theoretical ideas on spatial issues developed within the fields of economic geography, business studies and history of science. Section 3 digs deeper into the heterogeneous and interacting nature of place and into its interplay with resources. Section 4 presents how IKEA deals with space and places in its handling of a series of resources. Section 5 suggests a framework for analyzing the role of space in *resource networks*. Section 6 concludes the chapter with a reflection on how IKEA uses space and places.

2. PLACE AND SPACE: AN INDEPENDENT OR A DEPENDENT VARIABLE?

Places, sites, space, territory, locations.[1] These are all germane terms used in social sciences to discuss a common issue: *where* do human endeavors occur and how important is this "where"? One can go further: "how does this *where* affect human endeavors?" For instance, business studies and economic geography have studied the different performances of firms depending on where and how close to each other they are located. Porter (1990, and 2000: 253) points out the advantages of being located in a geographic cluster. More than one hundred years ago, Marshall (1890) had already stressed the advantages of proximity between firms involved in similar or related businesses. This idea was further developed by *industrial district* researchers (e.g., Brusco, 1989).

Research on international business has also been attentive to spatial issues, especially with reference to multinational companies (MNCs). Hofstede (1983) reviews how the culture of the country of origin affects the particular managerial styles and strategies of an MNC. The MNC's performance may even be hindered when its culture and managerial style differ from those of the countries hosting its subsidiaries (Ibid). In general, the various locations where these large firms perform their business activities affect their performance, which reflects how different places can be utilized within the framework of

MNCs' worldwide strategies. "Locational" aspects, such as societal and infrastructure provisions or international transport and communication costs, are stressed by Dunning (1995: 476, 479–480, and 1998: 49–54). At a more fine-grained level of analysis, country-specific issues also imbue the local *networks* that embed the subsidiaries of an MNC (Forsgren et al., 2000: 52–55). These local embedding structures can contribute to developing the knowledge and competence of local units (Ibid: 55), but they also create problems when headquarters try to control the latter (Andersson & Forsgren, 1996, and Andersson, 1997).

Economic geography and international business research studied why firms chose a specific location or why they are simply located there: what kinds of advantages were they seeking? Porter (1990) stresses the *local* nature of competitive advantages, making place a key variable to explain why some firms perform better than others. Economic geographers also focus on the reasons why many firms, especially small and medium enterprises (SMEs), are *co-located* inside local clusters or industrial districts. Malmberg & Maskell (2002) claim that such traditional explanations as access to raw materials and cheap labor, market proximity or urbanization economies do not explain why firms co-locate, as often happens, in areas far from raw materials, cheap labor, end-markets or large cities and logistic nodes. Agglomeration of related businesses seems to offer *different types of* coordination advantages (Ibid). These entail not only reduced costs, but also easier access to and joint development of *tacit knowledge* (Ibid: 438–442): the argument is that only by being close to each other is it possible to observe, compare, imitate and understand each other at deeper and more hidden levels of knowledge.

All the approaches reviewed above share, however, the limitation of treating space as an *independent* variable that affects firms, social interaction, knowledge creation, etc. But place or space can also be treated as a *dependent* variable. This implies asking "Why is a place what we see? What is behind it? Which processes made a place what it is today?" Several geographers (e.g., Soja, 2000: 6; Harvey, 1990: 422; and Pred, 1984) point out that places are not *given* arenas, but are shaped through a process of social construction and interaction. The constructed nature of places is also stressed by science historians, who often focus on physical buildings. The process through which such places are constructed may be evident, as when new laboratories are built: here architects, financiers, politicians and scientists interact to give a concrete shape to the building (Gieryn, 1998 and 1999). But the process that imbues a place with symbolic values may stretch over centuries and be outside human control, as in the case of old university buildings (Rothblatt, 1997). Whatever the nature and time span of the process that shapes places, this process creates spatial structures that also *affect* social interaction: from scientific knowledge creation (Ophir & Shapin, 1991), even when performed in ascetic isolation (see Hannaway, 1986), to the exercise of power through panoptic mechanisms (Foucault, 1979).

3. INTERACTING AND HETEROGENEOUS PLACES: WHAT HAPPENS TO RESOURCES?

While suggesting the constructed nature of space, the history of science literature also recognizes the effects of places *on* human endeavors (i.e., the focus in economic geography and business studies). Place is seen both as a dependent variable, created by social construction and interaction, and as an independent variable that affects social processes. For instance, scientific buildings (e.g., laboratories), utilized as symbolic weapons, affect power and legitimacy conflicts between researchers (see Widmalm, 2001). We can therefore conclude that *spatial* structures and *social* structures interact: the latter shape the former as much as the former constrain and affect the latter. The result of this process is that the socially shaped and interacted places (buildings, cities, regions and nations) are highly *heterogeneous* (Foucault, 1986: 23). Their features are not fixed once and for all, but vary depending on: (1) the social processes and structures in which places are immersed, and (2) the other places they are connected with physically, symbolically, or economically.

This heterogeneous and multidimensional nature of space and places is also explicitly recognized in recent contributions from the business network perspective: Håkansson, Tunisini & Waluszewski (in this volume) stress how places are *shaped by* and simultaneously *affect* the interaction between firms and, especially, how firms combine resources. These places can both *enable* and *constrain* inter-firm interaction and resource combinations (Ibid). The fundamental idea is that space and resources interplay, that is, they affect each other. Much of a resource's heterogeneity (Penrose, 1959: 74–75) depends on the places to which the resource is related, while places are shaped by the very resources they include. In other words, certain features are first *embedded* in places, while they interact with social structures and processes. Then, these features affect, in turn, the social and physical resources that are *located inside* or symbolically *related to* these very places.

To summarize, the features of heterogeneous spaces become embedded in the resources related to these locations. In particular, such key resources for doing business as *products, facilities, organizational units* and *business relationships* (Håkansson & Waluszewski, 2002) acquire space-related features from the places with which they are associated. Firms can therefore more or less actively exploit these place-related features of the resources important for their businesses. Exploiting these features, however, is not a matter of linearly or straightforwardly "managing" the space-related features of resources. Things are more complex than that, for two main reasons related to the connection between places and resources: (1) the very same place can embed into one resource *conflicting* features, in relation to different managerial goals or to the *interfaces* (Ibid.) with other resources; and (2) every resource is simultaneously exposed to *more than one* social or physical place: these different places can therefore embed conflicting features into the same resource.

In order to systematize how firms utilize space, we need to specify what *types* of places we are dealing with. Spatial issues can, in fact, be studied on three analytical scales: a *micro*, a *meso* and a *macro* level. These three levels are anchored to *geographical* places, physically delimited from other places (see also note 1). Micro-spaces (or places[2]) are confined in buildings, such as offices, factories, laboratories or retail stores. Analyzing places at this micro level focuses on the construction, design and functional details of such artefacts and on the social processes unfolding inside these restricted spatial structures (see Gieryn, 1998 and 1999, or Brandt & Sloane, 1999). Meso-spaces range from collections of buildings, such as campuses and cities, to the areas surrounding the latter, such as provinces and regions. But besides including many micro-places, meso-places also include the *connections between* micro-places, both the physical and the symbolic ones: for instance, the links signifying power relations, like the rigid organization of a city during an epidemic (Foucault, 1979: 195–199). The physical and symbolic structures within one and the same meso-space can either reinforce or counteract each other: for instance, missing transportation links negatively affected the inclusion in Stockholm's scientific community of a monumental building conceived as a tool to unify this community (Lindqvist, 1997).

Finally, macro-spaces are the largest analytical arenas, extending to whole nations and countries. These are not only a physical collection of meso-places and their links, but result also from the aggregation of cultural, historical, ethnical and political aspects. Shifting from one macro-place to another gives rise to a fourth spatial scale of analysis: a "global" or "trans-national" level. However, we consider this simply a logical extension from the macro-level. The three levels reviewed above are not only "spatial scales" (Livingstone, 1995: 27) on which to study social processes; all three types of places— the *house*, the *city* and the *country*, in the terminology used by Beckman (1999)—also have properties that become embedded into the resources physically transiting or anchored to them, or symbolically related to them.

The above reasoning need not be restricted to *geographical* places and spaces, but also holds good for metaphorical spaces. For instance, a "business network" (Håkansson & Snehota, 1995) can be considered to be a space connecting different actors that occupy certain places (or "positions"). The network is itself composed of nodes and their connections, which makes it a spatial metaphor. Business networks include elements that are spread across micro-, meso- and even macro-spaces, mostly because the firms interacting within such networks are seldom located near each other (Markgren, 2001). Indeed, business networks *connect* elements (i.e., firms and resources) belonging both to places widely separated and to places located very close together.

Section 4 now provides an empirical illustration of the theoretical ideas developed in the two previous sections. The empirical material was collected through 70 in-depth interviews at several IKEA units and suppliers, visits to a dozen production sites, IKEA stores and offices (in Sweden, Poland, Italy and the US), and written material such as internal documents and newspaper articles (for a complete list of sources, see Baraldi, 2003). The next section stresses the role of micro-, meso- and macro-places in IKEA's efforts to handle resources. The various examples are used as *illustrations* pointing at a series of relevant issues that are then brought together in an analytical framework in section 5.

4. RESOURCES AND SPACE IN THE IKEA "UNIVERSE"

This section describes how IKEA uses the space-related features of its internal and external resources. Resources are presented according to the so-called "4Rs model," which classifies them as *products* (IKEA's own and the related components), *facilities* (e.g., the equipment and buildings used in production or distribution), *organizational units* inside and outside IKEA, and the *business relationships* between these units (Håkansson & Waluszewski, 2002; Wedin, 2001; and Baraldi & Bocconcelli, 2001). Each resource is clearly marked by the places they are associated with, physically or symbolically. But IKEA is not a passive beholder of how these spatial features become attached to the resources that it handles or that affect its business. IKEA strives to have embedded in the four resource types those spatial features that are *favorable* to its managerial goals, in terms of costs, revenues, reputation, development possibilities etc. However, spatial features unfavorable to or conflicting with these goals also emerge regularly and IKEA needs to cope with them. Let us now delve into how this happens with a few examples from the IKEA "universe" of places and resources.

4.1 IKEA, Shaping and Creating the Places and the Space for Resources

IKEA is constantly engaged not only in using places, but also in creating them, especially at the micro and meso levels. IKEA is, in fact, in a special position for *shaping* spaces. At the micro level, the products developed and sold by IKEA enter customers' homes and partly shape the environment in which they are used. But IKEA actively designs and builds other micro-places as well. Some of these are very apparent to an external observer: IKEA's retail stores are designed to include functional and symbolic features that will produce favorable economic consequences, whereas other micro-places are more hidden, such as IKEA's distribution centers. IKEA's own architects and production and logistic experts design and supervise the creation of all the above facilities. More indirectly, IKEA exerts an influence on how the factories of its suppliers are constructed, by persuading them to introduce specific machines or production processes. IKEA and its suppliers even invest *jointly* in equipment, which increases IKEA's ability to influence such micro-spatial issues as factory design, production flows and work organization.

Indirectly, IKEA also shapes meso-places, including the links between its own facilities or those owned by its suppliers or logistic partners. Many of IKEA's units are located in the same or adjacent buildings (e.g., a retail store and a nearby purchase office). This aggregation inside the same meso-space is particularly evident in the Southern Swedish town of Älmhult, where IKEA's story began 60 years ago. Today, this is the center for many business functions within IKEA's universe. The key function of product development is orchestrated from Älmhult by a 600-employee business unit, "IKEA of Sweden." But more than 10 other IKEA units are located in Älmhult, bringing to over 2,500 people the number of "Ikeans" working in this small town of about 15,000 inhabitants. Älmhult is the largest stable agglomeration of IKEA employees, covering about 4% of a workforce spread over 70 countries.

Besides exerting its hierarchical role toward the periphery of IKEA's "empire," Älmhult has also an important *symbolic* value. This is the place where the first IKEA store was opened in 1958, where salesmen from all the 180 IKEA stores gather twice a year to meet product developers and see IKEA's product news, and where selected executives participate in IKEA's career development courses. IKEA's influence on a place like Älmhult is easy to understand; but IKEA also affects the places that it has met since starting its international expansion in the 1970s. The urban landscape where IKEA's stores are located is often transformed by the opening of such units: starting very much as "green field" sites (literally among open fields, on the outskirts of major cities), these locations become filled with such infrastructures as parking lots (often built by IKEA), and enough activities and traffic to attract other retailers to co-locate. This in turn favors IKEA, because it further increases the traffic volumes to these meso-places. The shopping area Kungenskurva in Stockholm, where IKEA's flagship store is located, catalyzes yearly retail sales of SKr 5 billion.

IKEA also affects meso-places by inducing its suppliers to locate their production facilities or service centers near to IKEA's units. Suppliers can even cross national borders to be near IKEA. For instance, the Swedish coating-technology provider Becker-Acroma "followed" IKEA to Poland by opening a local technical support office as soon as the number of IKEA-owned factories or first-tier suppliers reached a critical mass. IKEA-related production sites in Poland are now so numerous and widespread that the Poznan office of Becker-Acroma is no longer adequate enough to service them all and new local offices may soon be opened.

4.2 IKEA, Using the Place-related Features of Resources

Let us now look at how IKEA *uses* the place-related features embedded in products, facilities, units and relationships. Since IKEA also actively intervenes to *shape* some of these spatial features, we point out which resources are most affected, and for what reasons.

4.2.1 The Importance of Place for Products

IKEA's products are all designed in Älmhult. Even if designers come from Denmark, the UK, Holland, etc., IKEA strives for a common identity across all its products. This identity is constructed not only around IKEA's look and concept, but also around such macro-spatial aspects as the Swedish (or Scandinavian) style and light-colored woods. Swedish culture is strongly embedded in IKEA's products in another way: they all bear very Swedish names (e.g., of persons and cities). These products carry this identity wherever they are sold around the world, even in countries where such names as "Lack" (a line of tables and shelves) or, even worse, "Jerker" (a line of desks) might make people frown or laugh. IKEA applies to all its products another Swedish feature: the furniture certification "Möbel Fakta," which has obtained international recognition.

Design, names and certifications, however, account only for the external features of IKEA's product. Indeed, construction details and technical solutions are seldom decided centrally in Älmhult and are not purely Swedish. Several places (at micro, meso and macro level) affect these hidden, but no less important, properties that define the key feature of all IKEA products, their *final price*, so essential for sales success. In fact, IKEA is a "production-led retailer," which means that the construction of each product emerges in *close interaction with* suppliers, on their shop floors and, consequently, in thousands of locations. All these micro-places contribute specific features of IKEA's products, important from a techno-economic point of view in keeping retail prices low.

Macro-places also impact strongly on products' costs, a large part of which depend on the country where they are produced. Labor costs, in particular, induce IKEA to purchase from low-wage countries, even if this can embed "negative" symbolic features in IKEA's product, for example if low wages are associated with child labor or exploitative work practices. The country of origin can therefore have both negative and positive economic, material and symbolic implications for IKEA's products. But IKEA has only a limited ability to directly affect these macro-places, its only choice being to avoid its products being connected with negative place features. Transportation costs instead lead IKEA to purchase from countries located near its major markets in Europe. In fact, having a low value in relation to their weight or volume, IKEA's products are very sensitive to transport costs.

Exploiting space to reduce labor and transportation costs creates conflicts, because countries that can embed low production costs in products (e.g., India or China) are far away from output markets and this implies high transport costs. Only a few meso-places, such as the Poznan area in Poland, allow a balance to be struck: Poznan offers good logistical connections with major markets and a local network of suppliers and sub-contractors that are both cost-efficient and technically proficient. But IKEA could solve the trade-off between low production costs (requiring large-scale centralized production and/or inexpensive labor) and transportation costs (requiring short distances to retail stores) only by introducing a particular product concept and technical solution: its furniture is sold to customers knocked down, inside "flat packs" that allow transport facilities to be filled more efficiently.

The effort to reduce transportation costs is extreme in the product "Lack," a series of tables and shelves: these are made out of empty structures that are cheaper to transport across the many countries separating the production sites in Poland and customers around in the world. But even if flat packs offer advantages in overcoming space-related problems, they may conflict with other place issues. Two examples concern the micro-place of customers' homes. Firstly, flat packs were behind a major problem involving the bestseller "Billy" bookcase in the early 1990s: when "Billy" flat packs were opened, formaldehyde was given off by the cellophane wrapping. The presence of hazardous chemicals in consumers' homes obliged IKEA to have all its suppliers change their lacquering technology. Secondly, consumers are confronted in their homes with the task of assembling the components inside the flat pack into a piece of furniture: this inconvenience is accepted by most people, but others may be deterred from buying IKEA's products. Interestingly, there are differences between countries: while the "do-it-yourself" idea behind IKEA's furniture is accepted in central and northern Europe, it is much less so in southern Europe (e.g., in Italy and Spain).

Space and places are important not only for final products, but also for their *raw materials* and *components*. Their geographic origin particularly affects their costs and functional features. When IKEA has identified advantageous sources of materials in a certain area, the company then pushes for its suppliers in other countries to utilize such sources. For instance, the supply of larch wood identified in China was considered so interesting that all IKEA product developers and suppliers were invited to make use of it. IKEA is also aware of the potential *negative* effect deriving from certain places of origin of raw materials. In order to protect corporate and product identity, IKEA applies a strict environmental policy based, among other ideas, on refusing wood from rain forests and areas endangered or overexploited. IKEA also participates in replanting programs of trees felled to satisfy its supply needs. The association of components with specific places is instead much less important than that of raw materials and finished products. What counts most are regular streams of components to the factories producing IKEA products. When production phases are outsourced to sub-contractors, these are usually located near to IKEA's first-tier suppliers.

4.2.2 The Importance of Place for Facilities

Many space-related features (e.g., costs) are transmitted to products *via* the facilities involved in producing or distributing them. We start by reviewing IKEA's own *distribution facilities*, moving then to *IT systems* and *manufacturing facilities* and, finally, to *transport equipment*.

Distributing products in over 30 countries in four continents required IKEA to invest heavily in 25 Distribution Centres (DCs) and 180 retail stores. DCs are large warehouses (300,000 m^3 in volume) that receive and handle products to be dispatched to the retail stores located in the geographic areas for which they are responsible. On the macro-level, IKEA first enters a country with retail stores, and introduces a DC hub only when more retail stores and volumes justify the investment of over SKr 1 billion that a DC entails. The connections between DCs and retail stores are also inspired by efficiency issues: most retail stores are grouped within a radius of 600 km around a DC hub, to limit transport costs and ensure punctual deliveries. Retail stores are in turn located in specific cities depending on key geographical and demographical indicators: only large and medium-sized cities justify an IKEA store (costing up to SKr 1 billion to establish); to the point that IKEA prefers to open two or more stores in the same city rather than to spread them too much, for transport cost reasons. Some customers are expected to travel over 300 km to visit an IKEA store. At the meso-level of the city, retail stores are located on the outskirts, where real estate prices are low, large parking lots can be built and access to major highways is secured: in this way IKEA exploits the space immediately surrounding its stores.

IKEA designed the details of its DCs and stores in order to ensure efficient product flows through these micro-places and easy docking of trains and trucks. Retail stores, as large as 55,000 m², are particularly important, because they are the physical space where customers come in contact with IKEA's products. IKEA shaped its stores to have customers flow through a showroom-like environment to a "self-service" warehouse and, finally, to the cash desks. But the "private" parts of retail stores are also carefully organized to allow incoming products to be swiftly placed in exhibition or storage areas. All IKEA retail stores and DCs are replicas of the first ones that IKEA opened in Älmhult, in 1958 and 1965, respectively. Retail stores, in particular, reproduce the architectural, aesthetic and functional features tested and developed during the expansion of IKEA in its home market. From Sweden, IKEA stores inherited many features visible to all visitors (over 200 million yearly): the blue and yellow of many exteriors, the restaurant serving Swedish delicacies and the "Sweden shop," present in all stores, from Singapore to Chicago. All the features shaping these micro-spaces are applied in accordance with detailed routines (e.g., those prescribing how IKEA flags should be placed). These details, symbolically related to Sweden, the macro-place of origin of IKEA, create uniformity among all IKEA stores.

IT systems are important facilities that sustain communication over the distances separating IKEA's units and suppliers. IKEA's 50 IT systems are standardized between countries to enable interlinking and coordination. IKEA's 500 business units use the same IT systems and models and the routines these support, so that the work practices of these units become homogenized around the world. EDI and order systems have important *indirect* space-related effects on other resources. For instance, these IT systems allow increased order volumes and require delivery times that obliged some supplying units to enlarge their warehouses to store larger quantities of finished goods for quick deliveries. Macro-level considerations are important here: not surprisingly such warehouses were built near factories in countries with low real estate costs, such as Poland. These indirect effects emerge across IKEA's supply network, where capacities are unbalanced. Within this network, IKEA stimulates capacity expansion where this is favorable: at micro level (e.g., in an unused warehouse), at meso level (e.g., in a warehouse well connected logistically) or at macro level (e.g., a warehouse in Poland).

Despite recent investments in production facilities, IKEA owns a marginal part of the equipment that manufactures its products. These facilities are owned by a network of over 2,000 suppliers spread across 60 countries. IKEA uses the space-related features of these facilities in two main ways: by exploiting their *geographical location* and their *area of origin.*

1. The location of production facilities affects the quality and costs of their operations and the costs for *transporting* their outputs to final markets. Country-specific macro issues affect labor costs and skills. Countries where facilities can be operated at low costs are often far away from markets and give rise to high transport costs. But in some countries, such as China, low operating costs and good and inexpensive raw materials (Chinese larch) outweigh the cost of transport. China is therefore, despite its distance, IKEA's largest supply country, providing 14% of its purchases. Meso-spaces are important, too, for facility operations and transport costs. In fact, many IKEA products rely on networks of first-tier suppliers and their co-located subcontractors, all equipped with advanced machinery and highly skilled personnel, even in such high-wage countries as Sweden. For instance, the Sydpoolen network, in Southern Sweden, produces the bestseller "Billy" bookcase, a large-volume assignment that requires large technology investments and tight coordination among all the firms involved.

2. The area of origin of production facilities is important because it embeds into them specific technical features and costs, including initial investments and operating and maintenance costs. A few areas of origin dominate here: most NC-millers and edge-banding machines come from Italy (e.g., Biesse) or Germany (e.g., Homag); the same is true of coating equipment, made for the most part by the Italian companies Valtorta, Sorbini and Cefla or the German Eisman and Bürkle. Competence from these specialized countries, or from their regions (e.g., the Rimini-Pesaro district for wood-working machines in Italy), is embedded in these machines.

Means of transport also allow the *physical* distances separating the nodes in IKEA's production and distribution network to be overcome. IKEA utilizes transport facilities owned by its logistics partners and selects the appropriate means to cover each one of over 20,000 routes: trucks cover shorter routes (between DCs and retail stores), while trains and ships cover the longer ones (from suppliers to DCs). Transport equipment needs to be as place-independent as possible, because its function is to *connect* different and widely distant sites, which requires standard interfaces, such as those of the containers shipped across four continents. However, the efficient utilization of these facilities depends on factors belonging to the three spatial levels: at micro level, loading on trucks or railway cars requires adequate docking stations at IKEA's DCs and retail stores; at meso level, IKEA's DCs and suppliers' warehouses need to be connected to inter-modal transport infrastructures; at macro level, motorways and railroads affect transportation. When these macro infrastructures are poor, as they are in many Eastern European states, they can cause delays or damage to IKEA's products.

4.2.3 The Importance of Place for Business Units

IKEA's *internal units* are over 500 in number and spread across 60 countries. These units are almost unmarked by the country where they are located, as IKEA strives for *homogeneity* in routines, identity and corporate culture across all of them (see also the contribution of common IT systems). Despite the cultural differences between countries, IKEA offices in Milan, Warsaw or Stockholm are strikingly similar in work style, hierarchical relations and interior design. For instance, IKEA's casual dress codes make IKEA's offices in Italy much more like any other IKEA office than like a typical Italian office. The differences between IKEA's units depend much more on their specific tasks: retailing for stores, purchasing for purchase offices, or product development for "IKEA of Sweden."

While IKEA's units are little affected by their location, IKEA locates them in those areas that appear most suitable for their diversified tasks. Purchase offices are opened in those countries where interesting purchasing opportunities (raw materials, components or finished products) appear. Some units are concentrated in the town of Älmhult, the center of IKEA's product development and retail universe. "IKEA of Sweden" also orchestrates from Älmhult the pattern of interaction between the above units: most communication goes through this center before returning to the units in the periphery.

Local specificities emerge instead in the interaction with external units, located across over 60 countries, and are consequently explicitly utilized by IKEA. Suppliers are for instance often selected because of such macro-spatial aspects as their location in countries with inexpensive labor and raw materials or near IKEA's final markets. But what counts most is that IKEA seeks very different space-related features in its suppliers. Most suppliers are located in three countries—China, Poland and Sweden—but for different reasons: Chinese units have access to good raw materials and low-cost labor; Polish suppliers have good competence, relatively advanced technology, lower-than-average labor costs and proximity to IKEA's key markets in Europe; Swedish units have very high competence, long-term experience and excellent technology. Swedish suppliers are accordingly involved in development projects, because of their proximity to "IKEA of Sweden" and their ability to cooperate on complex technical issues, as in the case of the lacquering suppliers Becker-Acroma and Akzo-Nobel.

IKEA's interaction with logistics partners takes place instead on a global scale. Their national identity is less relevant and the space-related feature in which IKEA is mostly interested is the widespread presence of these units, controlling terminals across most countries through which IKEA's products pass. Finally, IKEA interacts with non-governmental organizations. When these units are widely known global players, they may help to strengthen IKEA's identity as a firm concerned with such key issues as the global environment: IKEA has cooperated with Green Peace on initiatives ranging from forest-replanting programs to the development of chlorine-free catalogue paper (see Håkansson & Waluszewski, 2002). This cooperation has given IKEA's initiatives global coverage and media visibility.

4.2.4 The Importance of Place for Business Relationships

IKEA's business relationships with suppliers and logistics partners and those between other firms in IKEA's business network allow IKEA to use the many spatial features of resources discussed above. These relationships link IKEA's units to other external units located in many different places: they are the channels through which IKEA can be present in and exploit other places without being *physically* there. Relationships are not "located" anywhere, but are important bridges to overcome spatial, cultural and competence distances between IKEA and its partners. However, "overcoming" does not mean eliminating these distances, which indeed IKEA is looking for when finding suppliers located in so many different places. Even if IKEA established 40 purchase offices in 33 countries in order to create spatially (and culturally) closer "interfaces" with 2,000 suppliers, in about 55 countries, the combined function of all these relationships is to exploit the particular spatial features of single supplying units, so different from each other. A certain "distance" between IKEA and its suppliers and between suppliers is indeed necessary to ensure some *variety* in the place-related features of the competences, facilities and inputs associated with these units. It is then IKEA's task to *combine* the variety that it accesses through its relationships in ways favorable to its goals, such as keeping prices low, improving deliveries or expanding sales.

Being located close to other units often failed to facilitate IKEA's relationships or lead to good ones. Having today only 14% of its suppliers in Sweden, IKEA seems to be very attracted to foreign partners. However, IKEA started establishing relationships with Polish suppliers as early as in the 1960s, when it was still satisfied with the price and quality of Swedish suppliers. The reason why IKEA could not maintain its relationships with Swedish suppliers was a "veto" on supplying IKEA imposed on Swedish suppliers by the Swedish furniture retailers, who saw IKEA as too big a threat. It was therefore this type of boycott that "obliged" IKEA to establish new relationships outside Sweden. Only when the "veto" disappeared could IKEA (re-)establish relationships with Swedish suppliers, though based on different premises from those with foreign ones. Today, Swedish suppliers are those most regularly involved in cooperation projects dealing with complex technical issues. For instance, IKEA created a joint venture located in Southern Sweden and involving Swedish furniture producers (Sydpoolen) and lacquering suppliers (Akzo and Becker) to tackle the formaldehyde problems associated with the "Billy" bookcase. This would have been more difficult to accomplish farther from Sweden and from the key actors involved, since they all had to meet regularly around a testing facility.

But other factors than nearness to IKEA's home bases are more important in explaining close cooperation with specific suppliers: the frequently recurring joint development projects with the Polish supply units of Swedwood (IKEA's production arm) show how common goals, shared values, authority and power relations matter more than physical proximity. However, close relationships, developed in a specific geographical context, say Sweden, play important roles in other countries, too. The same Swedish lacquer manufacturers involved in the joint venture mentioned above also supply many foreign plants that in turn supply IKEA. IKEA is thus capable of transferring to new geographical contexts relationships developed elsewhere.

Handling many relationships and accessing through them different places also creates *conflicts* for IKEA. Many of these conflicts appear in the resources that these relationships connect, such as products from suppliers located in sites that allow low production costs but entail high transportation costs. Relationships themselves may be in conflict just because of "spatial" reasons: IKEA does not utilize two suppliers for the same product in the same geographic region, even if these two would be the best ones in the world for that product. Using co-located parallel suppliers is usually ruled out by the problem of having two suppliers neither of which can attain sufficient scale economies in production (unless low transport costs allow them to supply IKEA's global needs). Relationships can also conflict for political reasons at the macro-place level: the idea of linking IKEA's Israeli franchisee with suppliers from Muslim countries implies conflicts.

5. ANALYSING THE SPATIAL ASPECTS OF RESOURCE NETWORKS

IKEA's experiences with a multitude of places illustrate the importance of space in handling resources. While IKEA can exert an influence on some places, many are outside its reach, but they still affect how IKEA handles its network of resources (products, facilities, units and relationships). Places affect key aspects of resources of pivotal economic and managerial importance. An indicative list of the effects of space on resources includes: costs and revenues, manageability, efficient utilization, development, and identities and symbolic values of resources.

(1) The costs and revenues of resources. The costs of IKEA's products depend largely on the factory and the country where they are produced, while their sales depend on the building (IKEA's stores), the city and the country where they are sold. Costs of facilities are affected by their location (because of different installation, power and labor costs) and by the places from which these facilities receive inputs; while output volumes are related to the places that a facility connects, depending on the closeness to customers or to other receiving facilities. The economic performance of units and relationships is partly affected by the places to which they are related. Units sustain such costs as labor, which are determined locally at the meso- and macro-level. But since units interact with other units, their costs also depend on the places where these other units are located. For instance, purchases from suppliers located in certain areas expose a unit to the place-related costs incurred by these suppliers. Places also impact the revenue side, from the building hosting a unit (especially retail stores) to the areas where customers are located. Whereas certain places pose techno-economic, social or cultural barriers to getting customers, others are a major source of customers and revenues for a unit.

(2) The manageability of resources. No matter whether they are inside or outside a firm, the more geographically dispersed the various resources are, the more difficult it should be to control and coordinate them. Resources spread between several distant places (at the three analytical levels) are less manageable than those contained in one place.

(3) The efficient utilization of resources. For a firm like IKEA, efficiency concerns the physical resource flows and the information flows between units. These flows are affected by the *distances* that resources and information need to overcome. Physical distances range from the micro-distances of in-store logistics to the macro-distances between continents. Cultural micro-distances, within and between buildings (and the units occupying them), and macro-distances between units located in different countries can affect information flows. The cost advantages of a place can easily turn into disadvantages because of its distance from other places where resources need to be transferred or where information needs to flow.

(4) The development of resources. What possibilities of, or obstacles to, *recombining* resources derive from spatial factors? Having distant resources interact is not necessarily a problem for development, as it is for manageability as such. In fact, distance opens the door to new influences and for new resources not present in the *nearest* local environment: think of the Swedish and Ikean expertise in developing inexpensive products combined with Chinese larch. However, concrete development can be obtained only if distant resources are brought together to be recombined, either physically (e.g., in practical tests) or metaphorically. Not surprisingly, IKEA's product developers travel extensively to meet local suppliers, on their shop floors. When new solutions are found, production can start in widely separated places.

(5) The identities and symbolic values of resources. These softer factors may also have such concrete economic impacts as sales growth or loss of customers. For instance, IKEA is aware of the negative effects on its products and corporate image of any association with such places as child-labor factories or countries. On the positive side, IKEA's retail stores are extremely important in creating its identity, which relies in turn on many Swedish symbols.

Places affect managerial action on these five aspects of resources, creating both possibilities and hindrances. However, these effects are complex and hard to identify. Here, an analytical framework is sug-

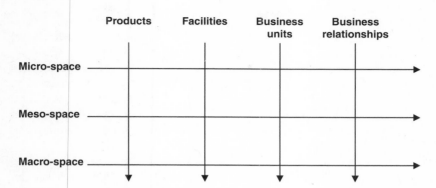

Figure 1. The Space-Resources analytical grid.

gested that helps in tracing these effects for each resource type, across *spatial scales* (Livingstone, 1995: 15, 27). The analytical grid of Figure 1 combines the three analytical levels for space with the four resource types, in a 3x4 matrix.

The grid in Figure 1 does not identify unilateral causal relations between variables (resources and places): it only helps analyze how the issues of *costs and revenues*, *manageability*, *efficiency*, *development* and *symbolic aspects* of resources relate to the three spatial scales. For each of these five items, positive or negative effects on a particular resource can be linked to micro-, meso- or macro-places. To start with, this "Space-Resources grid" can be used to *specify* (i.e., to identify as a specific location) and *count* the micro, meso and macro-places that affect a product or a unit, for instance. Then one can proceed to define *how much* a firm has invested (time or finance) in these places and in the resources considered: this provides an overview of a firm's pattern in utilizing space. The sheer number of places and the investments in specific places indicate, respectively, the *variety* and *heaviness* (Håkansson & Waluszewski, 2002) in a firm's space utilization patterns. Section 6 will apply this reasoning to IKEA.

The Space-Resources grid can be used for an even deeper analysis: evaluating how much specific places affect the five issues above. This exercise points out the *importance* of specific places and *why* they are important for certain resources, considering also the investments made in each place. However, these spatial aspects create *conflicting* pressures on resources. Many of these conflicts derive from the *processes* through which space-related features become embedded in resources (see section 3): these processes are highly complex

because they involve the various "interfaces" (Håkansson & Waluszewski, 2002: 190–200) between resources. For instance, the place-
related costs of a product derive from all the facilities handling it,
from its inputs, from the know-how of the units handling it and from
the volumes exchanged with specific suppliers and customers. All
these resources around the product have "cost features" associated
with their geographical location or origin: the country of a supplier,
the rural or urban location of a facility, the competence of a particular local workforce, etc.

The Space-Resources grid offers no solution to these space-related conflicts, but it may help to highlight them. Unravelling the
processes by which spatial features are embedded in resources is
so complex as to be beyond the scope of a matrix like the Space-
Resources grid of Figure 1. Actively using space is difficult not only
because of the limits to *affecting* places, but also because of the *complexity* and *often-conflicting* nature of the effects that places create on
resources. Firms are obliged to accept trade-offs: no optimizing solution for such complex and conflict-ridden resource networks as
IKEA's can ever be found in relation to spatial issues.

6. CONCLUSION: PLACES AND RESOURCE COMBINATIONS

The view on spatial issues presented in this chapter transcends theoretical approaches to space as a given or as an independent variable,
typically found in economic geography (see Malmberg & Maskell,
2002) and in business studies (Porter, 1990 and 2000). Places and the
spatial features of resources were considered here as tools that firms
can, within limits, affect and that they can utilize for pursuing various
goals. However, places and spatial features are not easily tamed and
manageable objects: they embed conflicting features into one and the
same resource, oppose resources with each other and often require
trade-offs when they are actively utilized. IKEA's experiences in
using places show how some spaces can be shaped by IKEA, such as
the retail store and customer home micro-places, whereas IKEA is
much more limited in shaping meso- and macro-spaces. Nonetheless,
IKEA actively utilizes important features that the latter types of
spaces embed in the resources it handles. More precisely, IKEA combines many place-related features that micro-, meso- and macro-
spaces reflect on such resources as products, facilities and units.
Business relationships are important linkages between units that fa-

cilitate this process of combination and that connect different places and the resources associated with them.

This chapter also stressed the importance for *technical development* of the interactive nature of space and of its interplay with resources. In fact, technical development requires the recombining of the features of resources, including those that are place-related. If places are seen just as given or as independent factors impossible to affect, the opportunities for developing resources are reduced. But IKEA's experiences show the importance of creating connections between several places and of finding ways to link and exploit the features that space embeds in resources.

IKEA approaches places in a dual way: by using them as stable "bases," but also by keeping them "at a distance." As far as the first aspect is concerned, IKEA is not afraid to become strongly connected with certain specific places. It does so in order to take advantage of the *friction of space* (see Håkansson, Tunisini & Waluszewski, in this volume) that embeds features in the resources located in or associated with some places, but not others. By *investing* in facilities, units and relationships "placed" in certain locations, IKEA becomes heavily related with these places. Such investments also help IKEA create long-lasting *symbolic* associations with places with which it has no longer a *physical* connection: for instance, IKEA's products are still perceived as Swedish, even if only 14% of them are made in Sweden. As for the second aspect, IKEA tries to overcome the potential limits that spatial friction imposes on short-term coordination and on long-term development, when resources that are *too* spatially embedded in one single place can be an obstacle. In the short term, distances create problems in coordinating so many widely dispersed resources. To overcome these problems, IKEA strives for homogeneous culture and routines across its internal units, for a uniform worldwide profile toward customers and for efficient product and information flows. In a long-term perspective, IKEA avoids the obstacles to development of too much spatial friction by relating itself simultaneously to *many different* places (via its relationships, and the placement of its units and of the facilities it utilizes).

Therefore, IKEA's investments in places are both *heavy* and *varied* (Håkansson & Waluszewski, 2002): this allows IKEA to get the most out of each single place with which it is related, while maintaining some flexibility. The pattern of space utilization reviewed in this chapter is certainly not unique to IKEA; rather it is typical of most large firms (especially multinationals) that have been operating for a long time in many different places. The approach proposed in this chapter could provide a more fine-grained view of the complex and conflict-ridden ways in which such firms gain advantages, by exploiting and affecting places. Conducting this type of research is, however, demanding from a methodological point of view: the units of analysis become *networks of resources* that are spread across multiple spatial scales. And covering these resources on the various spatial scales requires a large amount of detailed, often qualitatively collected, empirical material.

NOTES

1. Even if this chapter focuses on *geographical* places (or territory), with physical boundaries, locating human endeavors in a place transcends the idea of *physical* space to include its *social* and *cultural* features.
2. "Place" and "space" are different but related concepts. *Place* identifies, within a larger *space*, a specific point, located at a certain distance from other places (Agnew & Duncan, 1989: 1). Whereas "place" suggests a non-dimensional single point (even though this article treats places as heterogeneous and multi-dimensional points), "space" refers to an at least two-dimensional *area* and *structure*. However, the distinction space-place loses relevance when one moves across different scales of spatial analysis: meso-*places* (e.g., a city) include many micro-*spaces* (e.g., houses). The notion of space becomes instead useful if the focus is on what goes on *inside* a place. Then the single point on a map (the place) can be recognized as containing something and it becomes a space. The notion of space is also useful for *relating* different places to each other, to see how distant from or close to each other they are. Distance is indeed a spatial concept that relates different points in space.

REFERENCES

Agnew, J., & Duncan, J. (eds.), 1989, *The Power of Place. Bringing together geographical and sociological imaginations*, Unwin Hyman: Boston.

Andersson, U., 1997, *Subsidiary Network Embeddedness. Integration, Control and Influence in the Multinational Corporation*, Doctoral Thesis, Department of Business Studies, Uppsala University.

Andersson, U., & Forsgren, M., 1996, Subsidiary Embeddedness and Control in the Multinational Corporation, *International Business Review*, Vol. 5, No. 5, pp. 487–508.

Baraldi, E., & Bocconcelli, R., 2001, The quantitative journey in a qualitative landscape. Developing a data collection model and a quantitative methodology in business network studies, *Management Decision*, Vol. 39, No. 7, Sept. 2001, pp. 564–577.

Baraldi, E., 2003, *When Information Technology Faces Resource Interaction. Using IT Tools to Handle Products at IKEA and Edsbyn*, Doctoral Thesis, Department of Business Studies, Uppsala University.

Beckman, J., 1999, *Naturens palats: Nybyggnad, vetenskap och utställning vid Naturhistoriska riksmuseet 1866–1925* (Nature's Palace: Construction, Science and Exhibition at the National Natural History Museum, 1866–1925), Atlantis: Stockholm.

Brandt, A. M., & Sloane, D. C., 1999, Of Beds and Benches: Buildings in the Modern American Hospital, In: Galison, P., & Thompson, E. (eds.), 1999, *The Architecture of Science*, MIT Press: Cambridge, MA.

Brusco, S., 1989, *Piccole imprese e distretti industriali* (Small firms and industrial districts), Rosengerg & Sellier: Torino.

Dunning, J. H., 1995, Reappraising the Eclectic Paradigm in an Age of Alliance Capitalism, *Journal of International Business Studies*, Vol. 26, 1995, pp. 461–491.

Dunning, J. H., 1998, Location and the Multinational Enterprise: A Neglected Factor? *Journal of International Business Studies*, Vol. 29, 1998, pp. 45–66.

Forsgren, M., Johanson, J., & Sharma, D., 2000, Development of MNC Centres of Excellence, In: Holm, H., & Pedersen, T. (eds.), 2000, *The Emergence and Impact of MNC Centres of Excellence. A Subsidiary Perspective*, Macmillan Press Ltd.: Houndmills, London, pp. 45–78.

Foucault, M., 1979, *Discipline and Punish. The Birth of the Prison*, Vintage: New York.

Foucault, M., 1986, Of Other Spaces, In: *Diacritis*, Vol. 16, pp. 22–27.

Gieryn, T. F., 1998, Biotechnology's Private Parts (and Some Public Ones), In: Smith, C., & Agar, J. (eds.), 1998, *Making Space for Science: Territorial Themes in the Shaping of Knowledge*, St. Martin's Press: New York, pp. 281–312.

Gieryn, T. F., 1999, Two Faces on Science: Building Identities for Molecular Biology and Biotechnology, In: Galison, P., & Thompson, E. (eds.), 1999, *The Architecture of Science*, MIT Press: Cambridge, MA.

Hannaway, O., 1986, Laboratory Design and the Aim of Science. Andreas Libavius versus Tycho Brahe, *ISIS*, Vol. 77, 1986, pp. 585–610.

Harvey, D., 1990, Between Space and Time: Reflections on the Geographical Imagination, *Annals of the Association of American Geographers*, Vol. 80, Issue 3, pp. 418–434.

Hofstede, G., 1983, The Cultural Relativity of Organizational Practices and Theories, *Journal of International Business Studies*, Vol. 99, 1983, pp. 75–89.

Håkansson, H., & Snehota, I. (eds.), 1995, *Developing Relationships in Business Networks*, Routledge: London.

Håkansson, H., & Waluszewski, A., 2002, *Managing Technological Development*, Routledge: London.

Håkansson, H., Tunisini, A., & Waluszewski, A., 2005, Place as a Resource in Business Networks, In this volume.

Lindqvist, S., 1997, Forskningens fasader. Wenner-Gren Center som symbol för svensk vetenskap (The Façades of Research. Wenner-Gren Center as a Symbol for Swedish Science), *Lychnos*, 1997, pp. 119–156.

Livingstone, D., 1995, The spaces of knowledge: contributions towards a historical geography of science, *Environment and Planning D, Society and Space*, Vol. 13, 1995, pp. 5–34.

Malmberg, A., & Maskell, P., 2002, The elusive concept of localization economies: towards a knowledge-based theory of spatial clustering, *Environment and Planning A*, Vol. 34, 2002, pp. 429–449.

Markgren, B., 2001, *Är Närhet en Geografisk Fråga? Företags Affärsverksamhet och Geografi—En Studie av Beroenden mellan Företag och Lokaliseringens Betydelse* (Is Closeness a Geographical Issue? Business Activities and Geography—A Study on the Connection between Firms and the Importance of Localisation), Doctoral Thesis, Department of Business Studies, Uppsala University.

Marshall, A., 1890, *Principles of Economics*, Macmillan: London.

Ophir, A., & Shapin, A., 1991, The Place of Knowledge. A Methodological Survey, *Science in Context*, Vol. 3, No. 4, 1991, pp. 163–189.

Penrose, E., 1959, *The Theory of the Growth of the Firm*, Reprint 1995, Oxford University Press: New York.

Porter, M., 1990, *The Competitive Advantage of Nations*, Macmillan: London.

Porter, M., 2000, Locations, Clusters and Company Strategy, In: Clark, G. L. et al. (eds.), 2000, *Handbook of Economic Geography*, Oxford University Press: Oxford, pp. 253–274.

Pred, A., 1984, Place as Historically Contingent Process: Structuration and the Time-Geography of Becoming Spaces, *Annals of American Geographers*, Vol. 74, Issue 2, pp. 279–297.

Rothblatt, S., 1997, *The Modern University and its Discontents. The Fate of Newman's Legacies in Britain and America*, Cambridge University Press: Cambridge.

Soja, E. W., 2000, *Postmetropolis. Critical Studies of Cities and Regions*, Blackwell: Oxford, Malden.

Wedin, T., 2001, *Networks and Demand. The Use of Electricity in an Industrial Process*, Department of Business Studies, Uppsala University.

Widmalm, S., 2001, *Det öppna laboratoriet. Uppsalafysiken och dess nätverk, 1853–1910* (The Open Laboratory. Physics in Uppsala and its Network, 1853–1910), Atlantis: Stockholm.

MAKING SPACE FOR CULTURE

The Visual Ordering of Space in The First Museums of Ethnography

OLOF LJUNGSTRÖM

This article addresses the ethnographic production and visualization of culture through the spatial configuration of the internal space of the museum.[1] Its purpose is to analyze a nineteenth-century discussion about the epistemology of ethnographic research in the museum (truth claims and verifiability), and through it to delineate the practices (collection and systematization) followed in the production of knowledge.[2] As such, it is a contribution to an analysis of the establishment of a modernity of a scientific visual order in the nineteenth century.[3]

The museum and/or collection of nineteenth-century science was a highly *social* place. It was a meeting place (almost exclusively, as it were) for men of science. Just as significantly, but perhaps less obviously, it was also the place where the material remains of nature as well as culture, between objects of natural history and the sciences of man, were presented. Here they were received, identified, named, and stored. Much more importantly, here they were brought together to be ordered, classified, compared and finally displayed. They were there to be seen by both the scholars and the public.

The establishment of a philosophic and scientific modernity of vision beginning in the latter half of the 18th century (its "point of emergence") has been dealt with in Jonathan Crary's influential *Techniques of the Observer*.[4] Crary charts the break-up of the classical model of embodied philosophical and scientific techniques of observation, exemplified by the *camera obscura*, in favor of the subjective and fractured process of observation established by the early nineteenth century. Roughly, the classical model presupposed a consistent Cartesian human soul supplied with a set of senses and looking out of its embodied self. Under the strain of simultaneous developments in philosophy, physiology and psychology, this unified objectivist notion of self and vision was dismantled in favor of the recognition of vision as a constructive process, the results of which had to take into account the newly discovered distortions inherent in the human visual apparatus, the eye.[5]

What is most important here is Crary's stress on the transformation of the scientist as observer from a self-sufficient absorptive onlooker into a much more problematic figure actively producing the visual knowledge of his science, as well as the notion of a "physiologization" of the object of study. As far as physiological studies were concerned with the study of living beings, a completely metonymic relationship can be said to exist between the organisms studied and the greater "Nature" that was the real interest of the scientist.[6] Physiologists would dissect animals in order to present the different internal systems of the animal. Once available, this model was successfully transferred to the scientists of culture, who would treat it as an organism. Instead of penetrating, for example, neurological or respiratory systems, they would detail cultural practices such as hunting or fishing. The tendency to deal with observed *cultural* phenomena as analogous to the internal function of a living being will be much in evidence throughout this article.

In doing this, I depart from Crary's interests in physiology, instead focusing on the notion of organisms as presented in the early nineteenth-century sciences of natural history, systematics, comparative anatomy (morphology) and palaeontology. As model sciences, these form a necessary stepping stone towards the sciences of culture such as archaeology and ethnography.

More specifically, I will revisit one of the better-known public debates from the first half of the nineteenth century. It focused upon the necessity of establishing ethnographic museums, their uses, and the best system to adopt for the ordering of the collections. Through this I will show how the new visual practices developed within natural history were transferred to the sciences of culture within their typical framework of the museum. For scientific purposes, the nineteenth century would treat man as an animal among others, and the methods for doing so were pioneered within the museum.

The museum and collection was also in a sense a *liminal place* (borrowing the concept in a very general sense from Victor Turner).[7]

The museum was an intermediary place between the field and its practices, and the finished texts of scholarly discourse and theory. However, the collection and the museum had their own set of conventions and practices. It was in the museum collections that the strange alchemy took place that transformed everything, from the most everyday utensils to objects of immense power and significance for a whole community, into an ethnographic "sameness," available to the scientific gaze of the ethnographer. In the process, and often more significantly for the scientists (since it was a problem inherent in their own social and cultural practices), this process evened out the intermediary stages of scientifically aberrant functions, which an object might have passed through as a souvenir of a sailor, a soldier in colonial service, and so on—that is, as the bric-a-brac of western colonialism. One of the scientific community's worst fears would be that the object had been selected for transfer to the museums of the West for monetary gain. (For centuries sailors had been in the habit of making extra money by stocking up on exotic goods, including animals such as monkeys and parrots and so on, a practice that could give any ship returning from the East or West Indies something of a carnival character.) The absolute nightmare was a scenario in which the natives themselves had manufactured it for sale to western travellers, a double stigma of cupidity and artifice from which no object could hope to recover.

This liminality can also be extended to the fact that museums functioned as central institutions of instruction. The collection was a repository of knowledge into which the uninitiated could be admitted in order to study and learn. Here the uninitiated would enter, later to emerge as a *savant*. There always remained some doubt as to the limits of autodidacticism in this situation, but guidance into the mysteries was a welcome aid to most. Regardless of this, access to the means of learning, i.e. the objects of the collection and the order in which they had been placed, was still guarded by the custodians of the place.[8]

All in all, the "nations" and their respective "material culture" represented in ethnographic collections and museums were strange beasts indeed, dependent on a levelling out of all problematic circumstances surrounding their arrival in their final resting place. It is not by chance that I have here labelled them "beasts." The first arrangements of a representation of culture within the museum were heavily indebted to the fields of comparative anatomy and palaeontology, i.e. "morphology" in a general sense.[9]

TAKING IT ALL IN—ETHNOGRAPHY
AS OBSERVATION

The ethnographic collection was in a sense a visual display of what
Mary Louise Pratt has labelled the "anti-conquest," the particular
gaze of the natural-history traveller since the 18th century:

> natural history asserted an urban, lettered, male authority over the
> whole of the planet; it elaborated a rationalizing, extractive, disso-
> ciative understanding which overlaid functional, experiential rela-
> tions among people, plants and animals. [...] At the same time, in
> and of itself, the system of nature as a descriptive paradigm was an
> utterly benign and abstract appropriation of the planet. Claiming no
> transformative potential whatsoever, it differed sharply from overtly
> imperial articulations of conquest, conversion, territorial appropri-
> ation, and enslavement. The system created [...] a utopian, inno-
> cent vision of European global authority, which I refer to as an
> anti-conquest.[10]

My contribution here is to stress that the knowledge produced
within the narratives of the "anti-conquest" depended on rhetorical
devices that stressed the characteristics of landscape, flora and fauna
as *displays*. As such they were accessible to the gaze and evaluation of
the western traveller. The traveller can be understood to be present,
but still in a sense positioned above and beyond the confines of what
he would take in. (Pratt's appellation of this is the theme of "Master
of all I survey.")[11]

The advantage of the visual categorizations implicit in the "anti-
conquest" was the fact that the privileged position of observation was
regarded as transferable along with the collected specimens. The account of the travel writer was still fixed at a certain time and place,
even if that which was observed was perceived as "eternal Nature."
As these objects of nature or culture were eventually transferred to
the museum, all the contingent factors relating to the voyage were allowed to recede. Consequently, their "nature" had now, in a sense,
been made accessible to a disembodied scientific gaze at the same
time. The very fact that "Nature" could now be perceived shorn of the
constraints of locality and the occasion under which the travel-writing
scientist operated served to strengthen the authority of the pro-
nouncements of those scientists primarily working in the museums.[12]

At a basic level, the museum display can be seen as a function of
the rhetorical trope known as *parataxis*—placing things side by side.

The centrality of this device in the modern language of scientific method has been pointed out by Barbara Stafford.[13] It is a rhetorical practice that establishes natural objects as visually accessible. Under normal circumstances for the production of travel narratives, ethnographical accounts, and so on, this mode of production of visual knowledge is most commonly imposed on exotic landscapes, but it has been shown to have been transferable to vistas closer to the home of the European traveller, such as the slums of the big cities.[14] The museum does not seem to have engendered the same kind of accounts, possibly since the constructed "landscape" it made accessible to the viewer never contained the same potential for subversion as did the "master of all I survey" accounts. The rhetorical act of domination of the European traveller created an interesting tension in these accounts. (Will the heroic European master the African landscape, the very landscape that often killed such travellers?)[15] In the museum, the act of domination over the selected set of natural or cultural objects was much more absolute. In the collection, all the hardships of the road had been evened out. There may have been less romance and heroism surrounding the men working there, but this loss was compensated by the fact that their conclusions could less easily be challenged by reference to the contingencies of the experience of the individual traveller.[16] Regardless of whether the objects of science were presented to the traveller or the museum visitor, they were accessible for visual consumption lined up in a meaningful sequence, maintaining the same basic paratactic structure.

GREAT PLANS FOR A GREATER FUTURE:
E.-F. JOMARD AND VON SIEBOLD ON ETHNOGRAPHY

A public discussion of the uses of ethnographic museums was initiated in 1843, between the Dutch naturalist traveller Philip Franz von Siebold and the French geographer Edme-François Jomard. The Frenchman was a member of the Institut de France and the former editor of the prestigious *Description de l'Égypte*, as he had been one of the young savants brought to Egypt by Napoleon in 1798. In 1843 he received an open letter, written in French and published in Paris, by the natural historian and Japan traveller Philipp Franz von Siebold. The title of von Siebold's 22-page pamphlet was *Sur l'utilité des musées ethnographiques* ("On the Usefulness of Ethnographic Museums"). It was a recognition of mutual interests and of Jomard's lifelong ambition of creating an ethnographical museum in Paris. His activities had spawned a number of published articles and petitions concerning such an institution and, most important in the context of this article, the way its contents should be displayed and what could be learned from its study. However, his definite version of a conceptual ordering of an ethnographic museum was set out in the open letter in reply to von Siebold that Jomard published in 1845.[17]

The public exchange of views between von Siebold and Jomard has to some extent gone down into the history of nineteenth-century ethnography. For the English-speaking part of the world, it has been pointed out that it was known of and read by Augustus Henry Lane Fox, i.e. Pitt Rivers, who also visited the Leyden museum in anticipation of the forming of his own collections.[18] These writings were never forgotten in France. The central French museum of ethnography, the Trocadero Museum in Paris, was opened under the direction of E. T. Hamy in 1878. The prodigious Hamy later collected the prehistory of the institution and the discipline of ethnography in France, and gave the Jomard-Siebold exchange considerable attention.[19] In Scandinavia, the writings and activities of both von Siebold and Jomard were known to the great Danish archaeologist and museum-builder Christian Jürgensen Thomsen.[20] Relatively little attention has so far been paid to the possible extent of this influence, perhaps since it would be most in evidence in the Museum for Ethnography, which in 1851 was the last to be added to the list of institutions established by Thomsen, and which was never as highly profiled as the archaeological Museum for Oldkyndighed.[21] It still made the Copenhagen museum the first museum collection in the world explicitly and exclusively dedicated to ethnography, and thus in a sense the "mother institution" of all the later museums. In the following pages, I will outline the Siebold-Jomard exchange of views, and in particular Jomard's plan, never realized, for an ethnographic museum in Paris. I will then add an outline of the first arrangement of the Copenhagen museum for ethnography as detailed by Thomsen and his unofficial assistant C. L. Steinhauer in the visitors' guide published in 1855.[22]

This will allow me to do two things: first it will establish the early appearance of the search for the ultimate "system" in the ethnographic collections of nineteenth-century museums. Secondly, and more important, this comparison of the ideas behind, and finally the execution, of the plans of von Siebold, Jomard and Thomsen will give me occasion to discuss how the ordering of such collections in space was underpinned and affirmed by the developing practices of visual modernity within the sciences.

Of the two men, Jomard was the more daring thinker. Von Siebold had in fact, with generous support from the Dutch government,
already placed his huge collections of Japanese *objets d'art* and craft
items in a large museum in Leyden, without really turning it into an
ethnographic museum. Its aspect was perhaps more that of a collection dedicated to Japanese arts and crafts. In his program for ethnographic research proposed in 1843, Siebold stuck to an argument for
the reconstruction of the histories of non-European nations derived
from the comparative study of languages, religion, and so on, in which
scholars had been engaged for at least a century, with or without direct reference to biblical history.[23] His text was considerably fleshed
out by extended quotations from Jomard's own earlier writings on the
subject.[24] He finally did admit a major point of difference in their
arrangements for the display of the objects:

> It is true that the systems we, you Monsieur, and I, have admitted
> for the classification of ethnographical objects are different. Yours
> facilitates comparative studies as it places, one after the other, objects
> of the same nature, the same use, borrowed from several nations.
> Mine, on the contrary, preserves the geographical order, and brings
> together the objects of one and the same people. In a cupboard in
> your collection one can for example at a glance embrace the entire
> series of bronze mirrors belonging to all kinds of peoples.[25]

However, there was no disagreement as to the objectives of the
ethnographic museum. After stating the interdependence of archaeological and ethnographical museums, Siebold brought up the topic
of "comparative" studies of culture that "are based on the striking
analogies present between now extinct and surviving peoples":

> The comparative studies will result in important clarifications that
> will lead us to find and recognise those peoples that thousands of
> years ago deviated from the society of primitive man and, as I have
> said, were separated by the Ocean or by mountain ranges.[26]

In effect this is a statement of the objective of ethnography (and
of archaeology) in direct analogy to the successful program of
palaeontology, but with the different species of extinct (and of extant)
animals supplanted by the many nations of the world. Despite their
disagreement over the primacy of displaying "ethnicity" or "function," Siebold also subscribed to the central feature of Jomard's system: the notion that nations and cultures could be thought of as
organisms with specific sets of functions that can possibly be displayed

either in their entirety or "exploded," i.e. subdivided into a set of functions. In this they were in a general manner following interests arising within the fledgling sciences of physiology and morphology. As far as the display practices were concerned, the galleries of comparative anatomy of the natural history museum would have provided the model in a much more direct manner.

The different (but in fact complementary) principles adopted by von Siebold and Jomard would resurface throughout the century in the debates of the merits and demerits of the principle of what I have here chosen to label "ethnicity" and "function." "Ethnicity" is what von Siebold adopted, and the nomenclature here is slightly anachronistic. It denotes the practice of presenting every "nation's" material culture separately, perhaps best known through Franz Boas's assault on the display practices of Otis Mason in the U.S. National Museum of the Smithsonian Institution.[27] "Function," on the other hand, here denotes the principle of the presentation of objects derived from a set of "functional spheres" within society and culture, regardless of their provenance in time and place. These functions later proved easy to rearrange into evolutionary sequences, as evolution was later included in the display practices of the ethnographic (and archaeological) museums. It is best known in the form in which it was placed at the center of Pitt Rivers's presentation of his own collections, but it was also the choice of, for example, Otis Mason.[28] As will be shown, Thomsen actually adopted a little bit of both, and for the Scandinavian evolutionists (here I include the Danes), archaeologists, and ethnographers, there never really was a conflict between the two sides of the coin, just as von Siebold acknowledged.[29]

Concerning modernity and its impact on the organization practices for ordering the visual knowledge in natural and cultural sciences, Michel Foucault singled out comparative linguistics (Bopp), natural history (Cuvier), and economics as key areas for an epistemic break between a *classical*, inventory *episteme* and a *modern* one, where the objective was no longer simply one of classification and systematization but one of reconstructions of origin and development according to hidden principles that it was necessary to uncover.[30] If the table was the central conceptual tool of eighteenth-century natural history, as Foucault states, this had in the nineteenth century to give way to a more organic conception of things and their origin.[31] The meaning of these objects now had to be recovered through the reconstruction of a set of historical processes. And in order to do this, plants, animals, humans and, in the end, human culture were splintered into several subsystems, which were related to one another, but assessed as singular entities. And it was the museum that first seemed to offer a useful solution, more specifically the Paris Museum for Natural History.

Evolutionism would become the hallmark of the sciences of man in the nineteenth century. As Tony Bennett, following Foucault, has summed it up in his *The Birth of the Museum*: "things ceased to be arranged as parts of taxonomic tables and came, instead, to being inserted in the flow of time, to be differentiated in terms of the positions accorded to them within evolutionary series."[32] Bennett acknowledges Jomard's plan for an ethnographical museum, but stresses that display practices for presenting evolutionary sequences were not developed until the establishment of Pitt Rivers's collections for his museum in South Kensington, London, in the 1870s, and that they did not become widespread until the late nineteenth century. This description may be valid for the English-speaking world, but, as I will show, Jomard's ideas did impact the way in which ethnographical and archaeological collections were displayed first in Copenhagen, and through its influence in the rest of Scandinavia.[33] Jomard's plan also resurfaced in France through the work of Ernest-Théodore Hamy in the establishment of the Trocadero museum for ethnography in the 1870s.[34] Admittedly, the evolutionist component was never radically developed to the exclusion of the other potential ways ethnographic objects could be understood and displayed on the European continent. Still, it was always present and a central feature for the understanding of such collections.

Returning to Jomard's 1845 reply to von Siebold, it is obvious that the impact of Jomard's thoughts on the subject of ethnography (and ethnology) were the impetus for this exchange of views. In fact, after quite an eloquently polite introduction, Jomard never really took the trouble of commenting on von Siebold. Instead he stated that the knowledge gained from former voyages of exploration had by now been digested and that as their main aim had been to establish the geographical positions of islands and to chart coastlines, the time was now ripe to tackle the interior of these islands and continents. This was to be done in order to gain deeper and more exact knowledge of the nations and peoples living there, and of the "distinctions between the races of men and the universal knowledge of their languages, of their physiognomic characters and of their social condition."[35] Furthermore, in Jomard's view, the spread of western civilization and Christian morality was dependent on "the deepened knowledge of all the different peoples and of their moral and physical state."[36] He fully endorsed this process of acculturation. He also acknowledged that the eventual victory of Western civilization would lead to the removal of those selfsame "social conditions" as well as the "moral and physical" ones that were the object of his research. Nevertheless, the point of these studies was one of historical reconstruction, not simply the stocktaking of humanity:

> The complete collection and comparison of all those points of view under which contemporary man can be imagined, in all climates, will not fail to clarify the history of the past. Many historical problems cannot be resolved or even attempted except with a complete knowledge of those ancient tribes that time has changed but little, whether by their language, by their physical make up or by the aspect of their customs, manners and institutions.[37]

Jomard gave the work of the comparative linguists their due, as had von Siebold, since to date the most successful attempts at dealing with the multi-faceted phenomenon of non-European humanity had been made by them, including the widely accepted practice of making ethnographical distinctions based upon the classification of language.[38] However useful these studies had proved, they could still be added to and improved upon, in particular by paying attention to material culture. For my purposes, however, the key sentence in the passage below is what is implied by the reference to the "scientific" classification of these objects for the purpose of a comparative study:

> The works of the hand of man, attentively considered, can often reveal to us that which escapes history, or has not been preserved by tradition. I here refer to the end for which they have been made, the objective their manufacturers had set before themselves, and the means to which they had resource for their execution. This is how, through reflective and diligent studies of the monuments of antiquity, we can guess the secrets of its architecture. It is even permitted to say, that all science can be understood, appreciated and judged by its products. I think this principle is universal and especially applicable to the science of ethnography.
>
> History has kept a most complete silence regarding the arts and industries of a multitude of nations, and most of the others have remained without historians. A large number of these peoples have always been ignorant, and remain ignorant, of the art of writing. Is this a reason to refrain from their study? I think not. All of these

peoples, no matter how little civilised, how crude they may be, have known how to work stone, wood or metal. All have had tools, instruments with which to modify the forms of matter according to their needs, their tastes, and their ideas. All have through force or cunning subjected the diverse living beings of creation, and all have acted upon the dead matter in order to appropriate it for their needs.[39]

As a statement of program for the ethnographical study of material culture, this is fairly straightforward. If anything could be singled out for comment, it might perhaps be that the assumed "state of nature" of man, redundant of anything in the form of culture and thus analogous to any beast in creation, is manifestly absent. All peoples and nations, no matter how "coarse," have culture.

Jomard himself presented his system for the museum of ethnography of his inner vision in tabular form. Despite this, it was in fact a system for ordering objects within the space of a museum and it took its cue from the zoological displays and Cuvier's galleries of comparative anatomy in the Paris Museum for Natural History. Jomard stuck slavishly to a hierarchical ordering of his material by *classe, ordre, genre* and *espèce* (class, order, genera and species). (Figure 1.) The ten classes were as follows:

Iere.	Images representing the physiognomy of the natives.
II.	Objects and utensils for the procurement of food.
III.	Objects relating to clothing.
IV.	Objects relating to lodgings and constructions.
V.	Household economy.
VI.	Objects for the defense of man.
VII.	Objects relating to different arts and crafts and to the sciences.
VIII.	Music.
IX.	Manners and customs.
X.	Cult objects.[40]

For want of a label other than Jomard's *classe*, these can be seen as functional spheres within the human production of culture. (Figures 2 and 3.)

Understood in Cuvierian terms, the *classes* would correspond the *embranchements*, i.e. the four fundamental structures into which all living beings could be divided—vertebrates, molluscs, radiates and articulates. And, just as in Cuvierian comparative anatomy, it was not an order that necessarily presupposed any kind of evolutionary process, though it was quite acceptable to trace these classes/embranchements

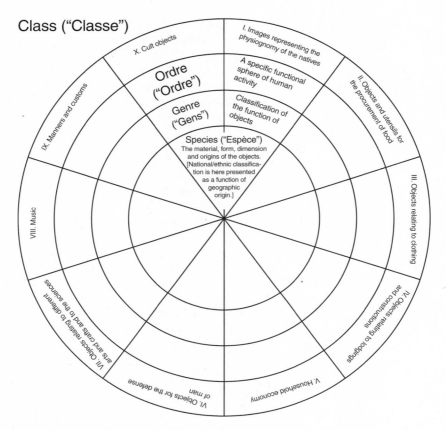

Class ("Classe")

Figure 1. The categories for classification proposed by Edme-François Jomard. Adopted by Jomard from natural history, most directly as proposed by Georges Cuvier. The ten major categories of Jomard, his "classes," have been included, as well as indications of the general content corresponding to the categories of natural history on the descending levels of classification in Jomard's system.

through time.[41] Of course, this was also the point at which evolutionary arguments could be inserted, as had already happened in natural history. Again, just as in Cuvierian comparative anatomy, the individual species and its analogy—according to Jomard—"ethnicity" or national provenance, would find itself at the bottom rung of the order of classification. In effect, this meant that culture should be understood as an analogy to nature, as species was an analogy to nation.

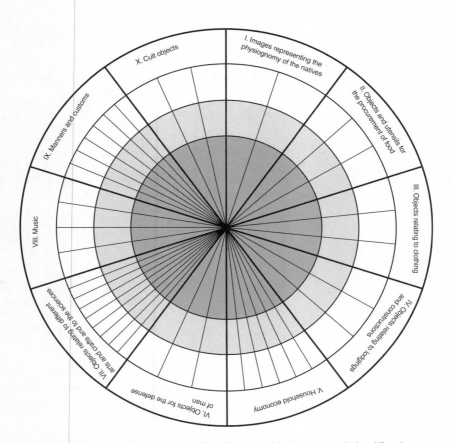

Figure 2. The categories of Jomard's ethnographical system of classification.

Edme-François Jomard's system of classification for an ethnographic museum represented as a many-spoked wheel. In the outer periphery is found the most general category of classification, that of the Cuvierian "class." Progressing inwards, this is followed by the other categories in a Cuvierian system of classification, those of order, gens and species in descending order. Each step inwards represents a further simultaneous increase in precision and subdivision. The concept of "nations," of ethnicity, is found at the lowest stage, that of species. (There is an increase in spokes as one moves towards the center of the wheel. Taking the metaphor of the machine one step further, this arrangement might perhaps be likened to a gear-box.)

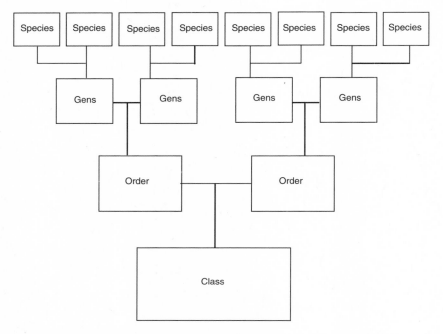

Figure 3. A Cuvierian system of classification as a branching "tree."

A Cuvierian system of classification can also be displayed in a classical tree-shape, which is also a more traditional tabular form of representing the different stages of classification within natural history. Instead of descending inwards like the circular graph in Figure 2, this one displays an open-ended ascent.

Both could be studied using the same research practices centered on the museum and the collection.

The analogy between the ethnographer's or archaeologist's nation or culture and the *embranchements* (or *types*), taxa and species investigated by natural historians was present in Jomard's plan. Cuvier established what Martin Rudwick has referred to as "the reality of extinction."[42] Central to Jomard's arrangements was the notion of what I would like to label the "imminence of extinction":

> The progress made by Christian civilization all over the globe in the last half-century, through war and all kinds of expeditions, has begun to profoundly modify the social conditions of far away peoples. Their manners, customs, the instruments of their arts and crafts and their utensils, everything up to and including their language, is

everyday changing for the better. Maybe soon, it will no longer be possible to collect these remnants of a past that is disappearing never to return. One must make haste in order to assemble that which still remains.[43]

That is, the ethnographer as a comparative historian of culture was not yet dealing with extinct forms of human life, as was the archaeologist, but that would shortly be the case. This ethnographical agenda implicitly reiterated the assumption that human civilization could and should be regarded as analogous to nature. The nations, the peoples, of this world represented individual organisms of higher or lower complexity, possibly each furnished with a specific life trajectory. Just like the notion of evolution, the ongoing process of extinction highlighted *time* and *change* as factors dominating the life of both organisms and cultures and our understanding of them.

Again, I would like to stress that the scientific results and their theoretical implications cannot be treated as something separate from the scientific practices centered in and around the museum. They were very much the products of the internal ordering of space in the museum displays. What carried over from comparative anatomy to ethnography (and by extension archaeology) was the practice of the subdivision of individual organisms into separate sets of functions that could be displayed and investigated side by side. Even a short walk through a comparative anatomy gallery makes it clear that what one faces is "exploded" organisms where the organs of several species are presented side by side. These animals can of course be reassembled, either in the minds of the naturalist or through the physical reordering of these specimens.[44]

METONYMY AND METAPHOR IN THE MUSEUM

The key scientific success of Cuvier and others in the Paris museum was palaeontology, which grew out of this "indoor version of comparative anatomy," as Dorinda Outram has labelled it.[45] Even if the research was dependent on the work in the museum, the scientific output was in the form of text available to the reading audience. These readers would approach the results that could be found through research in the museum in, for example, Cuvier's *Recherches sur les ossemens fossils* (1825). There never was any opposition between the practices of the museum and the scientific text. Both were necessary and complemented each other.

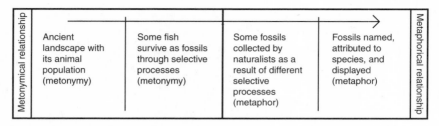

Figure 4. Metaphorical and metonymical relationship of fossils presented in palaeontology displays.

In the two sections to the right there exists an unproblematic relationship with the original conditions that they represent; i.e. metonymy (synekdoke, pars pro toto). In the two sections to the right, that which is displayed is presented as similar unproblematic metonymies. In actual fact they are rather constructed images, metaphors, presented as if they were unproblematic representations of past conditions.

Looking at Jomard's plans, and even von Siebold's endorsements of them, it is clear that in fact their objective was not simply the display of contemporary exotic material culture. What was hoped for was a scientific breakthrough similar to that of palaeontology. However, as far as the practices of display and scientific conclusions are concerned, there was an interesting effect that carried over from the study of fossils into the study of culture. Before I describe it, I would like to invoke a very simple Saussurean semiotic analysis.[46] (Figure 4.)

The disjunction occurs where the human agents enter, i.e. beginning with the processes of selection of fossils for collecting. The first two sections can be viewed as actual metonymies, while the last two are actually metaphorical, but they carry persuasive effect only if they are perceived as "natural" and metonymic.

Unlike palaeontology, the ethnographic collection presents a decidedly *human* aspect of the world, and it thus seems not only to be immediately accessible but also unproblematic to the observer, which is of course a part of its metonymic function. It incorporated no problematic viewer positions such as existed in the reconstructions of past landscapes included in the palaeontology exhibitions of the time, where the construction of an imagined position of a human viewer was a long and arduous process.[47] Instead, the ethnographic collection operated for the most part according to the same logic as the ordinary natural history exhibit. Things presented were assumed to be those that could at least in theory be inspected during a long-distance voyage or would have been accessible to a human viewer of events in history.

However, just as in the palaeontology displays, the ethnographic museums actually worked on the premise of a ruptured metonymic chain. It differed somewhat from that of fossils, but certain links had a metaphoric function, while being presented as series of unproblematic metonymies. Of course the ethnographic displays relied on a similar process of collection and selection, first in the "field" and then in the museum, to that of the palaeontological ones. I am, however, mainly talking about the fact that the cacophonic polysemy derived from the various origins and histories of ethnographic objects needed to be suppressed in order to make them useful within the framework of a museum display. The process of "shutting up" possibly divergent voices was quite simple and relied on the framing of individual objects by describing their meaning using catalogue texts.[48] As in Jomard's "ideal" museum, one was left with a set of ethnographic objects with a dyadic semiotic function. In a sense, they can be seen as "indexes," simultaneously of an all-embracing shared "humanity" and of a maximal divergence of nationalities, or "ethnicities," for display purposes. On the one hand, the display reinforced the idea of culture as universal human nature, and possibly of the brotherhood of man. Also, unlike later explicitly evolutionary ethnographic museum displays, the writings of Jomard still present a very eighteenth-century notion of exotic humanity as worthy of study in order to improve the arts and crafts of western society.[49] (Von Siebold in particular praised the skill of Japanese craftsmen.[50]) On the other hand, all objects were also to be understood as representative of a specific nation and its culture. A foreshortening of perspective suppressed all information surrounding the circumstances in which an object had found its way to the museum. If available they were mostly disregarded in favor of the overriding concept of "culture," i.e. the ethnographical "sameness," initially presented.

Sometimes it was not even necessary to present authentic ethnographical objects. It remained preferable to display the original objects, but in fact, and as Jomard expressly stated, when the objects themselves were missing or had proved too cumbersome and impractical for transportation, they could be substituted with representations. In a descending hierarchy, it was preferable to substitute them with three-dimensional models crafted by the "nation" representing itself, followed by three-dimensional models of European make, down to the still sufficient two-dimensional representation as detailed drawings in the genre of realistic art.[51] For purposes of overview, maps and charts would be introduced, thus marshalling the entire range of what Bruno Latour has labelled "techniques of inscription" (though their use for representation differs from their use in the kind of experimental science Latour has analyzed).[52]

THOMSEN'S MUSEUM

That the wellsprings of ethnography, including the practices of collection, display and public consumption, are derived from more sources than natural history is obvious. There is a caesura between the plan of Jomard explicitly molded upon "Cuvierian" comparative anatomy, and the Copenhagen museum of Thomsen, who was considerably less interested in natural history. Nevertheless, the influences from natural history lie as a subtext under the arrangements of the Copenhagen museum, which means that such an explicit order by analogy with the natural history museums of the time could almost effortlessly be introduced if one was so inclined. This was also done, but more obviously in the late nineteenth century than in the pioneering Danish museum.

So what were Thomsen's interests? He seems to have picked up the two texts by von Siebold and Jomard when they first appeared. This evidently piqued his curiosity sufficiently to make him undertake a trip first to the museum in Leyden, and from there to Paris, and "upon a visit and conversation with the famous geographer Jomard in Paris, the idea matured of a general ethnographical Museum, that would encompass not just a single, but as far as possible all Nations not in possession of the European Culture."[53]

The arrangements of Thomsen and the assisting C. L. Steinhauer give evidence of the influence of the ideas and practices of both von Siebold and Jomard. Thomsen almost apologetically admitted that the system used "still only has very general subdivisions."[54] The guiding principle followed was a division primarily into different nations, i.e. "ethnicity," much like von Siebold's. However, these were further placed within a two-tiered framework of classification based upon the presence or absence of metalworking and literacy, on the one hand, and upon climate zones, on the other. Thus, in Copenhagen, the system was based upon three sections, each with three subdivisions. Section I was dedicated to illiterate nations with no metalworking, effectively living under stone-age conditions. (Thomsen was after all the inventor of the archaeological system of the classification of prehistory into the stone, bronze and iron age.) These were further subdivided upon the basis of whether they lived in a cold, temperate or warm climate. Section II dealt with nations in possession of metal-working, again under cold, temperate or warm conditions.[55]

Finally, in Section III, the arrangement deviated considerably from that of the other two. In this section dedicated to the civilized nations of the Far East, which were literate and had impressive arts and crafts (i.e., Japan, China and India), Thomsen finally applied a system reminiscent of Jomard's division of the display into social and cultural "functions." China had five of these subdivisions, for example: (a) Religion (including the arts of writing and printing); (b) Man as represented in the arts; (c) Wars, weapons in particular but including hunting, fishing and shipbuilding; (d) The house, including instruments, household utensils, craft tools and agricultural implements; (e) The conditions of the arts and crafts, peculiar modes of production and the materials used. Somewhat surprisingly, it was when addressing those exotic societies generally held to be most advanced, that the principles of classification most strongly placed the study of culture on a par with the study of nature. (Figure 5.)

To sum up, in the Copenhagen museum the levels of classification for Sections I and II in descending order would be: Climate, place, nation/"ethnicity" (though not always very consistent), and finally the identification of individual objects (name, use, etc.). In Section III the order would instead be the more "Jomardian": Climate, nation/"ethnicity," sphere of social/cultural function, and finally the identification of individual objects.

VISUAL TECHNIQUES OF THE MUSEUM

Did the visual displays and practices of ethnographic exhibitions really indicate that they formed part of the process of replacing older forms of visual order with a "modernity of vision"?[56] To some extent, the examples from the 1840s show how they form part of the older forms of visual order. Jonathan Crary has indicated that the 1840s and 50s were a formative period in the scientific formulation of modern visual culture. It would be surprising to find the full range of implications of this process at that time. To some extent, the presupposition underlying the museum exhibitions was still that they would be traversed and consumed by a Cartesian subject, an individual soul equipped with the full array of sensory perceptions but with primacy given to vision. The scientific museum exhibitions never did take the

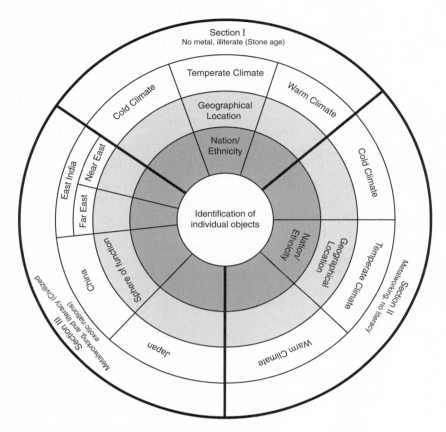

Figure 5. System adopted in the Copenhagen museum for ethnography.
Thomsen has inverted several of the layers of Jomard, in many sections adhering
to a style more in keeping with von Siebold's classification according to national-
ity. Most similarities are found in section 3. The "ethnic" and geographical classification is more central.

final step of inserting individuals into the kind of full-scale multime-
dia dioramas that the nineteenth century loved, the kind of mechanical multi-sensory machinery, where their perceptions would be the
product, but where the autonomy of movement and vision were
highly inhibited. In comparison, the museum seemed to offer autonomous individuals a free range of the place. At the same time, the
panoramic function of the museum cannot be denied, and even in this

less elaborate form it was dependent on the adoption of the forms of visual representation, perhaps most of all the static panorama paintings that began to appear in the 1790s.[57]

In all the museums concerned here—the ethnographical and archaeological museums, as well as the one to which they all hark back, the gallery of comparative anatomy erected by Cuvier in the Paris Museum for Natural History—the adopted order for the presentation of the subject matter was itself an indicator of "the division and fragmentation of the physical subject," which was the prerequisite for the development of a modernity of vision.[58]

The presentation of the functional subdivisions of an organism that lay at the core of Cuvierian comparative anatomy, which was later (roughly 1840–70) transferred to ethnography and archaeology, was in itself dependent on the fragmentation of the organism. Crary's examples are mainly derived from the work of French anatomist Xavier Bichat at the very beginning of the nineteenth century: "With Bichat begins the progressive parcelization and division of the body into separate and specific systems and functions that would occur in the first half of the nineteenth century."[59] Physiology would become a major success story of nineteenth-century science, but was still a long way from being a scientific discipline in its own right. It might be preferable to think of it rather as a set of interests. Still, the physiological discoveries at the start of the nineteenth century concerning the human eye as a device producing visual effects in itself is at the core of Crary's argument. However, as far as the intertwined practices of ordering and displaying not necessarily Nature, but individual organisms, is concerned, one has to look to the Paris Musée de l'histoire naturelle, and the success its researchers, in particular Georges Cuvier, enjoyed in the decades following its establishment in 1793. The Paris museum became the center for research in zoology, comparative anatomy and what Goethe would popularize as "morphology."[60] Crary might thus have chosen his examples equally well from the burgeoning and intersecting fields of geology, comparative anatomy, morphology, palaeontology, archaeology, and ethnography.

The above-mentioned subdivisions of functional spheres of culture adopted by Jomard mirrored the organs and their functions in Cuvier's museum. As ethnographical museums sprang up, or quite often were included within natural history museums, all over Europe (see Beckman's article in this volume), the model for a comparative science of culture spread parallel to the model for the comparative study of morphology, and it was the museum that provided the "natural history connection" for the study of ethnography. Here I would like to stress that the aspect of "comparative" science at this stage was to a very high degree tied to the practices of the collection and the museum. The "comparative" principle in the study of culture has been invented many times over and certainly before the nineteenth century. The ethnographers and anthropologists of the day would themselves point to the French Jesuit Lafiteau, active in North America in the first half of the eighteenth century, as a precursor.[61] Presented in its simplest form, the principle meant that those customs and beliefs observed among contemporary "exotic" or "primitive" peoples (as it were) can be taken to mirror similar arrangements in the distant past, European or otherwise. However, in placing this kind of comparative study on what was at the time considered a sure scientific footing, the practice of comparative studies of culture was meshed together with the study of material culture in the museum.

CONCLUSION

As I have done here, it can be argued that the human sciences, including ethnography, were part of a much more general reordering of vision in the nineteenth century. Popular spectacle, the aesthetics of art and scientific research all shared a set of common traits. In the case of the museum-based science I have addressed here, it hinged on the ordering of space within the collections of museums. Museums would become the typical scientific institutions for ethnographic, archaeological and anthropological studies in the nineteenth century. That these sciences at the time were heavily dependent on museums has always been common knowledge. In fact, as Simon Schaffer has pointed out, the museum was the typical nineteenth-century scientific institution. (Despite the contemporary rise of laboratory-based experimental research.)[62]

I have indicated one of the ways in which this was to a high degree due to the transference of scientific practices developed within natural history since the late eighteenth century. The natural history connection also makes it reasonable to assume that the specific case of the ethnographic museum has a wider significance. Much of the scientific "character" of nineteenth-century ethnography derived from its status as a "natural history of man."

In fact, the kind of knowledge that could be gained from the ethnographical visual order of the museum was perceived as something impossible to experience anywhere else. It would be a rare traveller, whether staying in one place or en route, who could hope to gain a similar expertise. The systematically ordered internal space of the museum was considered a truer representation of the material culture of humanity than anything possible to observe in "nature." The reaction in the early twentieth century became all the more pronounced, as the museum-based research was superseded by the new scientific ideals of fieldwork and "participant observation."

A further point is that the common lack of representation of a temporal progression in both natural history and ethnographical exhibits was often not an oversight. At the core lay assumptions about the natural world and human nature. The fact that time and progress could conceivably be added to the basic framework did not in itself make it imperative to do so. Ethnographical exhibitions would often have as their primary function the representation of a series of seemingly stable "nations" ("nations" or "peoples" in French, "Völker" in German, "folk" in Swedish; we might somewhat anachronistically for expediency's sake refer to these as "ethnic groups"). Just as the late nineteenth-century natural history exhibition would often present its purpose as the synchronic representation of the fauna of the world, "as is," so would the ethnographic exhibition represent the peoples of the world (the "ethnographic present"). In both cases, there would be an underlying agreement, at least on the part of the scholars, that this situation could be assumed to be the outcome of some kind of evolutionary process, though often its exact nature, mechanism, and so on could not be agreed upon. Neither was there necessarily a stable consensus about the actual sequence of events leading up to the situations represented. The aspect that was central to palaeontological and archaeological exhibits would thus often be excluded from the ethnographical exhibition, but included in the scientific publications of the scholars working in the museums.

The motivation for the study of man in the nineteenth century was to make him "an object of knowledge so that man could become the subject of his own liberty and his own existence."[63] The study of his material culture formed a part of this ambition. Like most research directed at man himself, it ended in a situation in which this elusive liberty was seen as an attainable hope for Modern Western Man alone. It would relegate un-modern, non-European humanity to a continued existence unconscious of itself and thus irredeemable except through the ministrations of its betters. This kind of conceptual domination of the world by European science was given physical shape in the museum.

NOTES

1. I would like to thank the Wenner-Gren Foundations, the Salén Foundation and Ragnhild Blomquist's Fund for research into the History of Medicine for funding this work. I would also like to express my gratitude to the staff of the Centre Alexandre Koyré pour l'histoire des sciences et des techniques, and the École des hautes études en sciences sociales (EHESS), Dominique Pestre, Claude Blanckaert and Pietro Corsi. I also owe a debt of gratitude to the staff of the library of the Paris Musée de l'histoire naturelle (MNHN), and to the archivists of the Bibliothèque de l'Institut de France and the Archive de l'Académie des sciences, Paris.

2. The parties involved were the French geographer Edme François Jomard and the Dutch naturalist Philipp Franz von Siebold. The former would stress the geographical distribution of functions within society as the key to classification, the latter the spatial distribution of different ethnicities. The differences between their approaches were evened out in the processes of visualization taking place in the display, but maintained by means of the textual apparatus of the exhibition catalogue. They were further united by a model for the establishment of scientific competence that positioned the museum researcher in the privileged position of arbiter of claims of verifiability and synthesis. This was done to the detriment of the field worker, whose collecting was relegated to the status of a mere assemblage of raw "facts," the material for research.

3. The research on modernity and vision now existing is considerable. The works of most interest to me, for the process of writing this article, have been Jonathan Crary, *Techniques of the Observer: On Vision and Modernity in the Nineteenth Century* (Cambridge, MA, 1990); Jonathan Crary, *Suspensions of Perception: Attention, Spectacle and Modern Culture* (Cambridge, MA, 2001); Timothy Mitchell, "The World as Exhibition," in *Comparative Studies in Society and History*, vol. 31, 1989, and Timothy Mitchell, *Colonizing Egypt* (Cambridge, 1988).

4. Crary, *Techniques of the Observer* (1990), 3.

5. In brief, Crary's main concerns are (1) with physiology, where the recognition of the subjectivity of vision and its potential fallacy had repercussions on the sciences by starting processes to check and counteract this tendency in order to safeguard the traditional truth claims of science; and (2) with artistic modernity, i.e. the ways in which this process simultaneously allowed for new modes of originality and expression and the advent of the artist of genius. See Crary (1990), introductory chapter, "1. Modernity and the Problem of the Observer."

6. I.e., nature itself could be grasped by studying the singular example. Metonymic would here be read a case of making the part represent the whole, the classical rhetoric figure of *synekdoke*.

7. Victor Turner, *Drama, Fields and Metaphors. Symbolic Action in Human Society* (Ithaca, NY, 1974), 87.

8. Nélia Dias, *Le musée d'ethnographie du Trocadero: Anthropologie et muséologie en France (1878–1908)* (Paris, 1991), 109–111, has in particular pointed out the German situation, in which a number of ambitious museums of ethnography were erected in the latter half of the nineteenth century. Combined with a tradition of team-work and research, the end result was a substantial cadre of museum-trained ethnographers.

9. The term "morphology" was coined by J. W. von Goethe. See Toby Appel, *The Cuvier-Geoffroy Debate: French Biology in the Decades before Darwin* (New York, 1987), 70.

10. Mary Louise Pratt, *Imperial Eyes: Travel Writing and Transculturation* (London & New York, 1992), 38–39

11. Pratt (1992), 201–208, in particular.

12. For example Barbara Kirschenblatt-Gimblett, "Objects of Ethnography," in Ivan Karp and Steven D. Lavine (eds.), *Exhibiting Cultures: The Poetics and Politics of Museum Display* (Washington, DC, 1990), 387ff.

13. Barbara Stafford, *Voyage Into Substance: Art, Science, Nature, and the Illustrated Travel Account, 1760–1840* (Cambridge, MA, 1984), 34, also reiterated in David Spurr's *Rhetoric of Empire: Colonial Discourse in Journalism, Travel Writing, and Imperial Administration* (Durham & London, 1993), 17–18.

14. For example in Felix Driver, *Geography Militant: Cultures of Exploration and Empire* (Oxford, 2001), Chapter 8, "Exploring 'Darkest England': Mapping the Heart of Empire," 170–198.

15. Pratt (1992), 209–210.

16. On the perceived need to discipline observers in the field, at its most extreme the ambition to implement a form of "remote control," see for example Driver (2001), the section "The Discipline of Observation: *Hints to Travellers*," 56ff.

17. Philipp Franz von Siebold, *Lettre sur l'utilité des musées ethnographiques et sur l'importance de leur création dans les états européens qui possèdent des colonies, ou qui entretiennent des relations commerciales avec les autres parties du monde* (Paris, 1843), and Edme-François Jomard, *Lettre à Monsieur Ph.-Fr. de Siebold sur les collections ethnographiques* (Paris, 1845). There is a sprawling literature devoted to the savants in Egypt and their chef d'œuvre *La Description de l'Egypte*. More specifically, Jomard's activities as a geographer have been dealt with by Anne Godlewska, *Geography Unbound: French Geographic Science from Cassini to Humboldt* (Chicago, 2000). Jomard's long-standing ambition of creating an ethnographic museum is borne out in, for example, Edme-François Jomard, *Considérations sur l'objet d'une collection spéciale consacrée aux cartes géographiques et aux diverses branches de la géographie*, in-8, 1831, and *Extrait d'un Rapport de la Commission nommée par M. le ministre du Commerce et des Travaux publics pour examiner la convenance de la formation d'un Musée ethnographique à Paris*, 1er novembre 1831, as well as *Bulletin de la Société de géographie*, février

1844; juin 1845. Regarding these efforts see also, "Rapport de la commission Cuvier au ministre, sur la création d'une collection ethnographique," *Bulletin de la Soc. de géogr.* année 1836, tom. VI, 2e série.

18. William Ryan Chapman, "Arranging Ethnology: A. H. L. F. Pitt Rivers and the Typological Tradition," in George Stocking (ed.), *Objects and Others: Essays on Museums and Material Culture* (Madison, WI, 1985).

19. Ernest Théodore Hamy, *Les origines du Musée d'Ethnographie: Histoire et documents* (Paris, 1890), and Dias (1991), Chapter IV, "Le débat Jomard/ von Siebold ou les origins de la muséologie ethnographique," 115–138.

20. Christian Jürgensen Thomsen, "Forerindring," I C. L. Steinhauer, *Kort veiledning i det nye ethnografiske museum* (Kjøbenhavn, 1855). See also Høyris, (1986), 16–17, and Jørgen Jensen, *Thomsens museum: Historien om Nationalmuseet* (København, 1992), 203–204.

21. The collection had in itself been established in 1849. It languished under Thomsen's equally influential successor Worsaae, who never had any real interest in the ethnographic material. Ole Høyris, *Antropologien i Danmark: Museal etnografi og etnologi 1860–1960* (København, 1986), 17–19.

22. Despite the lack of any kind of officially recognized status vis-à-vis the museum and its collection, Steinhauer seems to have retained an informal control of it until the last decades of the nineteenth century. His role comes out for instance in the personal correspondence between the Swedish late nineteenth-century ethnographer Hjalmar Stolpe and his friend and colleague Kristian Bahnson, the assistant to the curator (Worsaae) of the museum since the 1870s and from 1892 the curator of it. Letter from Hjalmar Stolpe to Kristian Bahnson 19/5 1890, the directors' archives, Etnografiska museet, Stockholm. See also Dias, (1991), 43, for E.-T. Hamy's recognition of Steinhauer as a founder of ethnography as a museum science.

23. For an example of this genre of argument see Siebold (1843), 7: "I have attempted to explain for myself how the original social and cultural stream has in all probability arisen in Central Asia, on the slopes of the highest mountains of Tubet [sic] and Chacmire [sic]." All translations into English in this article are by the author.

24. Ibid., 9, 12–13, 18.

25. Ibid., 16: "Les systèmes que nous avons admis, vous, Monsieur, et moi, dans la classification des objets ethnographiques, sont, il est vrai, différents: le vôtre facilite les recherches comparées en rangeant les uns auprès des autres les objets de même nature, de même destination, empruntés à plusieurs peuples; le mien, au contraire, conserve l'ordre géographique, et rassemble les produits divers d'une seule et même nation. Dans une armoire de votre collection on pourrait, par exemple, embrasser d'un seul coupe d'œil la série entière des miroirs en bronze, de toute sortes des peuples."

26. Ibid., 11: "Les recherches comparées auront pour résultat des éclaircissements importants qui pourront nous conduire à retrouver et à reconnaître les peuplades déviées depuis des milliers d'années de la société humaine primitive, et separées, je l'ai dit, par l'Ocean ou par des chaînes de montagnes."

27. Ira Jacknis, "Franz Boas and Exhibits," *Objects and Others . . .* (1985), 77–83, and Douglas Cole, *Franz Boas: The Early Years 1858–1906* (Vancouver & Seattle, 1999), 127–129.

28. On Pitt Rivers, see Chapman (1985), 23–26. On Otis Mason, see Jacknis (1985), 77–80. Mason actually published his system. Otis T. Mason, "Methode de classification dans les musées d'ethnographie," *Revue d'ethnographie* (E-T. Hamy ed.), no. 6, mai/juin 1887, 239–242. About this see also Dias (1992), 142–143.

29. Siebold (1843), 16.

30. Michel Foucault, *The Order of Things: An Archaeology of the Human Sciences* (London, 1970), 250ff.

31. Ibid., 75.

32. Tony Bennett, *The Birth of the Museum: History, Theory, Politics* (London, 1995), 96.

33. The notion that no practices for displaying evolutionism in ethnographical museums existed before Pitt Rivers's can also be found in the chapter "Serial killers" in Susan M. Pearce's *On Collecting: An Investigation into Collecting in the European Tradition* (London, 1995). Since this is not the case when looking at Scandinavia or France, a different genealogy has to be found for these countries.

34. Dias, 168ff.

35. Jomard (1845), 5: "distinction des races humaines et de la connaissance universelle de leurs idiomes, de leur caractère physiognomonique et de leur état social."

36. Ibid., 6: "la connaissance approfondie de toutes les différentes peuplades et de leur état moral et physique."

37. Ibid., 6: "Le rapprochement complet et la comparaison de tous les points de vue sous lesquels peut être envisagé l'homme actuel, dans tous les climats, ne peuvent manquer d'éclairer l'histoire du passé. Bien des problèmes historiques ne pourront être résolus ou même abordés qu'avec la connaissance parfaite de ces anciennes tribus que le temps a peu modifiées, soit sous le rapport du langage, soit sous le rapporte de la constitution physique, soit enfin sous l'aspect des usages, des mœurs et des institutions."

38. Ibid., 8.

39. Jomard (1845), 7–8: "Les œuvres de la main de l'homme, attentivement considérées, peuvent souvent nous révéler ce qui a échappé à l'histoire, ou bien n'a pas été conservé par la tradition: je veux dire le but de leur composition, l'objet que leurs auteurs se sont proposé, les moyens mêmes dont ils ont fait usage pour les exécuter. C'est ainsi que, par l'étude réfléchie et persévérante des monuments de l'antiquité, on peut deviner les secrets de son architecture. Il est même permis de dire que toute science peut être comprise, appréciée et jugée par ses productions: ce principe, que je crois général, est surtout applicable à la science ethnographique.

L'histoire a gardé le plus complet silence sur les arts et l'industrie d'une multitude de peuples, et la plupart d'ailleurs sont restés dépourvues

d'historiens. Un grand nombre des ces nations ont toujours ignoré et ig-
norent encore l'écriture. Est-ce une raison pour renoncer à les étudier?
je [sic] ne le crois pas. Toutes ces peuplades, si peu civilisées, si grossières
qu'elles soient, ont su travailler la pierre, le bois ou le métal. Toutes ont eu
des outils, des instruments avec lesquels elles ont modifié les formes de la
matière, suivant leurs nécessités, leur goûts, leur idées. Toutes ont soumis
par force ou par adresse les divers êtres vivants de la création, et toutes ont
agi sur la nature morte pour l'approprier à leurs besoins."
40. Ibid., 13.
41. About this rather extensive and complex matter see for example William
Coleman, *Georges Cuvier, Zoologist: A study in the history of evolution theory* (Cambridge, MA, 1964), "Morphology Between Type Concept and
Descent Theory," *Journal of the History of Medicine and Allied Sciences*, vol.
31, no. 2, 1976, Toby Appel, *The Cuvier-Geoffroy Debate* (New York, 1987),
Martin Rudwick, *Scenes from Deep Time: Early Pictorial Representations of
the Prehistoric World* (Chicago, 1992), Claudine Cohen, "Stratégies de la
preuve," *Le Muséum . . .* (1997), and Dorinda Outram, "New Spaces in Natural History," in N. Jardine, J. A. Secord and E. C. Spary (eds.), *Cultures of
Natural History* (Cambridge, 1996).
42. Rudwick (1992), 30 and 56.
43. Jomard (1845), 9–10. This was acknowledged also by von Siebold, quoting
Jomard, 6: "Les progrès que fait sur le globe la civilization chrétienne depuis
un demi-siècle, par suite des guerres et d'expéditions de toute espèce, ont
commencé à modifier profondément l'état social des peuples lointaines; les
mœurs, les usages, les instruments des arts et les ustensiles, tout jusqu'au langage, va s'altérant chaque jour davantage. Bientôt peut-être in ne sera plus
temps de recueillir ces restes d'un passé qui disparaît et s'évanouit sans re-
tour. Il faut se hâter de rassembler ce qui subsiste encore." It was repeated
by Thomsen, "Forerindring," in Steinhauer (1855).
44. Lee Rust Brown, "The Emerson Museum," *Representations* 40, 1992, 65–66.
45. Outram (1996), 250.
46. This analysis is taken from Susan Pearce's *On Collecting* (1995), 268.
47. Which is the subject of Rudwick (1992), in particular Chapter 2, which details how the necessary theoretical inferences used when constructing such
scenes were assembled.
48. The use of written labels placed by objects on display does not seem to be the
first practice adopted. It is sometimes attributed to Pitt Rivers, but final
judgement may need to be withheld. I have found it mentioned in the correspondence between the museum ethnographers Hjalmar Stolpe and Kristian
Bahnson, Letter from Hjalmar Stolpe to Kristian Bahnson 19/2 1893, the directors' archives, Etnografiska museet, Stockholm.
49. Jomard (1845), 11–12: "Les objets d'art étrangers, s'ils sont disposés dans un
ordre méthodique et instructif, ne seront pas examinés sans fruit par les in-
dustriels, soit pour certains usages qui pourraient entrer dans notre
économie domestique, soit pour des produits qui manquent à nos arts, soit

pour la beauté des nuances tirées de certains substances colorantes. Il existe en Afrique, par exemple, des alliages ou plutôt des plaquésincon nus à notre industrie."

50. Siebold (1843), 21.

51. Jomard (1845), 11: "pour être complète, la collection doit renfermer des dessins ou des modèles, partout où les objets manquant, et là aussi où les originaux sont de trop grande dimension, par exemple s'il s'agit des navires, des machines et des appareils divers plus ou moins volumineux."

52. Bruno Latour, *Science in Action: How to Follow Scientists and Engineers Through Society* (Cambridge, MA, 1987), in "Part B: Centres of calculation," 232–247.

53. Christian Jürgensen Thomsen, "Forerindring," in Steinhauer (1855): "vid Besøg og Samtaler med den berømte Geograph Jomard i Paris, modnedes først Ideen om et almindeligt ethnographisk Museum, der skulde omfatte ikke den enkelte, men saavidt muligt alle Nationer, der ikke besad den europeiske Cultur."

54. Ibid.: "endnu har meget svage Underafdelinger."

55. Ibid.: "Inledning."

56. This analysis is indebted to Jonathan Crary, *Techniques of the Observer: On Vision and Modernity in the Nineteenth Century* (Cambridge, MA, 1990).

57. Crary (1990), 111–112.

58. Ibid., Crary (1990), 81.

59. Ibid., 79.

60. Appel (1987), 159.

61. Michel de Certau, "Histoire et anthropologie chex Lafiteau," Claude Blanckaert (ed.), *Naissance de l'ethnologie? Anthropologie et missions de l'Amérique XVI–XVIII siècle* (Paris, 1985), 72–74. For Swedish readers, information on Lafiteau can be found in Christer Lindberg, *Den gode och den onde vilden* (Lund, 1998), 151f.

62. Simon Schaffer, "What is Science?," *Science in the Twentieth Century*, eds. John Krige and Dominique Pestre (Amstedam, 1997), 40.

63. "Foucault responds to Sartre," *Foucault Live*, trans. John Johnstone (New York, 1989), 36, after Jonathan Crary, *Suspensions of Perception: Attention, Spectacle, and Modern Culture* (Cambridge, MA, 2002), 45.

How Does Knowledge Production Take Place?

On Locating and Mapping Science and Similar Unruly Activities

HENRIK MATTSSON

INTRODUCTION

This chapter explores the relation between *space* and *knowledge production* from the perspective of an economic geographer. It does not explore this relation by seeking causal inference between an independent (space) and dependent variable (knowledge production). Instead it contributes to the understanding of how knowledge production *takes place* as a non-universal process: knowledge production as an encounter in time-space between several things: scientists, industrial agents, institutions, infrastructure, machines, technology, and so on.

In concrete terms, this chapter involves the following. First, it discusses the relation between space and human activity in general, focusing on how a surrounding environment is perceived to influence human activity. This exercise serves to introduce how we might think about space. The discussion starts off on a rather general level, before focusing on the geography of knowledge production. Three common ways of understanding the relation between knowledge production and space are identified. It is suggested that although these *modes of explanation*[1] are different in their understanding of the role of space, they are united in their understanding of knowledge production. It

I wish to particularly thank my supervisors Anders Malmberg and Dominic Power for their insightful comments and suggestions. I am also indebted to Sarah Whatmore and Jamie Lorimer for discussing issues addressed in the chapter and to the interviewees for sharing their stories. Finally, I thank Enrico Baraldi, Gordon Clark and Johan Jansson for reading and commenting on drafts of this chapter.

is further recognized that within these modes of explanation, knowledge production can be understood as either (a) bounded in space; (b) free from space; or (c) bounded or free from space, depending on the circumstances.

Second, the chapter argues that although the three identified alternatives, combined, seem to cover every aspect of the relation between knowledge production and space, it is actually possible to move outside these, and approach the question from a fourth perspective. In this part a theoretical tool with which to do this is constructed. In the following third and fourth parts, this theoretical tool is applied to an empirical case to illustrate how it might work in reality. Time-geography is used here, to arrive at a knowledge production taking place in dynamic time-space constellations, as opposed to taking place in more rigid governing structures such as institutional settings, industrial districts, clusters, and so on. Finally, in the fifth part of the chapter, some conclusions are drawn and future avenues of research are discussed.

BACKGROUND—THINKING ABOUT HUMAN ACTIVITY IN SPACE

Time exists so that everything doesn't happen all at once.
Space exists so that everything doesn't happen to you.

Anonymous

The relationship between an individual and the space in which she lives is strange indeed. On the one hand, we are all bounded in space: our bodies seem highly dependent on a home base that is geographically fixed, and a major part of our lives is spent in the immediate proximity of such home bases (Hägerstrand 1982; Pred 1977, 1981). On the other hand, we are all wandering minds. In addition to being more or less frequent travelers in physical space, we travel widely via mediated narratives of other places and times (Crang & Thrift 2000). We have knowledge of places we have never visited and we can go online at any time to communicate with anyone else on the web (Castells 1996). Subsequently, it is—if we take it to the extreme—really impossible to map our lives on a piece of paper. We live in spaces that, although they are all related to physical space in some ways, are at the same time impossible to map onto each other in visually graspable relations (Crang & Thrift 2000).

We are free from space yet stuck in it.

How can this be? The answer is simple but its consequences are complex, namely: space is both static and in flux—both being and becoming. As we know, space has given characteristics that are static, such as "costing time to move through." Thus we can measure spatial distance and speed and formulate general laws concerning their relation (Velocity × Time = Distance). A law like this will be accurate in all practical cases, even though instant travel is nowadays theoretically possible (practically possible for photons) using quantum teleportation.

However, this is not all that space is about. Space also creates distances indirectly which cannot be measured objectively or deduced to general law. Language and culture, for example, along with financial and judicial restrictions, create relational distances that depend on the characteristics of space itself, but also on inhabitants of space (Törnqvist 1997). Different geographical imaginations also create distances and proximities (Gregory 1994) that are "only" mentally constructed but whose materiality is highly evident in, for example, the ways urban dwellers move through city landscapes: using city space at night, being more influenced by Hollywood movies than by crime statistics; moving through crowded spaces in which the risk of being assaulted is high, instead of choosing unpopulated streets in which the same risk is minimal (Cf. Pain 1997).

In the academic community we often study science and similar activities from a specific geographical perspective that cannot handle this paradox. When we study knowledge production, for example science, as a human activity we often focus on certain cities, countries or universities. But this is arguably too simplistic a geography of knowledge production. It is after all not the city/university per se (e.g., Cambridge, England, or Stanford, USA) that is important to scientists, but rather the spaces constructed by "Cambridge biochemists" or "Stanford physicists" (Lefebvre 1991): these spaces are relational and less tied to the city landscape and more to the social, personal and academic relations of which they are made up. So, in this example Cambridge biotech involves "Cambridge" spaces that are highly "extra-local": causing places around the world to become important suburbs to the particular city story/landscape.

FOREGROUND—THINKING ABOUT THE GEOGRAPHY OF KNOWLEDGE PRODUCTION

Economic geographers and others have for some time now been intrigued by the relation between location on the one hand, and a variety of economically important processes on the other. Broadly

speaking, such processes used to be all about "Fordism" and "economies of scale," but now knowledge processes such as innovation and
learning are considered prominent (See Asheim 2004 for an overview).
In this field, the role of universities and scientists, especially in terms
of their relation to the rest of the knowledge economy, is the center of
much attention. However, this shift of focus is not homogenous.

Despite the apparent novelty of some of the concepts being used
to describe "the new spatiality" of knowledge, the underlying phenomenon has been studied for some time. Thus there exist quite a few
hypotheses and theories, making claims about the relationship being
explored in this chapter. Although heterogeneous, these claims can
be sorted into three modes of explanation.

It can all be said to have started about a century ago when Alfred
Marshall, in an attempt to explain competitive advantage provided by
spatial co-location, made his famous claim that "it is in the air" (Marshall 1919:284), thereby inspiring thinking about places as essentially
promoting or impeding knowledge production. This strand of thinking constitutes the first of the three modes of explanation. This economic geography, which draws its line of heritage from Marshall,
takes geography seriously indeed. But it generally understands geography as places, cities, districts, regions and so on. And it generally
studies knowledge processes as bounded in clusters, technopoles,
agglomerations, milieus, etc. (e.g., Asheim 1992; Feldman 2000; Porter
2000; Saxenian 1994).

A second mode of explanation stands in opposition to the first
one. This claims that geography is dead, killed by improvements in
transport and information technologies. The main argument of this
mode of explanation is that knowledge and information flow around
the world in networks and that subsequently the time has come to lift
our gaze from the local level, and start focusing on global(ized)
knowledge production (Castells 1996).

Lately, attempts have been made to combine (a) notions of place-
bound knowledge production—claiming that certain spatial agglomerations continually produce a disproportionately large amount of
knowledge, with (b) notions of network-bound knowledge production—claiming that it is not places, but rather certain social constellations, that continually produce a disproportionately large amount of
knowledge.

These efforts, which can be said to constitute a third mode of explanation, have among other things resulted in the conclusion that
"socio-institutional settings [. . .] and interactive processes of learn-

ing play decisive roles in processes of innovation and growth" (Bathelt et al. 2004:37), meaning that knowledge production takes place in settings where room is given both to people inhabiting the setting (the networks) and to the laws, regulations, norms and culture characterizing it (the milieu per se).

However, for all their dissimilarities, these three understandings of knowledge production and space are similar in the sense that all of them assume at a general level some kind of inert knowledge production process that is mainly formed by place, networks or a socio-spatial process. The three modes of explanation all assume a framework or governing structure of some sort, within which knowledge production takes place on a global, national or local scale.

Now, can we understand knowledge production in space in a different manner? Is it possible to assume that knowledge production is not mainly formed by the part of space in which it takes place, nor by the nodes or connections of networks; nor by a combination of the two? This chapter argues that it is. Assume that there is no governing structure. Assume that knowledge production is merely a series of events that has to take place somewhere and that therefore sometimes seem bounded in space and sometimes not. What does this kind of assumption leave us with: a world in which the ambitions, successes and failures of knowledge production are entirely due to coincidence? Not necessarily.

The idea that developments in science and other forms of knowledge production are results of pure coincidences can quickly be discounted. If this were the case, we would arguably not see any significant agglomerations of successful knowledge-producing activities. But statistical evidence, for example the fact that 20% of scientific discoveries awarded the Nobel Prize originate from only five universities, seems to suggest that such agglomerations do exist, for one reason or another. There is arguably something out there that makes knowledge production behave this way, but if it is not a governing structure of the kinds described above, then what is it?

Some of those considering human activity in space like to think about it as taking place in different types of time-spatial constellations (see for example Hägerstrand 1982; Deleuze and Guattari 1988; Whatmore 2002). Dynamic time-space constellations constitute an alternative to the traditional structures above. The former are less stable than the latter and they do not as easily get stuck in the dichotomy of things, being either spatially bounded, ubiquitous or a combination of the two. This chapter is much inspired by these approaches in that it strives to construct a theoretical tool, the aim of which is to handle knowledge production as desires/strategies/projects struggling to become satisfied/carried out/fulfilled within certain time-spatial constellations. What this means is explained below.

THEORIZING KNOWLEDGE PRODUCTION AS STRATEGIC STRUGGLES IN TIME-SPACE

Deleuze and Guattari claim that events are the result of things arriving either too early, too late, or just in time for a certain outcome to take shape (1988:282). Now, this does not imply that events are purely coincidental. They are often unpredictable, but not believed to occur suddenly out of thin air. Instead, this perspective implies that components of potential constructions travel through time and space, creating different outcomes depending on their relative speeds and directions.

This way of describing the world is reminiscent of a theory called time-geography. The basic idea of time-geography is to produce and analyze something called a "time-space-trajectory model": that is, a three-dimensional map or matrix, in which things can be plotted on their journey through time-space (Hägerstrand 1982). In addition to the time-space-trajectory model, time-geography also consists of a set of concepts that aim to keep the things mapped in the matrix together under a unifying perspective. Here, the pros and cons of time-geography, in relation to the study of knowledge production, are described and discussed. Some additions and modifications are made to original versions of time-geography.

This following theorizing process starts with a notion of knowledge production as being a result purely of desires, strategies and projects of agents: a notion which differs diametrically from the three modes of explanation. Gradually, this is then nuanced and modified until it arrives at a theoretical tool capable of handling knowledge production in the way described above.

Desires, Strategy and Projects—The Role of Agency

At the core of time-geographical understandings of society is the assumption that people try to create their own destinies. A basic assumption is therefore that people set up projects and strive to accomplish them—in other words, that they relate strategically to life in the world (Hägerstrand 1985).

However, claiming that any participant in the process relates in some sense strategically to the conditions of the game she is playing is not the same as recognizing perfect rationality or access to perfect information. It is merely a recognition that humans have desires that they try to satisfy; that this in turn will result in different types of strategy formation (Cf. Bower & Doz 1979; Biggadike 1979; Burgelman 1983; Hart 1992); and that strategy has an impact on social projects, e.g. knowledge production. In the words of Torsten Hägerstrand, "at the core of geography is the study of struggles of power over the entry of phenomena and events into space and time" (Hägerstrand 1986:43, translated from Swedish).

A project (strategy) can be of any scale: from making dinner to finding the cure for AIDS. Whatever the scale, projects can only be accomplished by bringing together so-called "existents" in time-space. Hägerstrand identifies three categories of existents:[2]

- *Physical objects and states*—inorganic and biological existents as well as all artifacts.
- *Mental states*—knowledge, perception, thinking, memories and emotions.
- *Cultural products*—stories and myths, works of art and mathematical theorems. (Hägerstrand 1985)

Time-geography aims at mapping these existents moving through time-space in order to understand events and non-events as an outcome of efforts to gather existents. If we return to the example above—making dinner—we can see that if someone wants to make food, this person has to get all the ingredients, equipment, power, a knowledge of cookery, etc. into one "bundle" (of things) in time-space. We cannot make a sandwich in our kitchen if the bread is still in the shop and we cannot make a gourmet dinner if the combination of skill, technology and information required is not present (embodied in ourselves, in a medium or in a consultant). Although the bundling process is more complex and more time-consuming in the other example used here—finding a cure for AIDS—it is in principle the same.

Projects or strategies are interesting because they create bundles and vice versa: for example, a professor with a lot of research to do will (try to) create a bundle of Ph.D. students, infrastructure, money, etc. to accomplish her project and from this bundle, in turn, new projects will emerge, create new bundles and so on. Some bundles are highly temporary, while others are materialized in the built environment (Hägerstrand 1982).

Projects or strategies do not necessarily originate from the bundle in which they are currently at play and they may (and most likely will) differ from one another. For example, the underlying motive for a professor to engage in a certain research project may be glory, fame or immortality; while a Ph.D. student, working on the same project, may be doing so only to finish her doctorate and get a job in a more stimulating department.

The Condition of Corporeality—Agency Complicated I

According to time-geography, bundles and projects/strategies are not formed randomly, but are governed by a rather harsh set of restrictions known as time-space constraints. One such constraint is, as mentioned above, the friction of distance: moving from point A to point B will take a certain amount of time depending on the means of transportation (Hägerstrand 1970). Although we have seen a revolution in transportation and communication technology over the last century, most people are still rather local beings. The need for face-to-face contact (Storper & Venables 2004), the importance of "being there" (Gertler 2003), to scan the "noise" (Grabher 2002), and so on is all a part of the explanation, but simple things also matter: e.g., the fact that all individuals, within certain time intervals, must return to a place to sleep and eat. Although this place of return does not have to be at the same geographical location at the time of every return, this principle in combination with the friction of distance certainly constitutes a strong time-space constraint (Hägerstrand 1970).

The constraints of time-space not only limit movement, they also limit (and subsequently render possible[3]) all action of individuals: i.e., they limit/render possible the realization of projects or strategies. Since only a highly limited number of projects can be carried out in a given time-space position[4] and therefore only a limited number of projects can be carried out in what we would commonly refer to as "a place," bundles are important for understanding the production and reproduction of spaces over time (Hägerstrand 1985).

Instead of assuming that all existents "behave" in the same way in, for example, one national context or one institutional system (which is the case in many other theoretical frameworks), time-geography argues that a resource, artifact, idea or person will have a different impact on events and non-events depending on the time-space constellation it enters or leaves.

Modalities and Power—Agency Complicated II

Of course, the environment in a bundle is not only sticks, stones and bodies: there are also other things present in bundles that affect human behavior. In short, these are things determining social power.[5]

Traditionally, time-geography has a rather mechanistic and simplified understanding of power, mainly because it was mostly developed in relation to computer-based simulation (Holm et al. 1989). However, the limiting aspects of the computer syntax, which forces things to be either on or off, one or zero, true or false, have at the same time forced those working with it to construct a detailed and all-encompassing conceptual framework for handling agency: the three modalities: *cans*, *wants* and *shoulds* (Holm et al. 1989). Although simplified and abstract, the result is arguably interesting in this context. According to Holm et al., human agency can be sorted into the following categories:

(a) CANS—things we can do; cannot do; cannot not do (must do)
(b) WANTS—things we: want to do; do not want to do
(c) SHOULDS—things we: should do; should not do.

The modalities are indeed capable of describing the output of all kinds of power, but they do not inform us about the way power actually works in time-space bundles.

We should not understand power as something one has: it is produced in social relations and not possessed as a quality of individuals (Foucault 1979; Said 1978). We can be given power temporarily in terms of so-called subject positions, but although certain characteristics, such as being of a specific sex, color, age, etc. highly affect this process, power in itself is not a characteristic: because the way sex, color, age, etc. determine power entirely depends on the time-space constellations they enter.

So, in the time-space trajectory model we cannot map power per se. What we can map is rather embodied discourses that can help us understand (the role of) power structures in the bundles we analyze. Allen Pred claims that discourse, since it is embodied, is situated and therefore just as manageable in geographic analysis as any resource or physical object (1984). Yet, although embodied in one sense, discourse is not only a mental part of individuals, it is also (re)produced on social arenas, where it actively regulates agency though the threat or reality of social punishment (Foucault 1979). The task is therefore to analyze bodies, not as containers of power, but as parts of a temporary constellation that creates different power-relations between the parts, depending on its momentary constitution.

Unfortunately, there is not room for a more thorough account of discourse theory and other concepts of power in this chapter. However, it is briefly mentioned since the things that regulate what can be said, by whom, and in which context, have a large impact on creativity and innovative processes and capacities. In terms of modalities, one can say that, in a sense, discourses are existents actively shaping social arenas (bundles) where action takes place. They influence, often covertly so, what (we think) we want or do not want; what (we think) we should or should not do; and, to an extent, also what (we think) we can, cannot and cannot not do. Therefore they need to be incorporated in a theory aimed at understanding knowledge production as desires/strategies/projects struggling to be satisfied/carried out/fulfilled within certain time-spatial constellations.

It is now time to apply what has been said in this section to a small empirical case. Doing this will help to further illustrate how the perspective introduced may be used to analyze knowledge production in space.

EMPIRICAL ILLUSTRATION—THE CASE OF BIOTECH RESEARCH

In this part, some empirical observations will be used to illustrate how the theoretical tool presented above might work in reality. The empirical observations and quotes used are picked from an ongoing research project about creativity in biotechnological research milieus. They were gathered during 2003 from interviews with a network of researchers and other actors who are, or have been, active within a biotech milieu in Europe.

Methodology

The population of interviewees is identified by names generated through interviews—a technique also known as the "snowball method." When using this sampling method, one starts off by interviewing one node in a network: usually some rather central figure in the milieu of choice (in this case the initial interview was with the professor/head of department/leader of the research team).

Using the snowball method means asking interviewees for names of, as far as they are concerned, suitable future interviewees, or finding them in the stories told by the interviewees. After this has been done for a while, a network starts to appear. When no new, or only a few new, names are being named, it is reasonable to conclude that the important part of the network has been captured—at least from the point of view of those forming a part of it. Multiple sources of network identification (i.e., employment records) might be rewarding to use since these can provide information about insider/outsider relationships and so on—this has been done in the present case.

When the network identification process is completed, the next step is to compare stories and biographies in order to get a picture of (a) how the network has been formed, (b) how/whether a network-specific "sub-culture" has formed/developed, (c) where its components have been, (d) the dynamics of the network members' strategies, and so on. This method will generate immense quantities of data. Following the time-geographical approach, we therefore focus attention on time-space bundles. Bundles are, as explained in more detail above, temporary contexts formed by the coming together of existents in time-space. What bundles help us do is to systematically limit a certain context and thereby limit the number of potential events and non-events resulting from it.

In an analysis (of an event or non-event) conducted at the spatial-temporal scale of European country X/ Year Y, the number of agents, projects, circumstances and so on is impossible to grasp. Bundle analysis helps us to comprehend better which agents, projects and strategies are actually involved in different events and non-events. This is not to say that time-geography can help us unravel the full complexity of a relational, contradictory, partly invisible and dynamic reality. As explained above, time-geography is used here to identify knowledge production as taking place in dynamic time-space constellations, as opposed to taking place in more rigid governing structures such as regional innovation systems, industrial districts, clusters, etc. In practical terms, time-space bundles are identified by plotting the different biographies and stories in a time-space matrix (see Figure 1).

The method used for analyzing the time-space bundles in this empirical material is inspired by the oral history tradition (Portelli 1997). Where oral history methodology strives to capture how one or several interviewees experience and conceptualize themselves as a part of history, the approach used here tries to understand how interviewees experience and conceptualize themselves as a part of place. This experience and conceptualization, or knowledge, is, in combination with strategies, an important explanatory factor in an analysis of why certain actions were undertaken or never happened, and why certain practices developed at the expense of others. Whether accurate or not, whether based on perfect rationality or paranoia, the way agents interpret their own relation to surrounding contexts, people and events will determine how they respond to them (Portelli 1997).

Telling the Story

In Figure 1, one of the stories emerging from the interviews is plotted. The figure sets the scene for the story, consisting of three locations: a biotech laboratory in Europe (being the point of departure), a biotech firm in the same European city and a laboratory in the United States. The spatial part of the figure (axis X and Y) is neither continual nor proportional: of course, in other contexts it might be suitable to base the matrix on a continual and proportional space, but it is neither necessary nor graphically possible in this particular case. The vertical axis (Z) represents time. Lines represent people, ideas and technologies (existents). Cylinders represent bundles.

The story plotted in the Figure is told here in text. Note, however, that this textual version is more complex than the plotted story: the story told is fuller than the example in Figure 1.

The leading part is played by the person currently a professor and head of the laboratory under study—let us call him Kohler (assumed names are used). Also featured are an American Professor Hunt and a chemist Smith. In a small but vital part of the story, we meet Mrs. Kohler. There are of course also numerous extras and secondary plots but for the sake of clarity these are omitted. The story is told in five acts represented in the time-space matrix of Figure 1 by bundles one to five.

The story begins in bundle one: the site is a university town. Kohler, who arrived 10 years earlier to study for a medical degree, has just finished his Ph.D. He has almost decided to go to a laboratory in another European country for his post-doctorate. However, Mrs. Kohler does not like the idea of going to this particular European country, so Kohler keeps his eyes open for other options.

At about the same time, Professor Hunt has arrived to visit a friend of his. This friend is also a friend of Kohler, and Kohler and Prof. Hunt end up eating dinner together at their mutual friend's house. During this three-course event, Prof. Hunt manages to convince Kohler that he should do his post-doctoral work at the U.S.

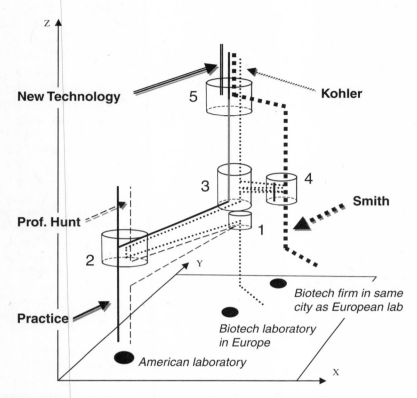

Figure 1. One of the time-geographical stories as plotted in a time-space matrix. The time-frame stretches from the early 1970s to somewhere around the year 2000.

laboratory that Prof. Hunt runs. This is quite an achievement, considering that it means Kohler disregards the advice of his supervisor and goes abroad with no other financial security than the goodwill of his three-hour acquaintance Professor Hunt. Anyway, this is what happens. Kohler goes to the U.S. laboratory and the story continues in bundle two.

At the U.S. laboratory, Mr. Kohler gets to learn Professor Hunt's way of doing things. He is intrigued by the way of thinking and working and he learns what it is about during his time in the U.S. When he goes back to Europe, five years later, he carries these ideas back with him.

However, back in Europe (bundle three), Mr. Kohler does not succeed in incorporating what he has learned from Prof. Hunt into the daily work at his old laboratory. There is simply too much resistance from other ideas of how things should be done. From his position as a Ph.D. recently returned from his post-doctoral work, Kohler does not have enough negotiating power to change the way things are done in bundle three. On top of this, he finds himself with very limited resources. This makes him look around for alternative sources of finance and competence. Inspired by Prof. Hunt, he starts associating himself with a large biotech firm a few blocks down the street.

In the firm—represented by bundle four—his views meet with sympathy. He also meets Smith, who is a chemist. One of the main traits of the ideas Kohler has learned in the U.S. laboratory is that a good laboratory should make efforts to get people from different scientific disciplines to understand each other and to work together—something that, at that time, was (and still is today) hard to achieve in academia with its strong boundaries between disciplines that have been established by differences in ontology, methodology, language, employment structures, and so on. Smith, the chemist, and Kohler, the biologist, engage in a co-operation that both of them later describe as highly rewarding.

However, all is not well, because, although their cooperation on projects is quite successful, their way of doing things is *non grata* in both bundle three—where at the time it is considered bad for an academic to collaborate with industry—and bundle four—where the more explorative nature of their research is not fully compatible with demands for short-term profit and low risk. An obvious clash of strategies emerges, resulting in a struggle over what things to introduce and what things to keep out of the time-space bundle. Smith has to leave the biotech firm but Kohler, in part at least, hires him. This is a rather notable reaction since at this time Kohler has significant difficulty in financing himself.

Time passes and we reach the happy ending. In bundle five—Kohler has reached a position strong enough to be able to implement the practices he first encountered in the U.S. lab. He is starting to get enough funds of his own and so is Smith. Together they develop a new technology. Today Smith has his own facilities and place of work in the same university building as Kohler, yet he is now financed by his own firm and not by the university.

So far the time-geographical story is descriptive in nature. The next step is to conduct a bundle analysis aimed at understanding how projects, strategies, and time-space constellations of existents formed events and non-events in this particular case.

Analysis

In bundle 1, the projects of Mrs. Kohler, the friend and Professor Hunt lead to the event of Kohler going to the U.S. and the non-event of him going to another European country which, otherwise, would have been the most likely event. Even though it would be too harsh to say that there is a straight causal relationship between these factors, on the one hand, and Kohler's decision to go to the U.S. laboratory on the other, they, according to himself, certainly affected his action space to quite a strong degree.

Furthermore, in bundle 1 Prof. Hunt has decided to defy some spatial restrictions and visits Europe. That he and Kohler actually end up eating dinner together is, arguably, more due to time-space restrictions on network formation than coincidence. It is probable that the university spaces of the European and the U.S. laboratory have a common network space that reproduces itself. We can also state that somehow Kohler trusts Prof. Hunt enough to go against quite a strong *should*—"one should secure financial security before going away." This can be explained by the trust emerging from their mutual relationship with the friend. If either one were to break the agreement, it would involve a cost in terms of a devaluation of this relationship. If their strategy is to maintain the value of that relationship, or increase it, then they will most likely not break the agreement.

In bundle number two, Kohler comes in touch with knowledge of how to conduct science. Because he stays in the proximity of the people carrying this idea through time-space for an extended period of time, he learns what it is about. In a way, it is tempting to think of knowledge as infectious, transmittable by intellectual interaction: it has been shown that learning works better in face-to-face interaction than if the teacher and the pupil are separated (Storper & Venables 2004). This is also in line with Gertler's argument about the importance of "being there" (2003).

When the "infected" Kohler returns to Europe, he carries the infection, but the group in bundle three seems immune to it. In classical time-geographical terms, one would say that there are people in bundle three who are implementing their projects at the expense of Kohler's project.

However, there is no clear project-domain in this European milieu because just a few blocks down the street (in bundle four) things are done in a very different way. In a way, one can describe these two spaces as two distinct time-space constellations, to a degree sealed off from one another. Although existing in the same national setting of culture and institutions (and governance strategies), and being part of the same innovation process, things work very differently within the two time-space constellations.

There are massive *shoulds* involved in protecting the boundaries between these constellations, but for a while Kohler manages to exist in both worlds. Though, at the time, "an academic should not associate with industry," he succeeds in doing so without too much punishment—perhaps his experiences from the U.S. laboratory helped Kohler in this matter.

However, when Smith wants to cross from industry to academia there are more than *shoulds* involved. This border crossing is guarded by some powerful *cans*. Organizational and collegial rules stop Smith from crossing between constellations. Since he lacks the proper academic title, he cannot get a job in this part of academia. Although he has a degree in both chemistry and biology, he is not admitted because he lacks a degree in medicine. The results of Kohler's and Smith's work, along with the testimony of Kohler, clearly show that Smith possesses adequate competence. Still he is stopped. Having corresponding competence is not of any help in this case. It is only due to the ability of Kohler and Smith to gather resources in time-space on their own that they can keep on breaking the *shoulds* and going around the *cans*. In a way, they create their own spaces within the boundaries of which they control events; within which they are the masters of the bundling process.

In the final bundle, the unholy alliance of Kohler and Smith bears fruit. A new technology is created that gains recognition in the scientific and industrial community. The interesting thing is that in many ways this technology was created in what was sometimes a fierce struggle against the frameworks set up, by policymakers and others, to work in its favor. It is of course impossible to say what would have happened if Kohler and Smith had followed each and every *should*; accepted each and every *can*; and given up on their *wants*—but after hearing the testimonies of the people involved, it is not far to a conclusion that the outcome would have been less productive from a knowledge-production point of view.

What can we learn from such a story? At a general level, the lesson is twofold. Firstly, we can learn things about how places of science and other forms of knowledge production are composed of complex time-spatial relations. The complexity of innovation processes means that in many cases what we see is far from linear or predictable: in reality innovation is most often an *unruly process*. The new technology that was created in this case in the European laboratory has just as much to do with journeys to other places and times as it has to do with the contemporary European city in which the laboratory is situated.

Secondly, this story implies that what we know is highly dependent on where we have been, and where we are at a particular moment: not only in terms of physical places, but also in terms of positions where physical aspects, institutions, discourses, languages, and so on come together, where we have both different subject positions and different spatial positions. Where we stand depends on where we sit, as the saying goes. In this view, for us to communicate successfully what we know is likewise highly dependent on where we have been; where the person we are communicating with has been; and the time-space constellation in which communication takes place.

At the more specific level, there are three points to be made. Yet, before making them it is suitable to discuss briefly what kind of conclusions one can draw from this type of study. The empirical material is after all of rather limited extent and, consequently, many would argue that it is impossible to know what the results really mean at a general level. To draw conclusions of a general character is, however, not the main point of this chapter. The point has been to use an example of how we can study spaces of knowledge production without getting stuck in the notion of this production process being either bounded in places or freely flowing around the globe.

On the one hand, the result might give a mundane, perhaps even trivial impression. On the other hand, however, what this approach shows is that sometimes trivial things have important impacts, especially on interactive processes such as science. Single events change the world.

CONCLUSIONS

The first conclusion relates to the question of agency and strategy. This case clearly shows that the way agents understand and react to the other elements in their shared time-space constellation can play a vital part in the outcome of a knowledge-production process. Agents do seem to relate strategically to the surrounding environment. In a way, this result is a consequence of the empirical object of study.

Biotechnological research of the kind studied here probably works as a resonance box for the mechanisms involved. This is so because of the high level of potential earnings in this field and the ease with which these kinds of technologies can be copied. A technology subject to patenting need not require large amounts of tacit knowledge per se in order to be used, something that would otherwise limit the risk of copying (Polanyi 1958, 1966). Tacit knowledge refers to things we know but that we do not know that we know or, alternatively, that we do not know how to explain to someone else (how to codify). A famous example of this is the knowledge of how to swim. We know how to swim but we cannot describe swimming on paper (Polanyi 1966). In the stages of the research process where the technology is near completion but not yet patented, trust and social control, therefore, become vital tools of a research group.

This in turn results in specific spatial patterns of controlled spaces in which trust, loyalty and social control can be practiced. This is the second conclusion: spaces within which a research team can develop and uphold certain practices without infiltration from external interests and projects are an important element in advanced, high-profit research of the kind studied here. However, we should keep in mind that this swings both ways. Although upholding certain practices by protecting them from external influence can be positive in some cases it can, of course, also result in lock-in and stagnation.

The final conclusion is related to governance. It is no secret that there is an ambition in most countries to govern science systems and industrial systems along with the interactions between them. The goal of this is to achieve technologies and tools leading to a better society and to higher levels of prosperity. In the empirical case used here, a new technology seems to have developed, thanks to a large extent to the ability of the involved agents to bend the national framework or even to break out of it. It is tempting to think about this in terms of the best innovators being those that do not have to care about the framework that is supposed to promote innovation. Of course, there is too little empirical evidence to draw this kind of general conclusion to its full extent, but the notion of this ability to disobey being a useful innovator skill lingers on. It also seems that the learning process leading to this skill is rather localized, since it requires high amounts of trust and face-to-face communication.

What can be said with some certainty, though, is that agents can control some time-space constellations quite easily, while other time-space constellations are harder, if not impossible, for them to dominate. In relation to national or regional governance of science and innovation, this would suggest that policy can be efficient under some time-space conditions but not under others. Some innovation processes are more unruly than others. A similar conclusion is reached by Bathelt et al. (2004). They suggest that local buzz (that is, local networking and interaction) is autonomous, while global linking and renewal can be subject to governance by national or regional actors.

This chapter has illustrated that, although dominating modes of explanation seem to provide an all-encompassing solution, it is possible to move beyond the dialectics of the "bounded in space–free from space" dichotomy. It has also shown that time-geography, if slightly modified, is anything but an out-of-date tool for studying knowledge production. Considering knowledge production as taking place in dynamic time-space constellations, instead of as taking place in more rigid governing structures (regional innovation systems, industrial districts, clusters, and so on), revitalizes several debates. Are governmental directives concerning research funding and employment regulations powerful tools of governance? What do managers of knowledge production really do with such things as science and innovation in space (do they build a science park / support a local network of firms / focus on international cooperation)?

Although perhaps giving the impression that it is promoting one approach over all others, this chapter, in fact, calls for a multitude of approaches. The explanatory "modes" referred to earlier can serve us well in our attempts to explain different forms of innovation. However, what such standard modes of explanation often lack is the capacity to get at the in-between, things that happen at the edges, the accidental, the unpredictable, and so on. This is a deficit we must strive to address, since the production of knowledge and innovation often resides in unruly spaces, times and processes.

NOTES

1. *Modes of explanation* will be used throughout the chapter to refer to these three ways of understanding knowledge production in space.
2. These categories and examples can be treated in several ways. We can interpret them as a rigid specification of what we need to put in a model in order to understand (even predict) society. I just take them as an illustration of what we might need to consider if we want to understand societal

phenomena. Hägerstrand's time-geography as presented in his writings points to several avenues of potential use, some very different from those actually chosen over the last 30–40 years.

3. Limitation of something often allows something else to exist: e.g., limitation of a thief's action space creates space for personal possession.

4. One person cannot perform more than a few tasks at a time. Also, when performed simultaneously, tasks are affected by each other.

5. Social power here is distinct from power over "sticks and stones" and "time and space." This is, however, only a simplified division. It is not to say that there are clear boundaries between different kinds of power or even between the social and the natural.

REFERENCES

Asheim, B. T. (1992) "Flexible Specialisation, Industrial Districts and Small Firms: A Critical Appraisal." In Erneste, H. and Meier, V. (eds.), *Regional Development and Contemporary Industrial Response. Extending Flexible Specialisation*. Pp. 45–63, Belhaven Press, London.

Asheim, B. (2004) *On the New Economic Geography of post-Fordist Learning economies*. In: Öhman, J. and Simonsen, K. (eds.), Voices from the North: New Trends in Nordic Human Geography. Ashgate 2003.

Bathelt, H., Malmberg, A. and Maskell, P. (2004) Clusters and Knowledge: Local Buzz, Global Pipelines and the Process of Knowledge Creation. *Progress in Human Geography* 2004.

Biggadike, E. R. (1979) *Corporate Diversification: Entry, Strategy, and Performance*. Harvard University Press, Cambridge, Mass.

Bower, J. L. and Doz, I. (1979) "Strategy Formulation: A Social and Political View." In Schendel, D. E. and Hofer, C. W. (eds.), *Strategic Management*. Boston, Mass.

Burgelman, R. A. (1983) A Model of the Interaction of Strategic Behaviour, Corporate Context, and the Concept of Strategy. *The Academy of Management Review*, Vol. 8, No. 1, 61–70.

Castells, M. (1996) *The Rise of the Network Society*. Basil Blackwell, Oxford.

Crang, M., Thrift, N. (eds.) (2000) *Thinking Space*. Routledge, London.

Deleuze, G., Guattari, F. (1988) *A Thousand Plateaus*. Athlone Press Ltd.

Feldman, M. P. (2000) "Location and Innovation: The New Economic Geography of Innovation, Spillovers, and Agglomeration." In: Clark, G. et al. (eds.), *The Oxford Handbook of Economic Geography*. Oxford University Press, Oxford.

Foucault M. (1979) *Discipline and Punish: The Birth of the Prison*. Vintage, New York.

Gertler, M. S. (2003) "Tacit Knowledge and the Economic Geography of Context, or The Undefinable Tacitness of Being (there)." *Journal of Economic Geography*, 3: 75–99.

Grabher, G. (2002) The Project Ecology of Advertising: Tasks, Talents and Teams. *Regional Studies*, Vol. 36, No. 2, pp. 245–262.

Gregory, D. (1994) *Geographical Imaginations*. Blackwell, Oxford.

Hart, S. L. (1992) An Integrative Framework for Strategy-Making Processes. *The Academy of Management Review*, Vol. 17, No. 2, 327–351.

Holm, E., Mäkilä, K., Öberg, S. (1989) *Tidsgeografisk handlingsteori—Att bilda betingade geografier*. Gerum, Umeå.

Hägerstrand, T. (1970) "Tidsanvändning och omgivningsstruktur." In: SOU 1970:14 *Urbaniseringen i Sverige, en geografisk samhällsanalys*. Appendix 1: Balanserad regional utveckling. Stockholm.

Hägerstrand, T. (1982) "Diorama, Path and Project." *Tijdschrift voor economische en sociale geografie*, Vol. 73, No. 6.

Hägerstrand, T. (1985) "Time-Geography: Focus on the Corporeality of Man, Society, and Environment." *The United Nations Newsletters*. Vol. 8, No. 3, p. 3.

Hägerstrand, T. (1986) Om geografins kärnområde. *Svensk Geografisk årsbok 1986*.

Lefebvre, H. (1991) *The Production of Space*. Blackwell, Oxford.

Marshall, A. (1919) *Industry and Trade*. Macmillan, London.

Pain, R. H. (1997) Social Geographies of Women's Fear of Crime. *Transactions of the Institute of British Geographers* Vol. 22, No. 2, 231–44.

Polanyi, M. (1958) *Personal Knowledge: Towards a Post-Critical Philosophy*. Routledge and Keegan Paul, London.

Polanyi, M. (1966) *The Tacit Dimension*. Doubleday, New York.

Portelli, A. (1997) *The Battle of Valle Giulia—Oral History and the Art of Dialogue*. The University of Wisconsin Press, Madison.

Porter, M. E. (2000) "Locations, Clusters and Company Strategy." In: Clark, G. L. et al. (eds.), *The Oxford Handbook of Economic Geography*. OUP, Oxford.

Pred, A. (1977) The Choreography of Existence: Comments on Hägerstrand's Time-Geography and its Usefulness. *Economic Geography*, Vol. 53, No. 2, pp. 207–221.

Pred, A. (1981) Social Reproduction and the Time-Geography of Everyday Life. *Geografiska annaler 63 B*.

Pred, A. (1984) Place as Historically Contingent Process: Structuration and the Time-Geography of Becoming Places. *Annals of the Association of American Geographers*, Vol. 74(2), pp. 279–297.

Said, E. (1978) *Orientalism*. Penguin, London.

Saxenian, A. (1994) *Regional Advantage: Culture and Competition in Silicon Valley and Route 128*, Harvard University Press.

Storper, M. and Venables, A. J. (2004) Buzz: Face-to-Face Contact and the Urban Economy. *Journal of Economic Geography*, Vol. 4, pp. 351–370.

Törnqvist, G. (1997) *Människa, teknik och territorium*. Nordrefo, Holstebro, Rounborgs grafiske hus.

Whatmore, S. (2002) *Hybrid Geographies. Natures, Cultures and Spaces*. Sage, London.

CONCLUSIONS

ENRICO BARALDI, HJALMAR FORS,
ANDERS HOULTZ

After a journey through the many places portrayed in the fourteen chapters of this anthology, it is now time to stop for reflection and to bring together the threads from the introduction. What have we learned from our travel across such disparate places as Swedish laboratories, clinics, and cities, the regions of Sapmi, Pesaro, Uppsala and the Silicon Valley, European ethnographic museums, and the many places of multinational corporations?

The articles have acquainted us with several physical, social and cultural places, and with our contributors' theoretical views on spatiality. Therefore, we try now to focus on what we have learned, first about the importance and meaning of places in general and then, more specifically, about the four questions that we raised in the introduction. As we shall see, the answers we provide to the four questions sustain and strengthen our general argument that places and their specificities remain of pivotal importance to scientific, technical and industrial life.

BACK TO WHERE WE STARTED: THE IMPORTANCE OF PLACES . . . AND OF SPACE

A strong message from this anthology is that *place matters*. This main conclusion clearly emerges from all fourteen contributions, spanning micro, meso and macro places and their roles in scientific, technical and industrial life. In stressing the relational and interactive nature of socio-economic processes, this anthology points to the *imprints* that such interactions have on the specific places where they unfold. Furthermore, it suggests that socio-economic interactions are seldom constrained within a single place, but connect several places, which thus end up affecting each other, often in unforeseen ways. All in all, these complex local and trans-local interactions imbue a place with particular and often unique features. Therefore, specific and well-identified places matter because they are clearly heterogeneous and differ from each other on several dimensions. Such differences result from the history of each individual place, both the historical processes that unfolded inside the place itself and those that connected it to other places. In a sense, *place matters* because *history matters*, and the history of each place is unique.

The introduction to this anthology took up a classic distinction made by geographers between "place" and "space"—a distinction that writers such as Manuel Castells have emphasized to the point of claiming that space has today *taken over* place in socio-economic processes.[1] Our conclusions go in another direction. In our opinion, to treat the relation between space and place as a dichotomy is misleading. In fact, *all places* include and can be seen as *spatial structure*: even small and limited places, such as a laboratory (see Fors and Widmalm in this anthology) or a hospital (see Shirran), are constructed as complex spatial structures. On the other hand, even *large spaces*, up to the very "global arena" itself, are composed of a wealth of *specific places* that interplay with each other, as shown by Ciabuschi and Forsgren and by Baraldi.

Moreover, the analytical distinction between micro, meso and macro places that we relied upon shows how places and space are *nested into each other*: for instance, what goes on inside the *space* of a city is clearly related to what goes on in the other *places* that constitute the broader national *space*, as shown by Kaijser's contribution on the Malexander parish. In a more extreme sense, there are even analytical perspectives that eliminate the place-space dichotomy: for instance, places and spaces coalesce and their distinction collapses into the "bundles" of time geography used by Mattsson in this anthology and inspired by Torsten Hägerstrand.[2]

The ambition of this anthology was to stress the importance of places to science, technology and business. This importance clearly emerged through all the various approaches applied by our contributors, from the time-space bundles of time geography to business networks and from historical to social analysis. But even more interesting are the inferences that we can draw from this anthology on the role of place in the *interplay* between science, technology and industry, a key topic for the whole field of STS (Science and Technology Studies). Starting from science, typically regarded as the most abstract and universal of all human endeavors, this anthology stressed that science is not simply an intellectual exercise conducted in a vacuum or in a placeless space of theories and conceptual disputes, but a highly social and material activity that needs to take place, literally, somewhere. These places of science possess physical features deriving from their architecture and the technical equipment that is used. Moreover, the places where science is performed are shaped and constructed by the very social side of scientific activities, including scientific and political ideologies, as well as interactions and power relations between scientific actors. These places in turn affect the daily performance of science. The same mutual relation holds for places of technology and industry, which, owing to their need for physical investments and embodied infrastructures, are tightly related to specific places.

As for the interplay between scientific research, technical development and industrial activities, we saw that their encounters never happen in a vacuum or on placeless markets, but in specific places where the three are brought together, typically through network-like connections. On the surface, science and industry may seem to be activities conducted separately from each other in highly specialized places, science in university laboratories, for example, and industry in factories or executive suites. However, taking a closer look, these places are not isolated, but interact and mutually influence each other through socio-economic interactions between the actors representing science and industry. Besides, "typical" scientific places often house industrial activities, such as the product development conducted at university laboratories or the business plans prepared in a professor's office; while scientific activities are conducted in "typical" industrial places, such as the experiments conducted in a test plant owned by a corporation or the scientific paper prepared in a biotech company.

The boundaries between scientific and industrial places appear to be becoming more and more indistinct, as in the case of the growing number of "industrial campuses" such as IBM's and Oracle's in Silicon Valley. But is this really such a new thing? Or is it rather only a recent example of the long-standing attempt by businesses to exploit the blurred borders that have always been a feature of the scientific, technological and industrial domains?

FOUR KEY SPATIAL QUESTIONS

Our introduction raised four specific questions about place to which we can now offer some systematic, although not definitive, answers:

1. *How are techno-scientific and industrial places constructed, by whom and for what purposes?*

2. *How are the ideals and the conceptualization of a place related to its concrete realization?*
3. *How do different places interact and what does this mean to the actors involved?*
4. *How do techno-scientific and industrial objects, ideas and actors move between places?*

We already pointed out that the first two and the last two questions are related and that, taken together, the four questions help to better specify why and how place matters—our main argument.

Question 1: Constructed Places

Throughout this anthology we have seen the conceptual and social interaction processes that led to several specific places assuming their particular features—physical, functional, cultural and aesthetic ones. These processes have been described in great detail for such micro-places as laboratories, university institutes, hospitals, ethnographic museums and the buildings in IKEA's network. As we moved along our spatial scale to meso-places, our descriptions became less detailed but broader, given the extension of the place concerned; but still we saw the main directions and actors in the construction of such places as a couple of areas in the city of Stockholm, and of Swedish cities in general. At the level of macro-places, things inevitably get so complex and broad that our descriptions catch only a few key aspects of construction processes, as done by Håkansson, Tunisini and Waluszewski in their discussion of the Italian district around Pesaro, or by Öhman for the Swedish region of Sapmi. In their analyses, our authors take account not only of the material and physical construction processes, but also of the ideologies, ideas and social interactions that lie behind the shaping of places.

The actors taking part in the construction of the places we visited are numerous, and together they shape, inhabit and use each individual place. For instance, doctors, patients and nurses in Essen-Möller's clinic; students, visitors and professors in Wallerius' laboratory; technicians and politicians in reactor sites; or the Swedish state and the local population around the dam on the River Lule. These actors clearly have different beliefs and interests, which are the sources of open or hidden *conflicts* arising within the places that we reviewed, both during the spatial construction process and in everyday life at such places. An easy way out of taking place seriously would be to claim that spatial structures simply *reflect* the underlying social processes, and in particular the structure of power relations involving groups of actors (so visible for instance in the architecture of hospitals that seclude nurses, doctors and patients), or that spatial structures are simply molded upon basic functional requirements (e.g., the configuration of modern Swedish cities and the location of nuclear reactors). However, claiming that the construction of place is only a reflection of the social order or of functional requirements ignores the fact that actors construct places through instrumental acts intended to bring about change. Moreover, places are not simply passive entities, but they influence, as much as they are influenced by, the interactions among actors.[3]

The construction of places, unwittingly or deliberately, serves to reinforce and strengthen certain social orders, while simultaneously changing and undermining others. This claim holds good regardless of whether a construction process is characterized by open strife and conflict between the actors concerned, or whether they agree with each other. In the latter case, closer scrutiny often reveals a hidden conflict in which the opposition has become marginalized by the mutual agreement of the powerful. When actors argue over the spatial arrangements or the norms pertaining to a certain place, some of these conflicts become perpetuated in concrete (literally, as in Essen-Möller's clinic), whereas other conflicts lead to unexpected breaks in the normal patterns of how actors should utilize and live in a space (like the scientist in Mattsson's chapter who breaks several spatially defined norms and rules).

That places do not simply reflect social orders and processes also appears from the *conflicting features* that social interaction embeds in one and the same place (see Baraldi). These conflicting features certainly arise because numerous actors are involved in the construction of a specific place and in its daily use or in simply living in it. But conflicting features also arise because other places are connected to the place under scrutiny, as we shall see in the answer to our third question. Some functions and uses of a place are necessarily in conflict, such as for example the *security* and *accessibility* to Stockholm's citizens of a nuclear reactor site or the *low transport costs* and the *low labor costs* of some countries supplying IKEA. Conflicts often exist between the functional and rational features of a place, on the one hand, and the cultural and aesthetic ones, on the other. In fact, while being constructed and inhabited over several years, places become suffused with *values* that go well beyond their originally "designed" function (as in the Frescati area discussed by Beckman).

It is especially in relation to micro- and meso-places that our contributors show the complex and conflicting nature of the above construction processes. The construction of such large macro-places as whole regions or nations is certainly even more complex. Therefore, by stressing the complexities of the real world, this anthology contains a clear warning against simple prescriptions for emulating hyped "model places," as for example Silicon Valley, in order to create economic growth and prosperity. For instance, the *innovation system* approach has inspired a growing body of literature concerned with *research policy* at the national and regional level.[4] This approach explicitly addresses the creation of techno-scientific dynamic and industrially innovative environments. In our view, the literature inspired by the innovation system approach has not taken seriously enough our second question, about the relationship (and often the lack of correspondence) between *idealized* and *concrete* places. Nevertheless, local public administrators all over the world try to reproduce in their regions such ideal models by applying a set of simplistic recipes.

We can advance here three major criticisms of overly rationalistic views on the designing and controlling of macro-places in order to create a science-driven economic development:

1. As pointed out by Timothy Sturgeon, the very characteristics of the role model, Silicon Valley, are poorly understood; there was in fact no instant industrialization directly driven by science in that place.[5] So it seems far-fetched to recommend other policymakers to create on the drawing board what Silicon Valley itself never actually was in reality.

2. Recognizing the interplay of a specific macro-place with other regions, the permeability of a place to external influence and the travels of ideas and objects (issues that we take up in our third and fourth questions) is more important than copying in loco a rigid template from outside. In this anthology, Widmalm, Håkansson et al. and Baraldi and Strömsten show how important these trans-local interactions and travels are for scientific, technical and industrial development. This implies that the economic development in a specific place, *if it is related to any scientific activity at all*, can very well be related to science coming from a completely different place. Alternatively, there is no guarantee that science will affect technical and industrial development in the very place where science is created—or in any other place at all. There is in fact no necessary causal and linear relation be-

tween science, technology and industry. And since such a relation does not exist in general terms, its artificial creation within a restricted territory requires so many right pieces (the right scientists, technical developers, capitalists, entrepreneurs, users, etc.) to fall exactly in the right place, that it is a miracle when the relation works more than once in the same place. At the same time, assuming that it is possible to create this linear relation within a given place imposes a controlling and mechanistic logic that goes against the complex, interactive and open nature of places.

3. Mattsson (in this volume) and the time-geography perspective of Hägerstrand imply that the three spatial scales (macro-meso-micro) interact with each other.[6] While contributing to making each macro-place even more complex and unique, this nested nature makes macro-places even less inclined to being designed and tamed, for instance, through any locally "imposed" pattern of science-industry interactions. Time-geography shifts the relevant arena for socio-economic interactions to a completely different unit of analysis: no longer a macro structure of rigid system components, but a more dynamic and fluid bundle of physically or mentally co-located material and immaterial resources. This insight leads Mattsson to conclude that if policymakers persist in designing empty structures they may totally miss what needs to be done to stimulate scientific and economic growth locally.

Question 2: Ideals and Conceptualized Places vs. Realized Places

Our second question is closely related to the first one. In fact, the construction of places, even though hardly a controllable process, is often inspired by some *ideal* or *model* in the mind of a laboratory leader, an urban planner or an R&D policy expert. These ideals range from the enlightenment values of transparency embodied in chemical laboratories (see Fors' contribution), to the modernism, functionalism and "pure" geometry applied to micro and meso places (and so evident in the superellipse of this book's cover and in Lundin's rendering of Swedish city planning) and to the free market and free trade models proposed on the macro scale by economists. Enlightenment sentiments and modernistic and liberal economic ideals eventually get blended in a striving for a frictionless and fully globalized world, typical of industrialists and technocrats. If these latter ideals, in particular, were to be implemented and fully realized there would truly be no meaning in writing a book on places, as these ideals tend to negate the importance of specific localities and seek their ultimate extinction in favor of a "placeless space" or a space where everything *flows* and never gets attached to any place, as suggested by the expression "space of flows" introduced by Castells.[7]

However, due to the complex and conflict-ridden nature of places that we stressed above and due to the social texture upon which such ideals are imposed, the way a place becomes concretely realized often turns out to be very different from the idealized place. For instance, the academic Frescati area of Stockholm in the early 2000s is worlds apart from the "Science City" envisaged by museum officials a century earlier. And Svedberg's functionalistic ideals of efficiency and open spaces for his laboratory had to give way to the competing needs of his heavy equipment, which requires solid foundations and secluded places. But the ambition to control space reaches its apex in modern city planning, as described in the chapter by Lundin: we can contrast the rationalistic, indeed Tayloristic, approach applied by city planners with the actual realization and daily use of the superellipse of Stockholm's Sergels torg, as presented in our introduction.

If realizing spatial ideals within contained places such as laboratories and cities is so difficult, one can wonder what chances there really are of successfully imposing models and ideals on whole regions and countries, as we saw above in discussing the innovation system approach. And what about the realized effects of large infrastructural projects on whole regions and their population? Öhman's account of the large dams on the Lule River shows how tragic the consequences of techno-scientific change can be to rural populations. To conclude the discussion of our second question, we stress that the necessary difference between template and ideal on the one hand, and the realized place, on the other, is a further explanation of why, despite the homogenizing and isomorphic pressures of such templates and spatial ideals, *places still matter*, that is they keep their identity, individuality and heterogeneity.

Our last two questions deserve special attention because if they were interpreted in a certain way, let us say unilaterally and mechanistically, they would seem to sustain the argument that specific localities and places do not matter any longer in the globalized space, which is precisely the opposite of the main argument of this anthology. We shall return explicitly to this point at the end of our review of our answers to the four questions.

Question 3: Interacting Places

Social and technical interactions are not only important in shaping a specific place *from within*, but also in shaping it *from the outside* (see Håkansson et al., in this volume). This happens because such interactions can seldom be constrained by physical or normative boundaries, as pointed out also by Mattsson: the fact is that we humans and our technologies are naturally prone to interact with each other; we, our artefacts and our ideas love to interact and cannot be prevented from meeting and creating, again and again, even more complex techno-social ensembles. It often happens then that an actor or an artefact finds its "kindred spirit" living in another place. These socio-technical interactions tend therefore to stretch outside, to the world of other places, making them more or less explicitly related to the focal one. In this way, two or more places, geographically separate, interact with each other. Such interactions certainly happen between places on the same level of our spatial scale, such as the laboratories in Uppsala and in the UK studied on the micro-level by Widmalm; but places at different spatial levels interact too: what goes on in a museum is clearly related to what goes on in the city where it is located, but it can also be related to what goes on in other continents, as shown by Ljungström.

How do places interact with each other, in practice? A first way is by means of socio-economic interactions between actors, individuals and organizations that *remain located in different places*. A second way involves actors, artefacts and ideas that *travel from one place to another*. As this second way is addressed in our final question, we focus now on the first one. One important type of socio-economic interaction that typically crosses spatial boundaries is addressed explicitly in the contributions of Håkansson et al. and of Baraldi, namely *business relationships* between distant firms buying and selling products or co-operating with each other. Similar interactions, although mostly filled with communication and softer types of exchange, also happen between individuals living in distant places, like the scientists in Widmalm's and in Baraldi and Strömsten's accounts in this anthology.

The interactions between actors located in different places can be reinforced and even institutionalized by the creation of particular *organizational structures* that span and tightly connect several places with the help of their physical presence and communication systems. While there are several such multi-site organizations, the *multinational corporation* is certainly the most prominent one for its capacity to act as a "place-connector," as shown in the chapters by Baraldi and by Ciabuschi and Forsgren. Within and because of multinational firms, interactions between different countries happen in accordance with a rather strict economic logic imposed by the goals and routines of the corporation.

What happens then to places when they interact with each other through social, technical and economic connections? The most obvious consequence is that they are no longer isolated, but that they assume certain positions in relation to each other: some places may become more *central*, while others more *peripheral*. For instance, the economic geographer Stephen Hymer proposed in the 1970s a strongly *hierarchical* model according to which the world would be dominated by a few big cities or hubs, where all power would be concentrated and key decisions made that affected the rest of the world.[8] While geographers are still arguing whether or how such a scenario could become reality, it is undeniable that some places are more central than others, maybe just on a single dimension: for instance, the Swedish town of Älmhult may be the center of IKEA's empire, but it has a very peripheral position on the global financial market.

But as soon as places become related to each other, the playground is open for them *to influence each other*. Power relations play a key role here: the places hosting the most powerful actors will gain in power and become strong instruments for controlling other actors and places on several levels: culturally, militarily and economically. This type of interaction between places is clearly unilateral, with one place (and its actors) in a dominant position and the others ending up by being dominated. This obviously holds good for a strong imperialistic country or for a multinational firm that imposes its products on the whole world or that relentlessly exploits the natural resources of a poor country. But this type of unilateral influence clearly appears also in Ljungström's account of how European ethnographic museums aimed to "control" the civilizations of other continents by displaying them in an orderly fashion and in Öhman's essay on the ambition of the Swedish government to dominate the Sapmi landscape and population in the course of producing electric power.

There are, however, also different types of influence, more bilateral and less hierarchic, that places mutually exert on each other: through the actors that populate them, places can in fact *cooperate* or *compete* with each other. Cooperation is evident between the Swedish and foreign laboratories portrayed by Widmalm and by Baraldi and Strömsten; but cooperation between places also arises when multinationals such as IKEA try to combine different locations to leverage the complementarities between places. When strongly place-bound actors such as municipalities or universities cooperate, they often do so because each place has features that complement those of other places. And if this cooperation is orchestrated by a multinational organization, the heterogeneity of places and their specific features play a major role in deciding where to locate, for instance, a company factory or a "center of excellence" in order to exploit the complementarities between places.

On the other hand, political, scientific and economic competition between places is very evident in the efforts of local public agencies to foster local innovations and industrialization by means of recipes drawn from territorial development models such as regional innovation systems and clusters.[9] And those actors who are strongly bounded in a territory, such as universities, compete too, for students, scientific publications and economic resources. At the same time, the actors least bound to specific places, namely multinational corporations, induce increased competition between places that are put against each other, in order to obtain the most favorable conditions for establishing their subsidiaries or sourcing their inputs. Competition, like cooperation, puts the accent on the individual and heterogeneous features of every single place that tries to outpace the others: in a world of competing places no one would like to be like any other, as pointed out by David Harvey.[10]

The interactions between places that we have seen (control, cooperation and competition) are grounded in the interactions between the actors attached to those places. And actors have vested interests in places, especially those actors, such as a county council or a university, that are closely bound to specific places. Actors also wield power through places, be they laboratories, regions or countries.[11] Moreover, as we discussed in our answers to the first and second questions, actors strive to (re)shape places to correspond better to their ideals. However, actors are in turn shaped and affected by the places they inhabit, or that they strive to control or alter.

What, then, do the interactions between places mean to the actors involved? What do they mean to scientists, businessmen or policymaking bodies? Generally speaking, they mean having more options open than if one were restricted to a single place. Scientists and technologists may seek connections in several countries to develop, spread or commercialize their ideas, as in the cases presented by Widmalm and by Baraldi and Strömsten; while multinational corporations can leverage the connections between different countries according to the logic of developing innovations locally and exploiting them globally (see Ciabuschi and Forsgren) or they can combine several heterogeneous places, as IKEA does.

However, not all actors will gain from the fact that places interact: what comes of Uppsala municipality's hope of stimulating local entrepreneurship if some of its best scientific ideas migrate to Silicon Valley? Or what about Malexander's chances of keeping its residents from moving to larger cities? In general, some actors may be damaged by the interaction between places because this also exposes them to the *competition* of new actors and places. And competition from other places is also a consequence of easier travel between places, an issue to which we turn now.

Question 4: Travelling Between Places

The journeys made by actors, artefacts and ideas are a second way to keep different places connected. But as economic geographers have noted since the time of Alfred Marshall, human activities tend to be concentrated inside specific places because of "economies of agglomeration."[12] This implies that while the above-mentioned entities can freely flow between places, the chances are that they will be attracted by some places and not by others. Thus, certain places such as Silicon Valley exert a stronger "force of attraction" than others. For instance, elite universities constantly increase their shares of research funds, publications and collaborations;[13] while multinational corporations, although playing in the global arena, invariably commit their resources to a handful of carefully selected places that are expected to foster their "centers of excellence."[14] Such processes lead to some places accumulating resources and concentrating power at the expense of others, and they strongly affect the relative position (central or peripheral) assumed by a place in relation to others. When such a spatial hierarchy is established, the travels of artefacts, such as those collected around the world and brought to ethnographic museums, reinforce symbolically and intellectually the control exerted by the center over the periphery.

But what happens to the "traveller" during the journey? When the traveller is an embodied object such as a research institution or a nuclear reactor that needs to be moved, we can expect some extensive changes in the object. Changes may be required simply because it is difficult to adapt material objects to the new context. Some of the object's features will need to be discarded or played down because the new place does not favor them concretely (i.e., the new place is less accessible) or symbolically (the new place is too rural), as shown by Beckman and Fjæstad. As for people, when they travel, they change too, in the sense that they learn, like the scientist in Mattsson's account: people may even learn to break the place-related rules if this helps them realize their projects. There are also material objects that need to travel along with a set of ideas that explains how to implement and use them, as in the cases of the ultracentrifuge and laboratory template described by Widmalm and of the innovations that multinationals try to transfer from a local subsidiary to another, as discussed by Ciabuschi and Forsgren. The ideas, the artefacts and all the people involved in such "transfers" seldom move to a new place and get *reassembled* at their destination in exactly the way they were assembled at their place of origin: adaptation to the new local context is essential for the innovation to work at all, but this can be costly and time-consuming.

Transformations and *translations* of the objects that travel, during and after their journey, are almost inevitable because they become exposed to different contexts inhabited by several new economic, political and symbolic objects that make certain demands on them, especially the objects located at the end points of the travel, where the travelling objects need to become re-embedded.[15] Some adaptations to the new context will be easier, as in the case of Svedberg's ultracentrifuge, while others will be more complex, as in the case of the museum institution portrayed by Beckman. A journey may accordingly have both negative and positive effects on the travelling object: being moved to the wrong place may mean the decline of an object, while moving to the right place can provide exposure to the resources necessary to transform a scientific idea into a stabilized product ready to be commercialized (see Baraldi and Strömsten).

Finally, travelling ideas behave quite differently from material objects. Even if ideas always travel embodied in concrete entities, such as people or texts, they have the capacity to adapt to new environments, changing themselves and the new places that host them in the process. But just like the more concrete travellers, ideas must flow through the right media and be given a conducive context. When such is the case, they travel quickly, and in their immateriality they are much easier to mold and transform to fit a specific context, compared with a person or a product. Ideas and ideals are in fact constantly reinterpreted before they are concretized in a new context, as the enlightenment ideal was in Wallerius' laboratory (see Fors). To their originators, ideas may even seem to have been corrupted or "misinterpreted" in the new context.

CLOSING ON THE FOUR QUESTIONS

We conclude our discussion of our four key questions by stressing that the act of asking and seriously addressing them is actually enough to breach the argument that places no longer matter in a globalized world. In fact, claiming with Heidegger and Castells that places are dead in favor of a global and modern space amounts to superficially accepting that the interaction between places leads *mechanically* and *unilaterally* to destroying their uniqueness and heterogeneity, as if the forces pushing to make every place become like any other would always prevail over those that drive in the opposite direction of variety.[16] Admittedly, Castells recognizes that the space of flow needs to be *territorialized* by linkages to certain locations and specific places.[17] But the importance of individual places, even in a "globalized" world, goes well beyond this recognition by Castells.

In fact, the geographer David Harvey points out that the collapse of several spatial barriers, the reduction of distances and the increased opportunities for places to interact with each other are being met by actors who cling even more closely to their own places in search of tangible marks of identity.[18] Increased trans-local interactions constitute the other side of the coin of globalization: the differences between specific places become essential for cooperation and competition between places, and for the multinational capital that exploits and combines them.[19] The sociologist Zygmunt Bauman summarizes this process, by which space is de-territorialized and simultaneously re-territorialized, in the idea of "glocalization."[20] In his own words: ". . . rather than *homogenizing* the human condition, the technological annulment of temporal/spatial distances tends to *polarize* it."[21] Thus, annulling spatial distances does not result in homogenization but in spatial *polarization*.

Even if there certainly are tendencies in the direction of spatial homogenization, such as the organizational similarity facilitated by more frequent travels and more and more global organizations, to assume that the "game is over" for the local versus the global grossly overstates the homogenizing forces. As well as the tendency of actors to cling even more closely to their places, another neglected issue is the existence of strong local variations across all spatial scales, from single laboratories through cities and to regions. But clearly, if one measures homogenization in terms of the diffusion of Coca Cola bottles, of the English language or of such templates as "Total Quality Management," one misses a great deal of local idiosyncrasies that cannot be easily quantified and measured. Moreover, the homogenizing imperative neglects the fact that the so-called global templates always undergo local *translations* before being adopted in a certain context, which further contributes to local variety. Finally, places do not interplay unilaterally, according to Hymer's hierarchical "centre-periphery" model that forces actors in peripheral places to passively accept and implement the ideas and templates coming from the center.[22] Instead, there is always a giving and taking from both sides, regardless of how unequal the relationship between two places may be.

Our texts suggest that places *mutually affect each other* and these mutual effects too account for a great degree of variation in localities. Places interact by competing, cooperating or simply "looking" at each other. Even if being drawn closer to each other implies that places can draw mutual inspiration, or maybe go the whole way and imitate *part of* each other's institutions or physical structures, places are so complex and multidimensional that they will always be different on some dimensions. Moreover, explicit attempts by policy officials to copy and reproduce places, or even only a few chosen spatial features, seldom succeed. And even those actors who are expected to exert the strongest globalizing and homogenizing pressures, namely multinational corporations, simultaneously search for and foster variety and uniqueness in the places they aim to combine through their international networks. On the other side of the barricade, local authorities may well try to copy some successful recipes from abroad, but they do so only in order to make their place a truly unique, privileged spot on the world map capable of attracting investments and people. While all this goes on, neglecting the forces behind the heterogeneity of places in favor of a deterministic model that unilaterally predicts homogeneity is a severe limitation on our ability to understand the role of places and space in scientific, technical and business life.

NOTES

1. Manuel Castells, 1996/2000, *The Information Age: Economy, Society and Culture*. Volume 1: The Rise of the Network Society, Blackwell: Oxford.

2. Torsten Hägerstrand, 1973, "The domain of human geography," in R. J. Chorley (ed.), *Directions in Geography*, Methuen: London, pp. 67–87; Torsten Hägerstrand, 1982, "Diorama, Path and Project," *Tijdschrift voor Economische en Sociale Geografie*, 73 (6), pp. 323–339.
3. See also Anthony Giddens, 1984, *The Constitution of Society: Outline of the Theory of Structuration,* University of California Press: Berkeley.
4. See, for instance, Bengt-Åke Lundvall (ed.), 1992, *National Systems of Innovation: Towards a Theory of Innovation and Interactive Learning,* Pinter: London; Richard Nelson (ed.), 1993; *National Innovation Systems: A Comparative Analysis,* Oxford University Press: New York; and Chris Freeman, 2002, "Continental, national and sub-national innovation systems—complementarity and economic growth," *Research Policy,* Vol. 31, pp. 191–211.
5. Timothy Sturgeon, 2000, "How Silicon Valley Came to Be," in M. Kenney (ed.), *Understanding Silicon Valley. The Anatomy of an Entrepreneurial Region*, Stanford University Press: Stanford, CA, pp. 15–47.
6. Torsten Hägerstrand, 1973, "The domain of human geography," in R. J. Chorley (ed.), *Directions in Geography*, Methuen: London, pp. 67–87; Torsten Hägerstrand, 1982, "Diorama, Path and Project," *Tijdschrift voor Economische en Sociale Geografie*, 73 (6), pp. 323–339.
7. Manuel Castells, 1996/2000, see pages 407–9.
8. Stephen Hymer, 1972, "The multinational corporation and the law of uneven development," in J. N. Bhagwati (ed), *Economics and World Order from the 1970s to the 1990s*, Macmillan: New York, pp. 113–140.
9. Bengt-Åke Lundvall (ed.), 1992, *National Systems of Innovation: Towards a Theory of Innovation and Interactive Learning*, Pinter: London; Michael E. Porter, 1998, "Clusters and the New Economics of Competition," *Harvard Business Review*, November–December 1998, pp. 77–90.
10. David Harvey, 1990, "Between Space and Time: Reflection on the Geographical Imagination," *Annals of the Association of American Geographers*, 80 (3), 418–434; see page 428.
11. See also Anthony Giddens, 1984, *The Constitution of Society: Outline of the Theory of Structuration*, University of California Press: Berkeley.
12. Alfred Marshall, 1890, "Industry and Trade," Macmillan: London.
13. See pages 263–66 in Walter Powell and Jason Owen-Smith, 1998, "Universities and the Market for Intellectual Property in Life Sciences," *Journal of Policy Analysis and Management*, 17 (2), pp. 253–277.
14. Ulf Holm and Torben Pedersen, 2000, *The Emergence and Impact of MNC Centers of Excellence*, Macmillan: London.
15. On translations, compare Bruno Latour, 1987, *Science in Action: How to Follow Scientists and Engineers through Society.* Harvard University Press: Cambridge, MA; pp. 108–32.
16. Martin Heidegger, 1977, "The Age of the World Picture," in *The Question Concerning Technology and Other Essays*, Harper & Row: New York; Manuel Castells, 1996/2000.

17. Manuel Castells, 2000, "Materials for an exploratory theory of the Network society," *British Journal of Sociology*, 51 (1), pp. 1–24; see page 14.
18. Harvey, 1990, 427.
19. Ibid., 428.
20. Zygmunt Bauman, 1998, *Globalization: The Human Consequences,* Polity: Cambridge.
21. Ibid., 18; emphasis added.
22. Hymer, 1972.

Notes on Contributors

ENRICO BARALDI is assistant professor at the Department of Business Studies and an associate of the Uppsala STS Center, Uppsala University. His research interests include industrial marketing, product development and technology management, with a special focus on the use of IT systems and biotechnology within business networks.

JENNY BECKMAN is assistant professor at the Department of History of Science and Ideas, Uppsala University, and an associate of the Uppsala STS Center. She has published on a range of aspects of natural history museums, as well as biology and education, botanical nomenclature, and scientific illustration. Her current research focuses on the history of modern systematics and amateurs in science.

FRANCESCO CIABUSCHI is assistant professor at the Department of Business Studies, Uppsala University. His research interests are within the fields of international business and strategic knowledge management.

MAJA FJÆSTAD is a PhD student at the Department of History of Science and Technology at the Royal Institute of Technology, Stockholm. The focus of her research is on the history of Swedish nuclear power and especially the plans for breeder reactors.

HJALMAR FORS is assistant professor at the Department of History of Science and Ideas, Uppsala University, and an associate of the Uppsala STS Center and of the Department of History of Science and Technology, Royal Institute of Technology, Stockholm. He has written on chemistry's emergence as a science during the eighteenth century. His present research is concerned with the Swedish Board of Mines as an intellectual environment for science and occultism circa 1690–1750.

MATS FORSGREN is professor of International Business at the Department of Business Studies, Uppsala University. His research during the last 20 years has been related to foreign direct investment theory, theories of internationalization, managing the multinational firm and business network theory.

ANDERS HOULTZ is assistant professor at the Department of History of Science and Technology, Royal Institute of Technology, Stockholm. His research has mainly addressed questions concerning the use of history, material culture and industrial heritage as means for creating identities.

HÅKAN HÅKANSSON is professor of Marketing at the Norwegian School of Management, BI Oslo. His research focuses on industrial purchasing and selling, technical development, and logistics. He is one of the founders of the IMP industrial network approach.

ARNE KAIJSER is professor at the Department of History of Science and Technology, Royal Institute of Technology, Stockholm. His research interest concerns the historical development of infrastructural systems.

OLOF LJUNGSTRÖM holds a PhD in the History of Science and Ideas from Uppsala University. He is currently employed by the Karolinska Institutet, Stockholm, as a researcher, and as a teacher at Uppsala University. His present research project is a critical appraisal of the university's medical research history in the period 1960–2010. Among his other research interests are the histories of anthropology, natural history and medicine.

PER LUNDIN is a PhD student at the Department of History of Science and Technology, Royal Institute of Technology, Stockholm. His research interests include large technological systems, professionalization, and the constructions of the objectivity ideal in science and technology during the 20th century. His dissertation deals with the adaptation of Swedish cities to the car during the postwar period.

HENRIK MATTSSON is a PhD student in Economic Geography at the Department of Social and Economic Geography, Uppsala University. He is also associated with the Centre for Research on Innovation and Industrial Dynamics (CIND), where he is writing a thesis on biotechnological innovation processes.

EMMA SHIRRAN is a PhD student at the Office for History of Science, Uppsala University. Her research interests include technical developments in obstetrics, and the success and development of the early 20th-century clinical ideal.

TORKEL STRÖMSTEN is assistant professor at the Department of Accounting, Stockholm School of Economics, and an associate of the Uppsala STS Center. His research concerns the interface between industrial networks, strategic management and organizational control.

ANNALISA TUNISINI is professor of business management and industrial marketing at the Facoltà di Economia, Università degli Studi di Urbino "Carlo Bo," Urbino, Italy. Her main research interests are inter-firm networks, supply chain management, industrial districts, and mergers and acquisitions.

ALEXANDRA WALUSZEWSKI is professor and director of the Science & Technology Studies (STS) Center at Uppsala University, Sweden. Her research relates the industrial network approach with the STS tradition, with a special focus on the interface between science and industry in the biomedical and biotechnical fields.

SVEN WIDMALM is professor at the Department for Technology and Social Change, Linköping University. His research interests include the social history of physics, astronomy and biology from the 18th century. He also works on policy aspects of modern science.

MAY-BRITT ÖHMAN is a PhD student at the Department of History of Science and Technology, Royal Institute of Technology, Stockholm. Her research interests include gender, ethnicity and postcolonial theory in relation to science and technology with water and energy as specific domains.

INDEX OF NAMES